Colour Television Theory

PAL-System Principles and Receiver Circuitry

COLOUR TELEVISION THEORY

PAL-System Principles and
Receiver Circuitry

GEOFFREY H. HUTSON

Formerly Principal Lecturer in Electrical and Electronic Engineering
Canterbury College of Technology

McGRAW-HILL Book Company (UK) Limited

London · New York · St Louis · San Francisco · Auckland · Bogotá · Guatemala
Hamburg · Johannesburg · Lisbon · Madrid · Mexico · Montreal · New Delhi
Panama · Paris · San Juan · São Paulo · Singapore · Sydney · Tokyo · Toronto

Published by

McGRAW-HILL Publishing Company Limited

MAIDENHEAD · BERKSHIRE · ENGLAND

---

07 094259 5

789 WCB 8321

PRINTED AND BOUND IN GREAT BRITAIN

Preface

This textbook is primarily intended for engineers, technicians, and students who already have a working knowledge of monochrome television principles and wish to extend their studies to embrace modern colour television engineering. It is mainly concerned with the PAL development of the NTSC system.

Every effort has been made to present the theory in a way which is logical and easy to follow. Wherever possible the subject matter under discussion in the text has been reinforced by the use of diagrams which illustrate the principle with a clarity which words alone often fail to achieve.

Although those who have already studied monochrome television will be better equipped to read this text, it is nonetheless felt that the approach is sufficiently comprehensive to allow general students of electronic engineering to understand the principles described without difficulty.

The book should prove very helpful to students preparing to take examinations which include colour television principles, in particular those conducted by the City and Guilds of London Institute and the Radio Trades Examination Board. It is also intended for those seeking technician engineer or professional engineering qualifications as well as students taking University Degree courses with a communications engineering content. The use of mathematics has been minimized so that the work will serve the widest possible range of readers. The aim is to give a clear understanding of the way in which colour television works, without the punishing experience of working through complex mathematical concepts. Those who wish ultimately to explore certain topics in greater depth, will benefit very much by first gaining the broad understanding of basic principles which it is the object of this book to provide.

Finally it is realized that the majority of those employed in the manufacture or servicing of colour television receivers, and in studio, transmitter, and distribution services, may not be intending to sit examinations in colour television engineering. They may merely aim to achieve an adequate understanding of the subject so that they may face this more sophisticated branch of television engineering with confidence. It is the author's hope that they will find in this textbook the information they seek, presented in a manner which will make the study interesting rather than arduous. Having grasped the fundamentals it is imperative that developments and innovations are studied as they appear because progress in this technology will continue to be thrusting and vigorous in the years ahead.

Diagram symbols. To minimize the congestion of information on the diagrams, the symbol Ω has been omitted from resistor values (e.g., 100 Ω, 100 kΩ, 1 MΩ, appear as 100, 100 k, 1 M).

With capacitors, μF has been omitted (e.g., 0·01 μF, 1·0 μF appear as 0·01, 1·0).

For the same reason, components have been numbered (e.g., R_3, C_2, L_4, etc.), only where this has proved to be the best way of identifying them in the text.

Historical note

All colour television systems at present in use owe their origin to the NTSC system which was invented and developed in the United States of America.

In 1953, the Federal Communications Commission approved the colour television signal specifications recommended by the National Television Systems Committee. This committee was formed in 1950 to make a searching examination of the problems associated with colour television. The Radio Corporation of America (RCA), played a predominant part in the development of the fully compatible system finally adopted by the committee and thereafter described as the NTSC system. The RCA tri-colour shadow-mask cathode ray tube was the major single invention which made a high quality colour television system possible, using mass-produced receivers at prices acceptable for domestic use.

Regular NTSC colour television broadcasts began in the U.S.A. in January 1954. In 1960, Japan adopted the NTSC system, followed by Canada and Puerto Rico in 1966, and by Mexico in 1967.

The PAL system, which is a variant of NTSC, was developed at the Telefunken Laboratories of Hanover, in the German Federal Republic. This system was developed to reduce the effects of phase distortion of the colour signal. Such distortion, in the basic NTSC system, can give rise to hue errors in the reproduced picture.

In 1967, the PAL system was adopted by the German Federal Republic and by the United Kingdom. Subsequently, the majority of countries which have started, or propose to start, colour television services, have adopted the PAL system. At the time of writing PAL is the chosen system for Australia, Austria, Belgium, Brazil, Denmark, Eire, Finland, the German Federal Republic, Hong Kong, Iran, Iceland, Italy, Netherlands, New Zealand, Norway, Portugal, South Africa, Spain, Sweden, Switzerland, Thailand, Turkey, the United Kingdom, and Yugoslavia.

The third main system is SECAM. This was developed in France where a service using the system was started in 1967. SECAM has also been adopted by Algeria, the German Democratic Republic, Hungary, Tunisia, and the U.S.S.R.

All systems have much in common. PAL and NTSC are particularly alike and this textbook, although primarily about the PAL system, contains a great deal of information about the closely related NTSC system. A substantial amount of the work is also equally applicable to SECAM.

Acknowledgements

The author's thanks are due to the following organizations for permission to publish extracts from circuit diagrams, technical manuals, or other published literature, and/or for their unfailing courtesy and co-operation in answering technical queries and extending any help requested:

Baird Television Distributors Ltd
British Broadcasting Corporation
Decca Radio and Television
Domestic Electric Rentals Ltd
Edward Arnold (Publishers) Ltd
Independent Television Authority
Mullard Ltd
Philips Electrical Ltd
Pye Group (Radio & Television) Ltd
Radio & Allied Industries
Radio Corporation of America
Radio Rentals Ltd
Rank Bush Murphy Ltd
Rediffusion Ltd
Sony Corporation of Japan
Standard Telephones & Cables Ltd
Telefunken Company of Germany
The Marconi Company Ltd
The Polytechnic of North London
Thorn Electrical Industries Ltd
Vision Hire Ltd

Sincere appreciation is expressed to Philip Darby, Head of the Quality Control Section of the I.T.A. Engineering Division, for his generous help in reading the manuscript and subsequently the proof copies of this textbook. His searching and helpful comments and suggestions proved of great value in the clarification of many matters arising during the development of this material.

Finally the author records his gratitude to his wife Betty for the very many exacting hours she spent typing the manuscript.

Geoffrey H. Hutson

To my wife Betty and my son John

CONTENTS

1
Light

Introduction

The object of an ideal television system is to create on a distant light-emitting screen a replica of what the eye would see if it were viewing the original scene directly. Since the natural world is one in which colour abounds, only a television system which reproduces colour can approach this ideal. It is only under near-dark conditions that the eye ceases to see colour and the world appears entirely in shades of grey.

Monochrome reproductions of natural daylight scenes are totally *un*natural in appearance. We accept them and interpret them within their limitations, because we have been conditioned to do so by constant exposure all our lives to black and white drawings, photographs, newspaper pictures, films, and monochrome television, etc. It is as well at the start of a study of colour television to be reminded that the presentation of a picture in monochrome is simply a device for conveying visual information in an abridged or incomplete form. It is a picture with a missing dimension, devoid of the infinite subtlety which is provided by the presence of what we know as 'colour'.

The problem which taxed the ingenuity of those in the U.S.A. who met and overcame the challenge of colour television, was to accept and retain the existing monochrome system but to modify it into one capable of giving a true facsimile of the original scene on a colour receiver, whilst ensuring that the transmitted signal gave a normal (i.e., in this sense black-and-white) picture on a monochrome receiver.

Colour has brought reality much nearer. The one major technique still to be evolved in an acceptably simple and economical way, is how to reproduce the sensation of depth which is created in the mind mainly by the stereoscopic effect of two eyes viewing the same scene from slightly different angles.

Basic requirements of a colour television system

It is helpful to summarize the main properties which a colour television system should possess.

General

The system must produce a picture of realistic colour, adequate brightness and

1

good definition. In designing it due account must be taken of the properties and limitations of the human eye.

Compatibility

(a) The colour television signal must produce a normal black and white picture on a monochrome receiver and do so without any modification to the receiver circuitry.
(b) A colour receiver must be able to produce a black and white picture from a normal monochrome signal. This is sometimes referred to as 'reverse compatibility'.

Conditions necessary to establish compatibility

To be fully compatible the colour television signal must:

(a) Occupy the same bandwidth as the corresponding monochrome signal.
(b) Employ the same location and spacing of the sound and vision carriers.
(c) Use the same deflection frequencies.
(d) Employ the same line and field synchronizing signals.
(e) Contain the same fundamental brightness (i.e., luminance) information as would a monochrome signal transmitting the same scene.
(f) Contain additional colour information together with the ancillary signals needed to allow this to be decoded.
(g) Carry the colour information in such a way that no visible sign of it appears on a monochrome receiver's picture.

Although conditions (e) and (g) are not entirely met, the departure from the ideal is not great and practical compatibility may be said to be achieved.

Basic elements of the theory of light

Few monochrome television engineers found it necessary to be knowledgeable about the subject of 'light'. To gain a thorough understanding of colour television, however, there are certain fundamental qualities of light which must be appreciated. The purpose of the remainder of this chapter is to summarize aspects of the theory of light which are likely to prove helpful to those engaged in colour television engineering.

Some, notably those engaged in studio lighting and camera technology, will need to pursue the subject in greater depth, including a detailed study of optics.

Electromagnetic radiation

Energy travels through space in the form of electromagnetic radiation. Light rays form a very small part of the large family of electromagnetic waves which in total embrace a frequency range extending from below 10^5 Hz to above 10^{25} Hz. The properties of e.m. waves are determined by their wavelengths. For convenience the total spectrum is divided into sections: e.g., cosmic rays, radio waves, ultraviolet rays, X-rays, etc. These sections have no precise boundaries since the behaviour of e.m. waves does not change sharply at given wavelengths. Figure 1.1 shows the family of e.m. waves.

The visible spectrum

The small range of frequencies to which the human eye is responsive, is known as the visible spectrum. This is centred upon a frequency of the order of 5×10^{14} Hz. When all of the frequencies in the visible spectrum reach the eye simultaneously, we see 'white' light. If, however, part of this range is filtered out and only the remainder of the visible spectrum reaches the eye, we see a colour.

The visible spectrum is expanded out in Fig. 1.1 to show the range of colours it contains. Again these merge into one another with no precise boundaries. However, seven broad areas are discernible and these are labelled:

Red   Orange   Yellow   Green   Blue   Indigo   Violet

As a useful aid to memory, the initial letters of the colours of the visible spectrum spell the name ROY. G. BIV.

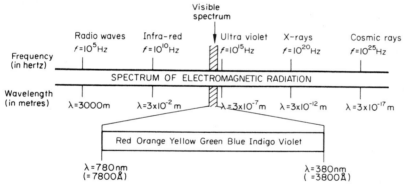

Fig. 1.1 *Electromagnetic radiation spectrum*

Note: 1 nanometre   = 10^{-9} metre (1 nm = 10^{-9} m)
1 Angstrom unit = 10^{-10} metre (1 Å = 10^{-10} m)

The scales in Fig. 1.1 are labelled in the fundamental units of hertz (i.e., cycles per second) for frequency and metres for wavelength. Because of the very small dimensions, it is necessary to use a smaller unit of wavelength to scale the visible spectrum and the standard unit for this work is the nanometre (symbol nm), where 1 nm = 10^{-9} m. The longest and shortest wavelengths to which the eye is responsive are approximately 780 nm and 380 nm. These are at the red and violet ends of the spectrum respectively. Another unit which is very widely used is the angstrom unit (symbol Å), where 1 Å = 10^{-10} m. Using these units the visible spectrum may be said to extend from 7800 Å to 3800 Å. For conversion purposes 1 nm = 10 Å.

Splitting up white light (Fig. 1.2(a))

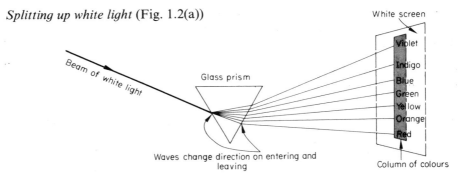

Fig. 1.2(a)   *Showing how a ray of white light is 'split-up' into the colours of the visible spectrum by unequal refraction of the component waves*

When an e.m. wave passes from one medium to another its direction changes at the boundary. The amount by which its path is refracted (i.e., bent) varies with wavelength; growing greater as the wavelength shortens. If a narrow beam of white light is directed onto a prism it is bent both on entering and leaving the prism. But, since white light contains waves of lengths varying from 380 nm to 780 nm, all the constituent waves are bent by differing amounts and instead of a single beam emerging, the various colours are separated so that the visible spectrum may be seen as a column of colours on a white screen placed near the prism.

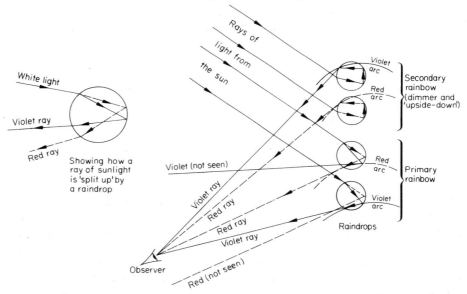

Fig. 1.2(b)   *Rainbows*

The second 'upside-down' rainbow which is sometimes dimly seen above the main rainbow is due to 'double refraction' in the raindrops.

4

A rainbow is a natural example of this process of the splitting up of white light by variable refraction (see Fig. 1.2(b)).

Since lenses are used to 'bend' light rays, it follows that in doing so they may also split up white light to give images with coloured fringes. Cheap lenses do produce this 'dispersion' of the various colours present in the incident light and this is known as chromatic aberration.

For optical instruments lenses are so constructed that they give the required refraction without dispersion. Such lenses, which may be formed from combinations of lenses made of glasses of different properties (e.g., crown glass and flint glass) are said to be achromatic.

Light units and terminology

In discussing light, various terms and units are used. Some of these are defined briefly below.

(a) LUMINOUS INTENSITY (I). This expresses the power of a light source. The main units, starting with the original but now deprecated one, are:
   (i) *Candle power (c.p.)*. 1 c.p. is the light emitted from a '*Standard Candle*'.[1]
   (ii) *Candela (cd)*. 1 cd is 1/60 of the light emitted from 1 cm^2 of a so-called '*full radiator*'[2] raised to the temperature of molten platinum; i.e., 2042 Kelvin.[3]

N.B. For practical purposes, one candela approximately equals one candle power (i.e., 1 cd = 1 c.p.).

(b) LUMINOUS FLUX (Φ). A source of light radiates energy in the form of e.m. waves. We speak of light energy as 'flux' and luminous flux is a measure of the flow of light per second. The unit is the lumen which may be defined as follows:

Lumen (lm). One lumen is the quantity of luminous flux which falls per second upon a surface of unit area placed unit distance from a light source of one candela; the surface being 'normal' to (i.e., at right angles to) the incident rays.

In more scientific terms, one lumen is the luminous flux emitted in one second per unit solid angle,[4] (i.e., per steradian) by a point source of 1 candela. (*N.B.* There are 4π steradians in a sphere so the total flux emitted per second from a source of one candela is 4π lumens.)

[1] A standard candle is made of spermaceti wax; weight six candles to one pound; burning rate 120 grains per hour (1 grain = 1/7000 of 1 lb).

[2] A full radiator is a substance, which, when heated to a certain temperature, emits light containing energy spread over the entire visible spectrum. Its spectrum at any other temperature may be worked out theoretically. A theoretical example of a full radiator, is a perfectly black body which, when cold, absorbs all radiation falling upon it.

[3] Temperature in (degrees) Kelvin = degrees Centigrade + 273, i.e., $t°C = (t + 273)$ K from which $0°C = +273$ K or 0 K $= -273°C$. *N.B.* The use of the word 'degrees' in front of Kelvin is now discontinued.

[4] A unit solid angle is the solid angle subtended at the centre of a sphere of radius r by an area of r^2 on the surface of the sphere. Since the surface area of a sphere is $4\pi r^2$, there are $4\pi r^2 \div r^2 = 4\pi$ steradians in a sphere.

The concept of a point source is useful, because from it light radiates out equally in all directions in an expanding sphere. The light rays are at all times normal to the imaginary surface of the sphere, since each ray passes along a radius. As the distance from the point source increases, the amount of flux passing through each square metre of the sphere's surface decreases, because the total flux is spread over a larger area. Since the surface area of the sphere is proportional to the square of the radius, the flux density is inversely proportional to the square of the radius (see section (i), page 9, on the *Inverse Square Law of Illumination*).

In specific rather than in general terms, *one lumen* may be defined as the quantity of luminous flux per second, which would pass through one square metre of the surface of a perfectly transparent sphere of radius one metre, if a point source having an intensity of one candela were located at the centre of the sphere.

(c) ILLUMINATION (E). This is a measure of the concentration of luminous flux falling upon a surface. It is expressed in lumens per unit area. The main units are:

  (i) *lux* One lux = 1 lumen per square metre (lm/m^2),
  (ii) *phot* One phot = 1 lumen per square centimetre (lm/cm^2),
  (iii) *milliphot* One milliphot = 10^{-3} phot (10^{-3} lm/cm^2).

N.B. The original non-metric English unit was the foot-candle. 1 foot-candle = 1 lumen per square foot. The unit is now deprecated. (Since $1 \text{ m}^2 = 10 \cdot 76 \text{ ft}^2$; $1 \text{ lm/ft}^2 = 10 \cdot 76 \text{ lm/m}^2 = 10 \cdot 76$ lux.)

Calculation of the illumination of a surface. If Φ is the luminous flux in lumens, A the area on which this flux falls, then the illumination is given by:

$$E = \frac{\Phi}{A} \text{ lumens per unit area}$$

(d) REFLECTANCE. Almost all 'seeing' is by reflected light. It is necessary to compare the reflecting properties of various materials and surfaces. This is done by the concept of a 'reflection factor', i.e.:

$$\text{Reflection factor } (\rho) = \frac{\text{lumens reflected from a surface}}{\text{lumens incident upon a surface}}$$

e.g., the reflection factor of a typical European forehead is $0 \cdot 3$.

(e) TRANSMISSION. Materials range from being fully transparent to completely opaque. The transmission property of a material is expressed in terms of:

$$\text{Transmission factor } (\tau) = \frac{\text{lumens transmitted by a material}}{\text{lumens incident upon the material}}$$

(f) DENSITY. This concept provides an alternative way of describing the transmission properties of photographic materials and is of particular interest to television studio engineers who are dealing with films. It is defined as follows:

$$\text{Density } (d) = \log_{10} \frac{1}{\tau}$$

where τ is the transmission factor. For example, if 10% of the incident light passes through a material, then $\tau = 0.1$ and $d = \log_{10} 10 = 1.0$. Similarly, for 1% transmission, $\tau = 0.01$ and $d = \log_{10} 100 = 2.0$.

The greater the density of a material, the smaller the amount of light passed by it. For photographic measurement purposes, a strip of material having a transparency which varies in steps along its length is often used. If the transmission factors of successive steps have a constant *ratio* to one another, the steps appear to the eye to change uniformly. Since the corresponding densities also change uniformly it follows that the density rating of a material gives a much more meaningful idea of its 'transparency' than the transmission factor itself. Suppose, for example, that the steps on the test strip have a constant ratio of 2:1 with transmission factors of $\tau = 1\%, 2\%,$ 4%, 8%, and 16%. The corresponding values for density are $d = 2.0, 1.7, 1.4, 1.1,$ and 0.8. The values for d thus change by regular steps of 0.3 and an observer easily correlates this linear reduction in density with the (apparently) linear increases in transmitted light.

(g) LUMINANCE (L). This is a measure of the light emitted from a surface. Light may be emitted by direct radiation from a source at a surface, or it may be reflected by a surface which is bathed in incident light. The word luminance is equally applicable to both cases since the result is the same; i.e., the surface emits light.

There are various units used to measure luminance. Some of these (e.g., group A below) express luminance in terms of light-source units (i.e., candelas) per unit area, whilst others (group B below) express the same thing in terms of light-flux units (i.e., lumens) per unit area. It should be mentioned that group A units are not restricted to describing the luminance of light 'sources' nor are group B units used only for non-directly radiating surfaces. The units are completely interchangeable.

Group A: using the luminous intensity unit; the candela.
(i) *nit*   One nit   = 1 candela per sq m (cd/m^2),
(ii) *stilb* (sb) One stilb = 1 candela per sq cm (cd/cm^2).
    (*N.B.* Since 1 m^2 = 10^4 cm^2; 1 stilb = 10^4 nits.)

Group B: using the luminous 'flux' unit; the lumen.
(i) *apostilb*   One apostilb = 1 lumen per sq m (lm/m^2),
(ii) *lambert* (L) One lambert = 1 lumen per sq cm (lm/cm^2).
    (*N.B.* 1 lambert = 10^4 apostilbs.)

Conversion. If the luminance of a plane surface of infinite extent is 1 candela per unit area, the equivalent rate per second of emission of luminous flux from a uniformly diffusing surface is π lumens per unit area (not 4π as may at first be thought). Thus:

$$1 \text{ nit} = 3\cdot14 \text{ apostilbs} \quad \text{and} \quad 1 \text{ stilb} = 3\cdot14 \text{ lamberts.}^{[1]}$$

It will be noticed from the above sections (c) and (g) respectively that 1 lux = 1 lumen per square metre and 1 apostilb = 1 lumen per square metre; i.e., in magnitude 1 lux = 1 apostilb. This appears to be an unnecessary duplication of units. However, the lux is a unit of illumination; i.e., it is a measure of how much flux falls upon a surface. Conversely, the apostilb is a measure of how much light flux is emitted *from* a surface.

An example serves to illustrate the point. Suppose that the illumination of a surface having a reflection factor of 0·4 is 100 lux; i.e., 100 lm/m². The luminance of the surface is $0\cdot4 \times 100$ lm/m² = 40 apostilbs.

In general for a given surface, the two quantities are related as follows:

$$\text{Luminance in apostilbs} = \text{reflection factor} \times \text{illumination in lux}$$

The concept of luminance in television. In monochrome television the amplitude of the video signal changes between its limiting black and peak-white levels, as the brightness of details in the scene varies between the minimum and maximum values accommodated by the system. At any instant, the video signal describes the amount of light falling upon the camera target-plate element being scanned at that moment. Since this in turn depends upon the amount of light being reflected from the scene, the camera describes the luminance of the scene, element by element.

The picture information during the active line is therefore properly described as a luminance signal. This signal is preserved as an essential part of the compatible colour television video signal and is designated by the symbol Y'.

Typical luminance levels of monochrome and colour receiver screens are of the order 120 nits (i.e., 120 cd/m²) and 80 nits respectively.

By way of comparison, a typical 100 watt filament lamp emits a flux of 1260 lumens, whilst the light output of a fluorescent tube may be of the order of 50 lumens per watt.

(h) SI PHOTOMETRIC UNITS. The proliferation of light units has led to confusion. The recommended SI (Système International d'Unités) units are reduced to four:

---

[1] The non-metric English units corresponding to the above are:
Group A (i) 1 candela per sq ft (cd/ft²),

     (ii) 1 candela per sq in (cd/in²);
Group B (i) 1 footlambert = 1 lumen per sq ft (lm/ft²).

Conversion factors
(a) Since 1 m² = 10·76 ft² it follows that:

$$1 \text{ cd/ft}^2 = 10\cdot76 \text{ cd/m}^2 = 10\cdot76 \text{ nits}$$
$$1 \text{ footlambert} = 1 \text{ lm/ft}^2 = 10\cdot76 \text{ lm/m}^2 = 10\cdot76 \text{ apostilbs}$$

(b) 1 cd/ft² = 3·14 lm/ft² = 3·14 footlamberts.

Table 1.1 SI photometric units

Quality being measured	SI unit	Abbreviation
Luminous intensity (I)	candela	cd
Luminous flux (Φ)	lumen	lm
Illumination (E)	lux (i.e., lm/m^2)	lx
Luminance (L)	candela per square metre*	cd/m^2

* This corresponds to the unit *nit* defined earlier. The 'nit' is not, however, included as a recommended SI term. It appears illogical to drop the word 'nit' but retain 'lux'. Dropping the word 'lux' would still further reduce the facts which need to be remembered.

(i) THE INVERSE SQUARE LAW OF ILLUMINATION. The illumination of a surface decreases as the square of the distance of the illuminated surface from the light source. At 1 metre from a source of 1 candela the illumination of a surface is (by definition) 1 lux (i.e., 1 lumen per square metre). At 2 metres the illumination is $1/2^2 = 0\cdot25$ lux.

In general, let I (cd) be the luminous intensity of the source; d (m) the distance of the surface from the source, and E (lux: i.e., lm/m^2) be the illumination of the surface. There are two cases to be considered (see Fig. 1.3):

(i) If the rays of light from the source are perpendicular to the surface at which the illumination is to be measured, then:

$$E = \frac{I}{d^2} \text{ lux}$$

(ii) If the rays of light from the source are at an angle θ to a perpendicular drawn from the surface, then:

$$E = \frac{I \cos \theta}{d^2} \text{ lux}$$

This is sometimes referred to as the cosine law of illumination.

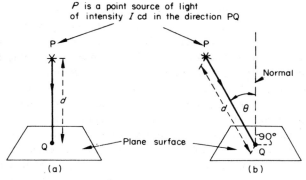

Fig. 1.3 Inverse square law of illumination

9

The human eye (Fig. 1.4)

Light passes into the eye through the pupil. The diameter of this aperture increases to allow in more light in twilight conditions and reduces to a very small size when the light intensity is high. A ring of muscular tissue called the iris regulates the size of the pupil.

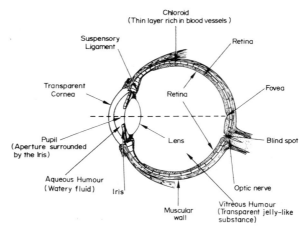

Fig. 1.4 *The human eye*

As with a camera, the sharpest image is formed when the aperture is small. In twilight our vision is blurred and indistinct.

A convex lens brings the image to a focus on the retina. This is the light-sensitive screen at the back of the eye which reacts to the arrival of light by translating the e.m. energy into information which is passed by nerve fibres to the brain. The retina consists of a very large number of light-sensitive cells. These are of two types; rods and cones, so called because of their shapes. Rods are sensitive only to the intensity of the incident light and not to colour. It is the cones which are responsible for normal colour vision. During daylight the process of 'seeing' is mainly by the action of the cones. When the lighting level falls below about 1 lux the cones cease to act. At night the rods alone are responsible for seeing. Their sensitivity is some 10,000 times as great as the cones but they create a 'monochrome' image only.

Exactly opposite the centre of the lens, on the axis passing through it, is a small area known as the fovea, of about 1 mm diameter, which consists of cones only. The fovea contains some 34,000 cones, each with its own separate nerve fibre going back to the brain in the bunch of fibres collectively known as the optic nerve. The fovea is the area of maximum visual resolution (but NOT maximum sensitivity). When the eye concentrates attention upon a small detail of the total scene in its complete field of vision, it is on to the fovea that the image of this detail is automatically directed. The fovea subtends an angle of about 1·7° only of the 180° or so total field of vision (see Fig. 1.5). At night, there being no rods in the fovea, a small detail in the twilight scene is only observed when the eye 'looks' slightly to the side of the object so that its image falls away from the fovea and on to an area where the very much more highly sensitive rods are present.

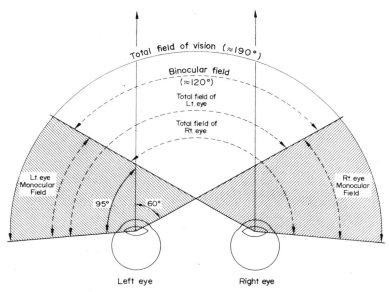

Fig. 1.5 *Showing the approximate visual field of the eyes*

Moving away from the area near the fovea, the cells no longer have individual nerve fibres but are arranged in groups; with several cells sharing one fibre. It has been estimated that there are some 6 to 7 million cones and 100 to 120 million rods in each eye with about 1 million individual fibres in the optic nerve. No cells are present in the centre of the region where the optic nerve is connected to the retina and this small point is known as the 'blind spot'. This passes unnoticed for two reasons. Firstly, the part of the image which falls on the blind spot of one eye is seen by the other (and vice versa), and secondly, incessant small movements of the eye continuously shift the position of the image on the retina so that all of it is seen.

Colour vision and colour mixing

The eye is not uniformly sensitive over the visible spectrum. Figure 1.6 shows the relative response of the 'average eye' to light of constant luminance projected at various wavelengths throughout the spectrum. The curve peaks in the yellow-green region and it is interesting to note that a curve showing the distribution of energy in sunlight, peaks in this same area. The full-line curve shows the average observer's subjective impression of brightness under daylight conditions. As shown by the second curve, under near dark conditions the response curve shifts to the left.

11

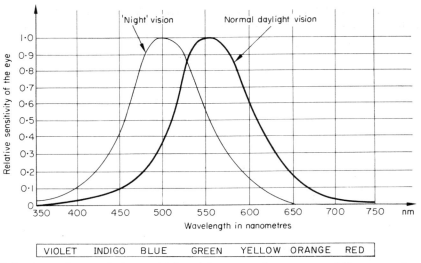

Fig. 1.6 *Approximate relative sensitivity of the average human eye to different wavelengths*

Light of a single wavelength is said to be monochromatic. Our ability to distinguish a variety of different colours might be supposed to indicate the presence of an equal number of different types of cones in the retina; each type being 'tuned' to only a small band of frequencies. If the cones were monochromatic in this way, then a given colour impression could *only* be produced by e.m. energy having the appropriate wavelength. This is not, however, true. Shining monochromatic light on the retina is not the only way of creating a given colour impression. For example, some monochromatic yellows may be matched by the simultaneous arrival at the retina of red and green light.[1] Almost all colours can be matched by mixing only three coloured lights. These are referred to as 'primaries' and those used are red, green, and blue.

This behaviour of the eye is consistent with there being three types of cones only, each having a different response curve; the three response curves overlapping in such a way that all spectral colours are beneath either one only, or else partly under two, of the three curves. Figure 1.7 illustrates this. It will be seen that yellow activates both red and green cones. It is logical to deduce that when red and green light reaches the retina at the same time, the simultaneous excitation of the red and green cones gives a mental impression which is indistinguishable from monochromatic yellow.

Coloured objects

In order for colour to be seen, e.m. energy has to reach the eye. We see an object by the light reflected from it. If it looks green in daylight, then this must imply that

---

[1] Not all yellows can be matched in this way; e.g., sodium yellow cannot be exactly reproduced by any mixture of red and green television primaries.

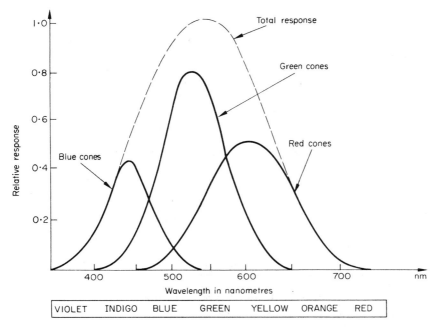

Fig. 1.7 *Hypothetical relative sensitivities of the suggested three types of cones in the retina*

although it is bathed in 'white' sunlight, it is only reflecting the green part of the light back to our eyes. The remainder of the spectrum is 'absorbed'.

An object therefore looks coloured because it only reflects part of the visible spectrum and absorbs the rest. The colour stems from the incident light. Grass does not look green under sodium lighting because there *is* no green light for it to reflect.

Spectral and non-spectral colours

The profusion of colours in the world around us very much exceeds the individual colours seen in the visible spectrum. The reason for this is not hard to see. As we scan the spectrum we look in turn at a series of individual monochromatic colours. Clearly if we choose to combine any two or more of these there is a vast total of possible combinations; the more so because the proportions as well as the 'colour' of the constituents may be varied.

As has been said already, it is possible to produce the sensation of many of the spectral colours (e.g., yellow) by the combination of two other spectral colours; one having a shorter and the other a longer wavelength than the spectral colour itself. It is important to realize, however, that there are many more colours which do *not* appear in the spectrum as monochromatic colours. Purples are notable examples of non-spectral colours. These are produced by combinations of reds and blues which are at opposite ends of the visible spectrum.

13

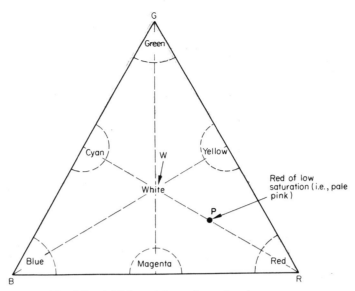

Fig. 1.8   *Additive mixing colour triangle*

In colour, this equilateral triangle would give a visual indication of the effect of mixing the red, green, and blue primary colours shown at the corners.

Figure 1.7 shows that the red and blue cones cannot be activated simultaneously by any single wavelength, without the green cones being activated at the same time. The region of overlap of the red and blue cones falls under the response curve of the green cones and the visual sensation to monochromatic light in this region is predominantly green. Separate red and blue lights however, falling outside—and on opposite sides of—the green response curve, when present simultaneously give the colour sensation we know as purple.

The colour of an object is determined by pigments. These are chemicals which create a given colour by subtracting parts of the spectrum of the incident white light. The remaining light is reflected and this gives the object its characteristic colour.

Making colours by mixing paint pigments may therefore be described as a process of *subtractive mixing*, since each added pigment subtracts more from the white light and leaves less to be reflected to the eye.

Conversely, it is possible to create colours by the addition of coloured lights. This is known as *additive mixing*.

These two distinctly different processes are now discussed in turn.

Additive mixing. To the colour television engineer, this is the most important aspect of colour theory to grasp. It is fortunately simpler to remember than the theory of subtractive mixing. A colour television receiver does not create colour by starting with white light and subtracting parts from it. Here colours are created by mixing

14

red, green and blue lights. This is vividly demonstrated if red, green and blue beams of light are made to overlap on a screen in a darkened room. Plate 1[1] shows the result. The following should be committed to memory:

$$\begin{aligned} \text{red} + \text{green} &= \text{yellow} \\ \text{red} + \text{blue} &= \text{magenta} \\ \text{blue} + \text{green} &= \text{cyan} \\ \text{red} + \text{blue} + \text{green} &= \text{white} \end{aligned}$$

Red, green, and blue are called primary colours, while yellow, magenta, and cyan are known as complementaries. If a complementary is added in appropriate proportions to the one primary which it itself does not contain (e.g., yellow + blue), white is produced.[2]

Subtractive mixing

This may be demonstrated by imagining that various colour pigments are superimposed one upon another. Plate 2[1] illustrates the result when the three complementary colours, yellow, magenta, and cyan are used. These are shown partially overlapping so that the effects of any combination of them may be seen. It must be remembered that it is no longer light sources that are being considered. White light is shining down on the pigments which then absorb parts of the spectrum and reflect the rest. The results are summarized below:

$$\begin{aligned} \text{yellow} &= \text{white} - \text{blue} \\ \text{magenta} &= \text{white} - \text{green} \\ \text{cyan} &= \text{white} - \text{red} \end{aligned}$$

$$\begin{aligned} \text{yellow and magenta} &= \text{white} - \text{blue} - \text{green} = \text{red} \\ \text{yellow and cyan} &= \text{white} - \text{blue} - \text{red} = \text{green} \\ \text{magenta and cyan} &= \text{white} - \text{green} - \text{red} = \text{blue} \end{aligned}$$

$$\text{yellow and magenta and cyan} = \text{white} - \text{blue} - \text{green} - \text{red} = \text{black}$$

These expressions are intended to show the sequence of events when the pigments are added in turn. For example, yellow on its own merely subtracts blue light leaving the red and green parts of the spectrum which when seen together look yellow. Magenta on the other hand, takes out green leaving only red and blue which we see as magenta. When the two pigments, yellow and magenta, are added, there is only one colour which both reflect. This is red, which is what is seen.

Sometimes the word 'primaries' is used in connection with artists' pigments. Three are quoted from which other colours may be made. These are often loosely described as yellow, blue, and red. Blue and yellow are said to produce green, etc. In fact, the colours referred to are yellow, cyan (blue), and magenta (red). The

[1] Inserted between pages 102–103.

[2] In the general sense, two coloured lights are said to be complementary if together they make white light. Used in this way it is equally permissible to say that yellow is complementary to blue or that blue is complementary to yellow.

15

description 'primary colour' is better reserved for the additive primaries, red, blue, and green, while the others may then be called pigment (or artists') primaries.

Grassman's law

It is found experimentally that the eye behaves as though the 'outputs' of the three types of cones are additive. The subjective impression which is gained when red, green, and blue lights reach the eye simultaneously, may be 'matched' by a single light source having a colour which is judged the same as that recorded by the eye when receiving the three separate primaries, and of *a luminance numerically equal to the sum of the luminances of the three primaries*. This apparent property of the eye of producing a response which depends upon the algebraic sum of the red, green, and blue inputs is referred to as Grassman's law. Because the eye behaves in this way, it is possible in studying the theory of colour (i.e., colorimetry), to deduce the net effect of various separate light sources by applying the simple rules of algebraic addition and subtraction.

Trichromatic units

In the whole of the remainder of this work, only additive mixing need be considered.

White has been seen to be reproduced by adding red, green, and blue light. Clearly the intensity of each may be varied. The following luminance equation expresses the approximate quantities of the three colour television primaries, which are necessary to produce one lumen of white light:

$$1 \text{ lm of white} = 0.30 \text{ lm of red} + 0.59 \text{ lm of green} + 0.11 \text{ lm of blue} \qquad (1)$$

These proportions are referred to many times during a study of colour television engineering. For some purposes however, they make things unduly complicated. To overcome this the concept of trichromatic units is used. By definition, when measured in T-units, white light is said to be made up of equal quantities of the three primaries. Further, the magnitude of the T-unit is such that:

$$1 \text{ } lumen \text{ of white} = 1 \text{ T-unit of red} + 1 \text{ T-unit of green} + 1 \text{ T-unit of blue.} \quad (2)$$

i.e.,

$$1 \text{ lm white} = 1 \text{ T(R)} + 1 \text{ T(G)} + 1 \text{ T(B)}$$

A comparison of (1) and (2) shows that:

$$
\begin{aligned}
1 \text{ T-unit of red} &= 0.3 \text{ lumen} \\
1 \text{ T-unit of green} &= 0.59 \text{ lumen} \\
1 \text{ T-unit of blue} &= 0.11 \text{ lumen}
\end{aligned}
$$

It is thus easy to translate a given number of T-units of any primary into lumens if necessary. Meanwhile, by the use of T-units, the awkward numbers are removed from a great deal of the discussion of colour theory.

16

Expression (1) is an application of Grassman's Law, i.e., the effective luminance of the three sources is the sum of the three. This law may also now be applied using T-units. It follows from (2) that:

$$3 \text{ T-units of white} = 1\ T(R) + 1\ T(G) + 1\ T(B)$$
$$\text{or} \qquad 1\ T(W) = \tfrac{1}{3} T(R) + \tfrac{1}{3} T(G) + \tfrac{1}{3} T(B)$$

Colour triangles and chromaticity diagrams

A colour triangle is a diagram which allows the relationship between given chosen primaries and the colours which may be obtained by mixing them, to be portrayed in a simple and convenient form. Carried to their most sophisticated form (e.g., in the C.I.E. chromaticity diagram), they become devices which allow *any* colour to be precisely designated numerically in terms of co-ordinates on the diagram.[1]

Although in their simplest form colour triangles often give an actual pictorial idea of the approximate range of colours which are available by mixing three given colours, this is not true of the more sophisticated diagrams. The purpose of these is to provide a means of numerical specification of any colour under discussion but *not* to give a visual impression of that colour. Whilst a true reproduction of the actual colour might be an added asset, it is not in fact possible to make such a diagram. The reason for this is that the range of colours which can be created by printing or photographic techniques falls short of the total range of colours which occur in natural scenes and may also be less than the range of colours obtainable by the additive mixing of the primary coloured lights used in colour television. Because of this limitation, diagrams in colour which purport to show the range of colours which can be obtained by the additive mixing of three colour television primaries, must be in part inaccurate. The areas and extent of the inaccuracies will vary according to the red, green, and blue primaries actually in use in a given television system.

A detailed study of the development of these diagrams is not, however, necessary to the majority of colour television engineers. They are therefore introduced only in an elementary way to show their basic principles and for the added insight they give into colour theory.

Figure 1.8 shows an equilateral triangle with the three primaries in the corners. The colours formed by mixing red and green are shown along the side RG. Yellow falls midway between red and green, with orange on one side of it and 'yellowish green' on the other. Similarly magenta falls between red and blue, and cyan is between blue and green. Contributions from *all three primaries* are needed to create all hues which lie *within* the triangle, as distinct from on its boundaries.

At the centre of the triangle the contributions of the three primaries are equal so that this is the position of white (see **W**).

The two colours connected by any straight line drawn diametrically across the

---

[1] C.I.E. stands for Commission Internationale de l'Eclairage. The methods of measuring colour recommended by this international committee are widely used.

triangle to pass through W are complementary colours; i.e., together they form white (e.g., red and cyan, blue and yellow, etc.).

HUE AND SATURATION. At point R, red is completely pure and is said to be *fully saturated*. On moving towards W on the line RW, the red becomes diluted with white so that the pure red changes to a pastel shade of red (pink) and finally the red tint disappears altogether at point W.

A colour is said to be *desaturated* when white is added to it. In colour technology, the word 'hue' is used to describe the characteristic which normally is known as colour.

To describe a given colour impression, three qualities have to be considered. These are brightness (i.e., *luminance*), *hue*, and *saturation*. A colour triangle is only two dimensional and shows hue and saturation but not brightness. In Fig. 1.8 point P represents a red hue of low saturation. Another dimension (e.g., out of the paper, along a line perpendicular to point P) would be needed to show the brightness of the red hue at P. However, in a television signal, it has already been pointed out that the brightness of a colour is transmitted as the *luminance* signal. The other two qualities of *hue* and *saturation*, hence represent the extra information which has to be transmitted in a colour television signal. A colour triangle is therefore helpful in demonstrating what it is that has to be accommodated by the 'chrominance' (i.e., colour-bearing) signal which, when transmitted with the luminance signal, will

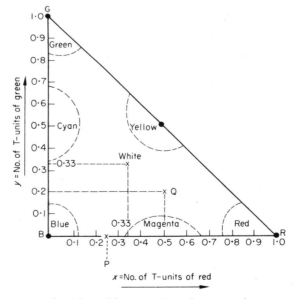

Fig. 1.9 *Additive mixing colour triangle*

In colour, this dimensioned right-angled triangle allows any hue available by mixing the given primaries, to be identified by quoting two ordinates, i.e., the number of T-units of red and green. Examples are given in the text.

18

provide the colour receiver with a complete description of the colour in the scene, i.e., its hue, saturation, and brightness.

Only the last of these qualities is of interest to a monochrome receiver.

A colour diagram of the form discussed, simply shows all hues which may be derived from the three chosen primaries shown at the corners. These hues all fall within the boundaries of the triangle.

The diagram becomes more useful if it allows the proportions of the three primaries which are needed to create a given hue to be read off and also allows the position of the hue to be designated simply by quoting co-ordinates. It is possible to use an equilateral triangle for this purpose but a right-angled triangle is simpler and more convenient to use.

Figure 1.9 shows such a triangle. Let the quantity of each hue shown, be 1 T-unit. Red is plotted along the x axis and green along the y axis. The amount of blue present in a given hue is deduced by a simple application of Grassman's Law. Since 1 T-unit of each hue has been specified, the sum of the red, green, and blue components of a given hue is unity. Hence the number of T-units of blue is found by subtracting the sum of the red and green T-units from 1.

Two examples will serve to show how the triangle is used:

(a) *The hue 'Q'* This hue is located by quoting the co-ordinates R = 0·5, G = 0·2. These numbers also indicate that 1 T-unit of the hue 'Q' contains 0·5 T-units of red and 0·2 T-units of green. It follows that the amount of blue is $1 - (0·5 + 0·2) = 0·3$ T-units, i.e., 1 T-unit of Q = 0·5 T(R) + 0·2 T(G) + 0·3 T(B).

(b) *The hue 'P'* This hue is located on the x axis. Its co-ordinates are $x = 0·25$, $y = 0$. One T-unit of the hue at P thus consists of 0·25 T-units of red, 0 T-units of green, and $1 - 0·25 = 0·75$ T-units of blue.

C.I.E. chromaticity diagram

The triangles discussed are not of universal application since they only show the hues obtainable from the specified primaries. No three primaries exist from which all the colours of the spectrum and all the non-spectral colours (i.e., the purples) can be produced.

In the C.I.E. diagram, hypothetical primaries are used and this allows an all-embracing colour diagram to be made. Figure 1.10 shows the form of this chromaticity diagram. The fictitious primaries are situated at the corners of the triangle and all the spectral colours fall along the curved part of the horseshoe-shaped diagram which lies within the triangle. This curved part of the horseshoe shape is marked in nanometres to allow monochromatic colours to be identified by reference to their wavelengths. No such calibration appears on the base of the horseshoe because it is there that the non-spectral purple colours are situated and for these non-monochromatic colours, wavelength has of course no meaning.

Inside the horseshoe shape some information has been added which would not normally appear on a C.I.E. diagram. The full-line triangle RGB shows the range of

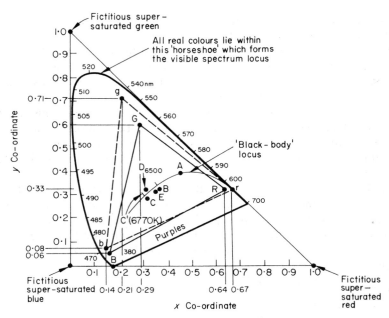

Fig. 1.10 C.I.E. chromaticity diagram

The triangles RGB and rgb enclose the ranges of hues which can be reproduced by colour television display tubes using red, green, and blue primaries having the *x* and *y* co-ordinates of the points, R, G, B and r, g, b respectively.

hues which can be produced by a colour television system using the primaries in use at the time of writing in the U.K., whilst the dotted triangle shows the traditional NTSC primaries. The latter have a somewhat greater chromaticity range but those now in use are chosen because the phosphors are brighter whilst the chromaticity range is perfectly adequate for high quality colour pictures.

The C.I.E. co-ordinates for the chosen primaries are quoted as part of the specification of a colour television system. Those for the two sets of primaries referred to are listed in Table 1.2.

Table 1.2 C.I.E. chromaticity diagram *x* and *y* co-ordinates for colour television display tube primaries

Colour	Present primaries used in U.K.			Previously used primaries (traditional NTSC)		
	x	*y*	Fig. 1.10 reference	*x*	*y*	Fig. 1.10 reference
Red	0·64	0·33	R	0·67	0·33	r
Green	0·29	0·60	G	0·21	0·71	g
Blue	0·15	0·06	B	0·14	0·08	b

Also shown on the C.I.E. diagram of Fig. 1.10 is the 'black body locus', the significance of which is discussed below.

Colour temperature

The spectrum of light emitted by a full radiator changes as its temperature is raised. The range of hues may be shown on a C.I.E. diagram by a line which is referred to as the full radiator—or black body—locus (sometimes called the Planckian locus). This locus is particularly useful in the classification of 'whites' (see Fig. 1.10).

Some light sources have a spectral energy distribution which corresponds to that of a full radiator when the latter is held at a particular temperature. For some purposes it is convenient to classify such a light source by quoting its *colour temperature*, which is defined as the temperature (in Kelvin) to which a full radiator would have to be raised to emit light of the same character. The colour temperature is not the actual temperature of the light source itself. To illustrate this, when a tungsten lamp filament is held at a temperature of 2800 K it emits a white light which is classified as corresponding to a colour temperature of 2854 K, since this is the temperature which a full radiator would need to have to radiate a matching white.

The term colour temperature is only strictly applicable to light sources which may be precisely matched by a full radiator. The concept is, however, extended to include sources which give light that can be nearly—but not exactly—matched by a full radiator. The expression *correlated colour temperature* is used to describe the light from such sources. This is the temperature at which a full radiator produces a light that most nearly matches the light from the given source. As an example, the point C in Fig. 1.10 may be nearly matched by point C' (which is the nearest point on the black body locus to point C) and hence the source C is said to have a correlated colour temperature of 6770 K. Expressed in another way, a full radiator at 6770 K yields a white which is very much the same as the white light corresponding to that which has the C.I.E. chromaticity co-ordinates of point C.

Standard illuminants (i.e., standard 'whites')

There are many different spectral distributions which we would subjectively classify as 'white'. These range from 'warm whites' which have a preponderance of energy at the longer wavelength (i.e., the red) end of the spectrum, to 'cold whites' which have more energy at the shorter wavelength (i.e., the blue) end.

It is sometimes necessary to specify what is to be used as the white for a given purpose (e.g., for colour television). There are five main 'standard whites'. These are referred to as Illuminants A, B, C, D_{6500}, and E. The approximate spectral distribution curves of these are sketched in Fig. 1.11 and they are also identified as points in the C.I.E. diagram Fig. 1.10. Their main characteristics are listed below:

ILLUMINANT A. This is a warm white which corresponds to a colour temperature of 2854 K. A tungsten filament lamp radiates light of this 'shade' of white when operating

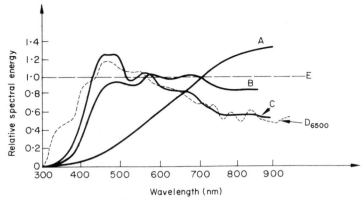

Fig. 1.11 *Curves showing the approximate energy distribution for the 'standard whites', illuminants A, B, C, D$_{6500}$, and E*

at a temperature of 2800 K. Note that because it may be *exactly* matched by a full radiator, Illuminant A appears as a point which lies on the black body locus of the C.I.E. diagram.

ILLUMINANT B. This approximates to direct noon sunlight (as distinct from light from an overcast sky). It may be obtained in a laboratory from an Illuminant A source by the use of special filters. Unlike Illuminant A it cannot be exactly matched by a full radiator but is nearly matched when the latter has a temperature of 4800 K and may therefore be said to have a correlated colour temperature of 4800 K. Note that in Fig. 1.10 B falls near to—but not on—the black body locus.

ILLUMINANT C. This is sometimes referred to as normal daylight and has the quality of the diffuse light from an overcast sky. Again it may be obtained from Illuminant A by using special filters. Like B it cannot be exactly matched by a full radiator but only nearly so. As shown in Fig. 1.10 the nearest point on the black body locus is at 6770 K and so Illuminant C is said to have a correlated colour temperature of 6770 K. It is the white which at one time was aimed at in colour television.

ILLUMINANT D$_{6500}$. This is the white now adopted for colour television. The previously chosen Illuminant C lies slightly to the magenta side of the black body locus whereas D$_{6500}$ is slightly on the green side. When compared with daylight, Illuminants B and C are deficient in wavelengths below 400 nm. Modern whiteners and fluorescent dyestuffs require the stimulation of ultraviolet light, since they absorb energy at these short wavelengths and re-radiate energy which falls in the visible spectrum. The spectral distribution of D$_{6500}$, as shown in Fig. 1.11, has a greater energy content below 400 nm than B and C and is designed to simulate 'standard daylight', which may be taken to be a mixture of direct sunlight and diffuse 'skylight'. D$_{6500}$ cannot

22

be obtained from Illuminant A (as B and C can be, by using filters), but a close approximation to it is possible using other physical sources. A light similar in appearance to it would be obtained using a full radiator at 6500 K but coloured materials requiring the stimulation of ultraviolet light for their true daylight appearance, would not be exactly matched. The white corresponding to D_{6500} may be matched by the right mixture of light from the three phosphors of a colour television cathode ray tube.

ILLUMINANT E. Otherwise known as 'equal energy white', this is a hypothetical white which would be produced if all the wavelengths in the visible spectrum were present with equal energy. Illuminant E is a concept which is of use in colorimetry work to simplify theoretical studies.

Colour charts or atlases

These allow a direct comparison under daylight between the colour of an object and carefully graded hues. They are arranged so that there is a just perceptible change from one hue to another. The best known is the American Munsell system. The chart is in the form of a circle, divided into ten main segments; e.g., green, green-yellow, yellow, yellow-red, red, etc. Each of these is sub-divided into ten smaller sections. Diametrically opposite hues are complementary and saturation reduces from maximum at the circumference through sixteen steps to the centre, where white is situated.

2
Colour Television Signals

A colour television receiver creates a coloured picture by the simultaneous production of red, green, and blue pictures which are so closely adjacent element by element that the visual impression is the same as though the three pictures were exactly superimposed upon one another. At any instant during the scanning process the transmitted signal must indicate the proportions of red, green, and blue light which are present in the element being scanned.

As indicated in chapter 1, the picture information in a compatible transmitted signal consists of two parts; a *luminance* signal representative of the brightness of the element being scanned and a *chrominance* signal which bears the extra data on hue and saturation necessary for a complete description of the colour of the picture element. The luminance signal alone serves the needs of a monochrome receiver, producing at the c.r.t. a voltage proportional to picture brightness. In a colour receiver, the ultimate requirement at the display device is three voltages proportional to the red, green, and blue content of the scanned element.

Symbols

The red, green, blue, and luminance voltages are often written as E_R, E_G, E_B, and E_Y. As a simplification, in this book, the prefix E is omitted and the symbols R, G, B, and Y represent these voltages directly, unless otherwise stated. These usually appear 'primed' as R', G', B', and Y', which indicates that the voltages have been 'gamma corrected'.

Gamma (γ) correction

Regarded overall a television system ought (as a first approximation) to be linear; i.e., the light emitted from the receiver should be directly proportional to the light falling upon the camera target plate. However, a receiver c.r.t. does not emit light in direct proportion to the voltage applied between grid and cathode. This is chiefly due to the non-linearity of the beam current against grid voltage characteristic, rather than the light output against beam current characteristic, which is largely linear. If the luminance (L) of the screen is plotted against the grid-to-cathode input voltage (V_g), the curve (for low values of V_g) is roughly parabolic, i.e., $L \propto (V_g)^2$.

In general terms the non-linear relationship between light output and voltage input may be expressed by writing $L \propto (V_g)^\gamma$. The symbol used for the index is the Greek letter gamma. To compensate for this non-linearity at the receiver c.r.t., an opposite distortion, referred to as gamma correction, is introduced at the picture source. If E is the camera voltage resulting from a given light input (L), then a gamma corrected voltage of $E^{1/\gamma}$ will yield a light output at the receiver which is directly proportional to the light input at the camera. Hence:

$$\text{Receiver light output} \propto (V_g)^\gamma \propto (E^{1/\gamma})^\gamma \propto E$$

It is presupposed that the camera voltage E has been arranged to be linearly related to the light input. In the U.K. the chosen value for γ is 2·2, i.e., the transmitted signal is said to have a *gamma* of $1/2·2 = 0·45$.

Figure 2.1 shows a plot of both the transmitter and receiver characteristics.

For the transmitter, the x axis is the camera voltage output (assumed to be directly proportional to the scenic luminance), and the y axis is the gamma-corrected version of this voltage (i.e., $y = x^{1/\gamma} = x^{1/2·2}$). For the receiver the x axis is the voltage input

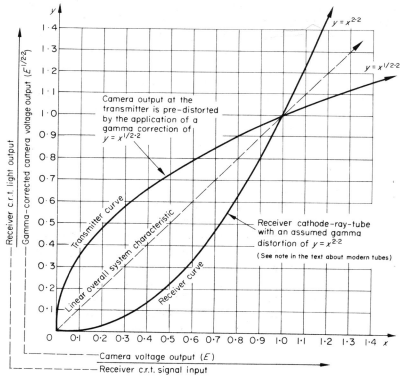

Fig. 2.1 *Transmitter and receiver 'gamma' curves*
(for $\gamma = 2·2$)

25

to the c.r.t. and the y axis is the c.r.t.'s light output (i.e., $y = x^\gamma = x^{2.2}$). Both axes are scaled in relative amplitudes, from 0 to 1.0; i.e., 1.0 represents the maximum value the quantity may have and all other levels then fall between 0 and 1.0.

Suppose a given scenic luminance produces a linearly proportional camera voltage of 0.7. An input of 0.7 (along the x axis) gives an output from the transmitter curve of 0.85. This represents the gamma corrected voltage which goes forward to modulate the transmitter vision carrier. To see what happens at the receiver an input of 0.85 is applied (along the x axis) to the receiver curve. The y axis shows that the output is 0.7. A scenic luminance of 70% maximum at the transmitter hence gives rise to 70% maximum brightness at the receiver.

If all the values on the x axis are processed in this way; i.e., passed successively through the transmitter and receiver characteristics, a straight line is produced which represents the overall linear characteristic of the system. This is shown dotted on the diagram. It is a graph of $y = x^n$ where the exponent n is the product of the exponents of the two curves: i.e., $y = x^{2.2 \times 1/2.2} = x^1$.

The section of the curves beyond $x = 1$, $y = 1$, is the region of overmodulation.

In a more general sense the words 'system gamma' are used to express the relationship between the light output at the receiver and the light input at the camera, i.e., to describe the overall 'light characteristic' of the entire system. Used in this sense the system described above would be said to have a gamma of unity because the 'net exponent' is unity.

Despite what has been said above, however, it has been found that many modern receiver cathode ray tubes have a gamma of the order of 2.8·rather than 2.2. Since, as stated earlier, the normal camera gamma correction factor employed is $1/2.2$, the overall system clearly has a gamma of approximately $2.8 \times 1/2.2 = 1.27$, i.e., the system has a rising characteristic such that:

$$\text{Light output} \propto (\text{light input})^{1.27}$$

It has been suggested that a rising gamma such as this is desirable when the ambient lighting level in which the receiver is being viewed is low, but that an overall gamma of unity is to be preferred when the ambient lighting is bright.

Looked at objectively, the aim of a television system is to provide an acceptable contrast ratio with a minimum of 'noise'. It may be true that optimum performance does not always coincide with an overall gamma of unity and because of this the gamma at various points in the system may be adjusted to optimize the performance (as judged subjectively) rather than to establish a strict overall linearity. With telecine the gamma correction factor may vary between figures of the order of $1/2.5$ and $1/4$ because of the differing characteristics of the film itself.

Colour-difference voltages

To drive a colour receiver c.r.t. (e.g., a shadow mask tube) the voltages R', G', and B' are required. A voltage Y' is available from the demodulated luminance signal. By providing three other voltages $(R' - Y')$, $(G' - Y')$, and $(B' - Y')$, referred to as colour-difference voltages, the required R', G', and B' colour voltages are obtained by simple algebraic addition. Thus:

$$(R' - Y') + Y' = R'$$
$$(G' - Y') + Y' = G'$$
$$(B' - Y') + Y' = B'$$

Production of luminance and colour-difference voltages

Figure 2.2 shows how these voltages may be derived at the transmitter. The scene is analysed into its red, green, and blue content by passing images of it through red, green, and blue filters to three cameras. On white, these three cameras are adjusted to give equal output voltages. On 'peak-white' (i.e., maximum brightness) let the common level be taken as unity, e.g., 1 V. On greys (i.e., on whites of lower brightness) the three voltages remain equal but have a level of less than 1 V.

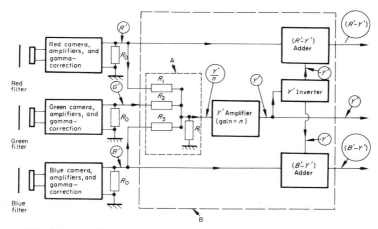

Fig. 2.2 *Production of luminance and colour-difference voltages*

To produce a voltage representative of the luminance of the scene, the proportions 0·3, 0·59, and 0·11 of R', G', and B' respectively are added.[1] Then:

$$Y' = 0·3R' + 0·59G' + 0·11B'$$

Colour difference voltages are derived by subtracting the luminance from the colour voltages. Only $(R' - Y')$ and $(B' - Y')$ are produced.

It is only necessary to transmit two of the three colour-difference signals since

[1] A separate fourth camera tube may be used to yield the Y' signal directly, but the inclusion of this is not an aid to understanding the system at this stage. It is more instructive to concentrate upon the three voltages R', G', and B' and process these. In due course the reader may find it interesting to make a study of the relative merits of three- and four-tube colour-television cameras.

the third may be derived from the other two. How this is done and the reason for not choosing $(G' - Y')$ as one of the two, is discussed in chapter 16.

A circuit in which signals are combined in given required proportions is called a matrix. The essential properties of a matrix are that it must:

(a) operate upon the input signals to establish them with the relative amplitudes and polarities needed for the combined signal;

(b) provide a method of combination which prohibits interaction (i.e., cross-talk) between the various signal sources.

Often a matrix may consist simply of resistors which act as attenuators to set the input signals at the necessary relative amplitudes. It may, however, include non-inverting and/or inverting amplifiers.

In Fig. 2.2 the dotted box marked A includes a simple resistor matrix for establishing the R', G', and B' signals in the approximate proportions 0·3, 0·59, and 0·11.[1] If the output impedances R_o of the cameras are low and R_1, R_2, and R_3 are all made much larger than both R_o and the common resistor R_c across which the Y' signal is developed, then cross-talk is minimized. If *peak-white*[2] is assumed to be present and the camera voltages are all at 1 V, the required immunity from cross-talk may be arrived at by reducing the Y' voltage across R_c to a level much lower than 1 V, and then passing the Y' signal through an amplifier to establish Y' at 1 V. This makes R_c small compared with R_1, R_2, and R_3. The resistor values for the three potential dividers $R_1 R_c$, $R_2 R_c$, and $R_3 R_c$ are therefore calculated not only to achieve the correct R', G', and B' relative levels of 0·3, 0·59, and 0·11 but also to scale down these three voltages by a factor n equal to the gain of the amplifier. In this way the resistors R_1, R_2, and R_3 serve the dual purpose of adjusting the relative amplitudes of the R', G', and B' signals and of isolating the cameras from one another.

To obtain $(R' - Y')$ and $(B' - Y')$, the Y' signal output from the Y' amplifier is first inverted (so that $+ Y'$ becomes $- Y'$) and then added to R' and B'.[3]

It follows from what has been said that the whole of the circuitry in the dotted area marked B in Fig. 2.2 could be described as a matrix into which R', G', and B' signals are fed and from which Y', $(R' - Y')$, and $(B' - Y')$ signals are taken out.

The chrominance signal

The two colour-difference signals are modulated on to sub-carriers and combined to form what is then called the chrominance signal. It is the method of modulation which marks the difference between the NTSC, PAL, and SECAM systems. This is discussed in a later chapter.

[1] In a practical encoder the proportions are corrected to three decimal places; e.g., $Y' = 0·299R' + 0·587G' + 0·114B'$.

[2] It has been suggested that the term 'peak-white', which has been widely used for years, should be dropped in favour of the expression 'white-level' and it is likely that this may be done in due course. The familiar term peak-white is used in this textbook.

[3] It is possible to obtain $(R' - Y')$ and $(B' - Y')$ directly from R', G', and B', without using the available Y' signal. Thus:
$$(R' - Y') = (1)R' - (0·3R' + 0·59G' + 0·11B') = 0·7R' - 0·59G' - 0·11B'$$
$$(B' - Y') = (1)B' - (0·3R' + 0·59G' + 0·11B') = 0·89B' - 0·3R' - 0·59G'$$

In the broadest sense the quality of *chrominance* defines the difference between a coloured area and a neutral grey of the same luminance, and the expression *chrominance information* embraces that part of a video signal which enables a colour receiver to describe an area in colour rather than in monochrome. For this reason, in colour television literature generally, the word chrominance is widely (and often confusingly) used in connection with any circuit dealing with a 'non-luminance' part of the video signal picture information; whether this be a modulated sub-carrier signal or a simple colour-difference signal.

For the sake of clarity, in this textbook the term *chrominance signal* has been reserved for the complete modulated sub-carrier signal which bears the colour-difference signals as modulation information.

Disappearance of colour-difference signals on 'whites'

The colour-difference signals equal zero when greys or whites are being transmitted. That this must be so, is easily seen.

(a) ON PEAK-WHITE. Here, $R' = G' = B' = 1.0$ but

$$Y' = 0.3R' + 0.59G' + 0.11B' = 0.3(1) + 0.59(1) + 0.11(1) = 1$$

hence

$$(R' - Y') = (1 - 1) = 0 \quad \text{and} \quad (B' - Y') = (1 - 1) = 0$$

(b) ON GREYS. Again $R' = G' = B'$ but the level is less than 1. In the general case, let the common voltage be V, then

$$Y' = 0.3R' + 0.59G' + 0.11B' = 0.3V + 0.59V + 0.11V = V(1) = V$$

hence

$$(R' - Y') = (V - V) = 0 \quad \text{and} \quad (B' - Y') = (V - V) = 0$$

The disappearance of the colour difference signals during the grey or white content of a colour scene, or completely during a monochrome transmission, is an aid to compatibility in the NTSC and PAL systems.

Values of luminance and colour-difference signals on colours

On colours, the voltages R', G', and B' are not equal. The Y' signal still represents the monochrome equivalent of the colour since the proportions 0.3, 0.59, and 0.11 taken of R', G', and B' respectively, represent the contributions which red, green, and blue light make to the luminance of the colour.

It is helpful at this stage to consider the luminance and colour-difference signals which correspond to various arbitrary colours.

(a) A DESATURATED PURPLE. The word desaturated indicates the presence of some white light so that R', G', and B' voltages must all be produced. The hue, however,

29

is purple which implies a mixture of red and blue. Hence R' and B' predominate and both must be of greater amplitude than G'. Suppose $R' = 0·7$, $G' = 0·2$, and $B' = 0·6$. The white content is represented by equal quantities of the three primaries and the actual amount must therefore be indicated by the smallest of the three; i.e., in this example G'. Thus, white is due to $0·2R'$, $0·2G'$, and $0·2B'$. The remaining $0·5R'$ and $0·4B'$ together represent the magenta hue.

(i) *To calculate the luminance signal*

$$Y' = 0·3R' + 0·59G' + 0·11B'$$
$$= 0·3(0·7) + 0·59(0·2) + 0·11(0·6)$$
$$= 0·21 + 0·118 + 0·066 = \mathbf{0·394}$$

(ii) *To calculate the colour-difference signals*

$$(R' - Y') = (0·7 - 0·394) = \mathbf{+0·306}$$
$$(B' - Y') = (0·6 - 0·394) = \mathbf{+0·206}$$

(iii) *Reception by a colour set.* In a colour receiver these three signals (i.e., the luminance at (i) and the two colour-difference signals at (ii) are recovered. In a manner described in chapter 16, the 'missing' $(G' - Y')$ colour-difference signal is recovered by combining suitable proportions of $(R' - Y')$ and $(B' - Y')$. Clearly $(G' - Y') = (0·2 - 0·394) = -0·194$, hence this—and the three signals whose values are worked out above—are recovered. Then, by a process of matrixing, the required original colour voltages are obtained. Thus:

$$R' = (R' - Y') + Y' = \quad 0·306 + 0·394 = 0·7$$
$$G' = (G' - Y') + Y' = -0·194 + 0·394 = 0·2$$
$$B' = (B' - Y') + Y' = \quad 0·206 + 0·394 = 0·6$$

(iv) *Reception by a monochrome set.* In a monochrome receiver only the luminance signal $Y' = 0·394$ is recovered. Since peak white to the same relative scale would be 1·0, it is clear that the purple colour described, shows up only as a fairly dull grey in a black-and-white picture. This is as would be expected for this colour.

(b) A DESATURATED ORANGE. To allow a comparison, let the degree of desaturation be the same as before. By interchanging the values for G' and B', so that $R' = 0·7$, $G' = 0·6$, and $B' = 0·2$, it is now red and green which predominate. These, in equal quantities would yield the complementary hue yellow, but with rather more red than green, an orange is indicated. The white content is again represented by $R' = G' = B' = 0·2$. The remaining amounts of R' and G', i.e., $R' = 0·5$ and $G' = 0·4$, together represent the orange hue.

(i) *To calculate the luminance signal*

$$Y' = 0·3R' + 0·59G' + 0·11B' = 0·3(0·7) + 0·59(0·6) + 0·11(0·2)$$
$$= 0·21 + 0·354 + 0·022 = \mathbf{0·586}$$

(ii) *To calculate the colour-difference signals*

$$(R' - Y') = (0\cdot7 - 0\cdot586) = +\mathbf{0\cdot114}$$
$$(B' - Y') = (0\cdot2 - 0\cdot586) = -\mathbf{0\cdot386}$$

(iii) *Reception by a colour set.* From the demodulated $(R' - Y')$ and $(B' - Y')$ signals, the missing $(G' - Y')$ signal is obtained. This must be of amplitude $(G' - Y') = (0\cdot6 - 0\cdot586) = 0\cdot014$. Matrixing then yields:

$$R' = (R' - Y') + Y' = +0\cdot114 + 0\cdot586 = 0\cdot7$$
$$G' = (G' - Y') + Y' = +0\cdot014 + 0\cdot586 = 0\cdot6$$
$$B' = (B' - Y') + Y' = -0\cdot386 + 0\cdot586 = 0\cdot2$$

(iv) *Reception by a monochrome set.* The luminance signal only is recovered. This is of amplitude $Y' = 0\cdot586$. As would be expected, the orange gives rise to a brighter grey (i.e., the screen is 'whiter') than the equal amplitude (and equally desaturated) purple discussed before.

Polarity of colour-difference signals

In (a) above, it is seen at (ii) that both $(R' - Y')$ and $(B' - Y')$ are positive. But in (b), at (ii), $(R' - Y')$ is positive whilst $(B' - Y')$ is negative. Both $(R' - Y')$ and $(B' - Y')$ may be either positive or negative, depending upon the hue they represent. Table 2.1 shows their polarities for various groups of hues. These will be verified when colour-bar signals are discussed.

Table 2.1   Colour-difference signal polarities for various hues

Hue	Polarity of $(R' - Y')$	Polarity of $(B' - Y')$
Purples (magentas)	+	+
Red, orange, yellow	+	−
Yellow-green, green	−	−
Blue-green (cyan), blue	−	+

Bandwidth of luminance and colour-difference signals

The luminance signal has the full video signal bandwidth of the system, e.g., 5·5 MHz for the U.K. 625-line signal. This implies that very fine detail may be described in 'black-and-white'. The eye is however, not capable of seeing such fine detail in colour. If broad parallel coloured stripes are painted on a white piece of paper and held say 5 metres from the eye, the colours are seen clearly. If the width of the stripes is now decreased in steps, there comes a point where the eye no longer sees the stripes as coloured, but gains only a 'monochrome' impression of them. It would be illogical to transmit colour detail which the eye cannot see. A bandwidth for colour-detail of about one fifth that allowed for the luminance signal, is found to give realistic results. In the U.K., colour-difference signals have a bandwidth of approximately 1·0 MHz,[1] and are not more than 3 dB down at 1·3 MHz.

Constant luminance

Ideally the reproduced luminance of every detail in a given transmitted scene would remain constant irrespective of whether the scene were transmitted in monochrome or in colour and this would be true both in monochrome and in colour receivers. In addition, in a colour receiver, arbitrary changes in level (e.g., due to noise) in the chrominance signal would not cause changes in luminance. (This last feature is particularly desirable since the eye is much more sensitive to changes in luminance than to changes in the information carried by the chrominance signals, i.e., hue and saturation.)

In practice this ideal of *constant luminance* is not entirely met but the discrepancy is not regarded as causing a significant degradation in picture quality. The following considerations throw further light on this subject.

Let a given scene be transmitted first as a monochrome, then as a colour picture.

(a) *Reception of the monochrome signal*

Both monochrome and colour receivers are capable of displaying a full band-width picture of correct luminance.

(b) *Reception of the colour signal on a monochrome receiver*

To produce the correct luminance the c.r.t. must be fed with an input voltage of correct amplitude, properly gamma corrected to offset the non-linearity of the c.r.t.

It is assumed under (a) above, that the monochrome signal meets these requirements, as indeed it does in practice. Unfortunately, on a colour transmission, the luminance signal is not truly 'gamma-corrected'. A true luminance signal, before gamma-correction, is expressed by:

$$Y = 0\cdot3R + 0\cdot59G + 0\cdot11B \tag{1}$$

Properly gamma corrected, this then becomes:

$$Y^{1/2\cdot2} = (0\cdot3R + 0\cdot59G + 0\cdot11B)^{1/2\cdot2} \tag{2}$$

But, in fact, the luminance signal is obtained from R, G, and B voltages which have already been gamma-corrected (i.e., from R', G', and B'). This is written as:

$$Y' = 0\cdot3R' + 0\cdot59G' + 0\cdot11B' \tag{3}$$

---

[1] The eye is able to see finer detail in some hues than others (e.g., detail in orange or cyan is seen better than say purple and yellow-green). Even this fact was taken into account in the original American NTSC system by transmitting more detail in the better-seen hues than in the remainder. However, experience has shown that the added technical complexity caused by this refinement is not in general justified. It has not been adopted in Europe. Those wishing to explore this point further should study the significance of the NTSC 'I' and 'Q' signals. (See Appendix A.)

This is equivalent to writing:

$$Y^{1/2\cdot2} = 0\cdot3R^{1/2\cdot2} + 0\cdot59G^{1/2\cdot2} + 0\cdot11B^{1/2\cdot2} \tag{4}$$

Mathematically this is clearly incorrect, when Y is defined as shown at (1), except in the special case when $R = G = B$, i.e., when grey or white information is being transmitted. If $R = G = B = V$, then substituting V for R, G, and B in eqs. (2) and (4) yields the same result; i.e., $Y^{1/2\cdot2} = V^{1/2\cdot2}$.

On colours, when R, G, and B are *not* equal, substituting arbitrary values in eqs. (4) and (2) shows that the amplitude of the transmitted luminance signal is smaller than it should be.

As an example, suppose that pure red of maximum amplitude is being transmitted. Then $R = 1\cdot0$, $B = 0$, and $G = 0$. The true luminance of the scene is then given by $Y = 0\cdot3R$ (from (1)). For simplicity, let the gamma of the system be $2\cdot0$ instead of $2\cdot2$. Then, from (2), a true gamma-corrected luminance signal would be:

$$Y^{\frac{1}{2}} = (0\cdot3R)^{\frac{1}{2}} = (0\cdot3 \times (1))^{\frac{1}{2}} = (0\cdot3)^{\frac{1}{2}} \tag{5}$$

But, from (4), the actual luminance signal produced is:

$$Y' = (0\cdot3)R^{\frac{1}{2}} = (0\cdot3)(1)^{\frac{1}{2}} = (0\cdot3) \tag{6}$$

At the receiver c.r.t. using the assumed value for gamma of $2\cdot0$, the light output is proportional to the square of the input voltage. Hence the luminance which would be produced by the truly gamma-corrected signal at (5) and the actual one at (6) may be compared as follows:

$$\text{True luminance} \quad = \{(0\cdot3)^{\frac{1}{2}}\}^2 = 0\cdot3 \tag{7}$$
$$\text{Actual luminance} = \{(0\cdot3)\}^2 \quad = 0\cdot09 \tag{8}$$

The reproduced luminance is therefore less than it should be.

To sum up, a monochrome receiver working on a colour signal produces a correct luminance level only when white or grey information is being transmitted. Every colour is produced at a lower than correct luminance. Calculations such as the one above, show that for the three primary hues the error is greatest on blue and least on green.

In practice this means that coloured areas of scenes are darker than they should be (or would be if the scene were transmitted in monochrome), and this represents a failure to achieve 'constant luminance'. The discrepancy is, however, reduced in an unexpected way. The chrominance signal which is present in the video signal when colour is being transmitted, is applied to the c.r.t. as a sine wave superimposed upon the luminance level. Due to the non-linearity of the tube's I_b/V_g characteristic (which, as described under the section on gamma correction, is of a form such that $I_b \propto V_g^{\gamma}$ where γ may be from $2\cdot2$ to $3\cdot3$), the increase of I_b due to one half cycle of the sine wave is greater than the decrease due to the other half cycle. The signal is in fact partially rectified and a net increase in beam current results due to the presence of the chrominance signal. This raises the luminance level above what it would be if it were due to the luminance voltage alone and makes it nearer to the true value which it would have if the luminance signal were truly gamma corrected. Moreover, the greater the degree of saturation of the colour the greater the amplitude of the chrominance sine wave and the greater the rectified component.

(c) *Reception of the colour signal on a colour receiver*

As explained, three voltages, R', G', and B' are responsible for the light emitted from the c.r.t. in a colour receiver. If these are faithful copies of the original gamma-corrected voltages at the transmitter, then the displayed luminance (and of course the hue and saturation) will be correct.

The incorrect value of Y' has been shown to be the cause of a luminance error in monochrome receivers. But, in a colour receiver, Y' is eliminated when the colour-difference signals are added to the luminance signal, e.g., $(R' - Y') + Y' = R'$. At first sight it may appear therefore, that the displayed luminance is unaffected by the error in Y'. This is only true, however, for picture detail corresponding to frequencies up to 1 MHz. Colour-difference signals are bandwidth restricted to 1 MHz, but the Y' signal has the full video bandwidth (i.e., 5·5 MHz in the U.K.).

Above 1 MHz the colour-difference signals progressively disappear and the amounts of red, green, and blue lights emitted are always in monochrome proportions, but because of the incorrect value of Y' the picture suffers the same degradation as a monochrome receiver picture.

To sum up, ignoring other factors such as noise in the chrominance channel which may impinge upon the problem, in a colour receiver constant luminance *may* be achieved for frequencies up to 1 MHz but not for the remainder of the video bandwidth.

Because constant luminance may be achieved when the colour-difference signals are present (i.e., below 1 MHz) but not when they are absent (i.e., above 1 MHz), it is sometimes said that this implies that some of the luminance information is carried by the colour-difference signals. This is a logical deduction. The argument is further extended by attributing the failure of constant luminance in the monochrome receiver to the fact that some of the luminance information is carried in the chrominance signal which the monochrome receiver cannot use. Despite the logic of this approach it is perhaps more meaningful to attribute the success of constant luminance up to 1 MHz in a colour receiver, to the presence of compensating errors in the colour-difference and luminance signals (i.e., the former contains $-Y'$ and the latter $+Y'$, with Y' equally wrong in both signals).

Returning to the question of noise in the chrominance channel, the extent to which luminance is affected by this is diminished because an increase in $(R' - Y')$ or $(B' - Y')$, or both, causes a decrease in $(G' - Y')$ which is partly compensatory.[1] This property of the system helps to achieve 'constant luminance' by making

[1] It is demonstrated in chapter 16 that:
$$(G' - Y') = -0{\cdot}51(R' - Y') - 0{\cdot}186(B' - Y')$$
OR
$$-(G' - Y') = +0{\cdot}51(R' - Y') + 0{\cdot}186(B' - Y')$$

luminance more independent of arbitrary changes in the chrominance signal than it would be if all three colour-difference signals were transmitted.

Choice of chrominance sub-carrier frequency

To meet the requirements of compatibility the chrominance signal has to be contained within the existing bandwidth of the corresponding monochrome signal.

In the U.K. 625-line system video frequencies extend from 0 to 5·5 MHz. The chrominance signal has to fit within this bandwidth. It is a self-contained signal and is simply added to the normal picture information (i.e., the 'luminance' detail) to become part of the video signal which modulates the vision carrier.

Figure 2.3(a) shows the bandwidth of the normal U.K. 625-line vision signal. In Fig. 2.3(b) the chrominance signal is added as a shaded area approximately centred on a sub-carrier frequency shown as f_{sc}, where $f_{sc} = 4\cdot43361875$ MHz.

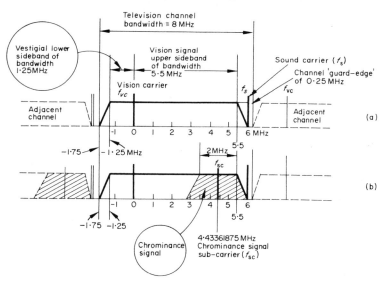

Fig. 2.3 *U.K. 625-line television signals showing frequencies expressed relative to the vision carrier (f_{vc})*

(a) Shows a normal monochrome signal.
(b) Shows the corresponding colour signal.

It is helpful to summarize some of the factors which govern the choice of the sub-carrier frequency f_{sc}:

(a) For minimum interference, f_{sc} must be as high as possible.
(b) Having specified a bandwidth of approximately 1 MHz for the colour-difference signals which modulate the sub-carrier, it must be sufficiently below 5·5 MHz to allow in the upper sideband of the chrominance signal.

35

(c) In the PAL system, the chrominance signal is amplitude modulated and 'equi-band' (i.e., its two parts are of equal bandwidth). It requires a total bandwidth of 2 MHz centred on the sub-carrier. The highest possible value for f_{sc} is hence $(5\cdot5 - 1) = 4\cdot5$ MHz, if both sidebands are to be fully accommodated.

(d) Cross-talk between chrominance and luminance information must be minimized.

(e) Since the sub-carrier falls in the normal video frequency spectrum it will pass through the video amplifiers in monochrome receivers. As it is a high frequency it will give rise to a 'dot-pattern' along each raster line. The numerical relationship between f_{sc} and the line frequency f_h must be chosen so that the dot-pattern shifts horizontally on successive raster lines in such a way that the visibility of this interference is minimized.

Frequency interleaving

When the spectrum of a television vision signal is analysed, it is found that the energy is not uniformly distributed throughout the channel bandwidth but exists in bunches of frequencies centred on harmonics of the line frequency.

The reason for this is easily seen. For simplicity, suppose that the vision carrier f_{vc} is modulated by a video signal of the form shown in Fig. 2.4(a). This represents 'black' raster lines. Figure 2.4(b) shows the negatively modulated vision signal bearing this information. For every frequency component in the modulating waveform, there will be a pair of side-frequencies one lying above and the other below f_{vc}. But the fundamental frequency of the modulating waveform is 15,625 Hz, i.e., f_h. Because it is a 'square' type shape, of an unequal mark-to-space ratio, this waveform is equivalent to the sum total of an infinite series of sine wave harmonics of f_h, i.e., f_h, $2f_h$, $3f_h$, etc. These sine waves grow progressively smaller in amplitude as the frequency gets higher. The spectrum of this vision signal is thus $f_{vc} \pm f_h$, $f_{vc} \pm 2f_h$, $f_{vc} \pm 3f_h$, . . ., etc. The highest harmonic accommodated in the vision signal is clearly $(5\cdot5 \text{ MHz} \div f_h) = 5\cdot5 \times 10^6 \div 15{,}625 = 352$.

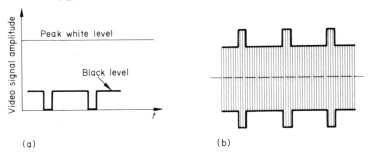

(a) (b)

Fig. 2.4 *(a) Shows the form of a monochrome system video signal on 'black' lines. (b) Shows the form of the corresponding negatively modulated vision carrier*

Figure 2.5(a) illustrates this distribution of line harmonics in the vision signal. If the video waveform on its own is considered, this itself is modulated by 50 Hz and

25 Hz components due to the field synchronizing signals. Each line harmonic therefore has groups of 'side-frequencies' around it, at 25 Hz intervals. For any static scene, since all detail repeats on successive pictures, the bunching is very marked. With normal pictures, where detail is constantly changing, the spectrum is more complex but there are still regularly spaced clusters of frequency components with intervening spaces which are only sparsely occupied. It is into these spaces that the chrominance signal is fitted.

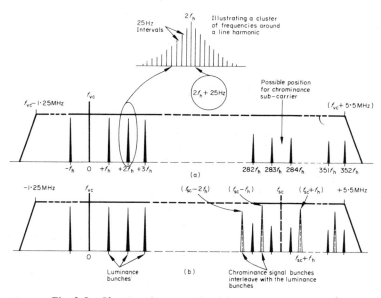

Fig. 2.5   *Showing the principle of frequency interleaving*

(a) Illustrates the spectrum of the vision signal when modulated by a simple 'static' video signal (e.g., of the form shown in Fig. 2.4).

(b) Shows how the chrominance signal produces bunches of frequencies which interleave between the 'luminance' bunches. Here the sub-carrier frequency is placed centrally between two line harmonics. This is true of NTSC where 'half-line offset' is used. With PAL (using quarter line offset) the chrominance bunches still interleave but do not fall centrally between the luminance bunches; the spacing between adjacent bunches being $f_h/4$.

Note: As the order of the harmonic increases, the amplitude of the bunches diminishes.

In the original NTSC system the chrominance sub-carrier was made to fit exactly between two line harmonics, i.e., its frequency was offset by half the line frequency from a line harmonic. This is known as 'half-line offset' and it involves choosing a sub-carrier of frequency equal to an odd multiple of half the line frequency. In the U.S.A., $f_{sc} = 455 \times f_h/2$. Since the chrominance signal is itself an r.f. carrier which is interrupted at line frequency, it also, has a spectrum consisting of bunches of side frequencies spaced at intervals of f_h. These range on either side of f_{sc}. In the composite vision signal the chrominance bunches clearly interleave with those of the luminance signal. This is illustrated in Fig. 2.5(b).

Dot-patterns (see (e) above)

The sub-carrier causes the brightness of a raster line to rise and fall sinusoidally from one end of the line to the other. If the positive and negative peaks are regarded as producing white and black dots it is possible to assess the overall pattern by working out how the white dots on successive lines are positioned relative to one another. The number of sub-carrier cycles per line is equal to f_{sc}/f_h. But in NTSC, $f_{sc} = n(f_h/2)$ where n is an odd number. Therefore

$$\frac{f_{sc}}{f_h} = \frac{nf_h}{2} \div f_h = \frac{n}{2}$$

Since n is an odd number, there is therefore an odd number of half cycles on each line. On any two successively scanned lines of one field, the white dots move along by half a cycle. Vertically this tends to give cancellation since white and black dots fall beneath one another.

Since one line contains an odd number of half cycles, it takes two lines to contain an even number of full cycles. But one picture contains an odd number of lines so that on *corresponding* lines of *successive* pictures the sub-carrier is in antiphase, again tending to give cancellation. As it takes two pictures to contain an even number of cycles the dot pattern follows a two picture, i.e., a four-field cycle. Working out the relative positions of sub-carrier cycles on raster lines over a four-field sequence, establishes that any remaining visible pattern is in the form of slanting black and white lines at an angle of about 45°. This gives minimum interference since slanting patterns of dim closely packed lines are far less visible than similar vertical lines.

The nature of the PAL system is, however, such that if the sub-carrier were chosen on the basis of half-line offset, then—on certain hues—dots tend to line up vertically to give an annoying interference.[1] To overcome this 'quarter-line offset' is used, i.e., f_{sc} is equal to an odd multiple of one quarter of the line frequency. For optimum results this is modified slightly by the addition of 25 Hz to create a phase reversal on each successive field and the actual relationship between f_{sc} and f_h in the PAL system in the U.K. is given by:

$$f_{sc} = f_h(284 - \tfrac{1}{4}) + \frac{f_v}{2}; \quad \left\{\text{i.e.} \left(1135 \times \frac{f_h}{4}\right) + \frac{f_v}{2}\right\}$$

$$f_{sc} = 15625(283 \cdot 75) + \frac{50}{2} = 4 \cdot 43361875 \text{ MHz}$$

With quarter-line offset, four lines are needed to contain an even number of sub-carrier cycles and four *pictures* are needed to produce a total number of lines which is divisible by four. The dot pattern therefore follows a four-picture or eight-field

---

[1] The reason for this will be understood when chapters 8 and 9 have been studied. One of the two sub-carrier components present in the PAL signal (i.e., the V component) is inverted on each successive line. This is equivalent to moving the dots produced by this component along by half a cycle on alternate lines, and this negates the simple corrective result which half-line offset gives on NTSC.

sequence. The pattern repeats once each 8/50 second, i.e., at the rate of 6·25 times per second. It is this which accounts for the apparent sideways drift of the dot-pattern.

Finally it must be noted that the chrominance signal is filtered out of the luminance channel in a colour receiver. Dot-patterns are essentially a compatibility consideration. They are of concern only in monochrome receivers working on a colour signal. With NTSC and PAL, the chrominance signal disappears on grey or white detail, so it is only in coloured areas of a scene that this interference appears. Since *all* colours appear as grey on a monochrome set this explains why dots are seen in some grey parts but not others.

The pattern is of very low visibility and is not a serious problem.

Chrominance signal bandwidth

In the radiated signal the attenuation slopes of the upper and lower sidebands of the chrominance signal are not identical, as they are shown to be for simplicity in Fig. 2.3. The upper sideband slope is dictated by the upper edge of the system's vision channel characteristic, but the lower sideband slope is made less steep and is shaped to give optimum performance.

In the U.K. 625-line system, with a video bandwidth of 5·5 MHz, the chrominance signal is double sideband up to 1·07 MHz (i.e., 5·50 − 4·43 = 1·07 MHz), but the attenuation of higher frequencies is thereafter more rapid in the upper sideband than in the lower.

Some other 625-line systems (e.g., in Europe), have a video bandwidth of 5·0 MHz but use the same chrominance signal sub-carrier frequency as the U.K. for PAL colour television signals (i.e., $f_{sc} = 4\cdot43361875$ MHz). Since the same colour-difference signal bandwidth of 1 MHz is also used, the chrominance signal is of vestigial sideband type. The upper sideband attenuation slope starts at 0·57 MHz (i.e. 5·0 − 4·43 = 0·57 MHz), but the lower sideband extends to 1·0 MHz before attenuation begins. Unless corrective measures are taken, this leads to some loss of saturation of fine coloured detail in the picture, since signal content describing such detail is present in only one of the two sidebands.[1]

[1] For a comparison of various television system standards and a study of vestigial sideband signals, see Chapter 4 of *Television Receiver Theory* by G. H. Hutson, published by Arnolds of London.

3

Colour-bar Signals (NTSC and PAL)

A standard colour-bar waveform produces on a colour receiver screen, eight vertical bars of uniform width. These include the three primaries, the three complementaries, white, and black. They are arranged in descending order of luminance from left to right. This places them in the order:

white   yellow   cyan   green   magenta   red   blue   black

On a monochrome set this produces a peak-white stripe on the left of the screen, followed by grey stripes which grow progressively darker from left to right. The luminance steps are not uniform.

A study of colour-bar waveforms is a great help towards gaining a clear understanding of the nature of colour television signals. Colour-bar signals are in practice entirely electronically generated so that actual light and cameras have no part in the formation of such signals. However, an electronically generated signal *represents* coded information about light and gives rise to the appropriate light output at the receiver. Because it is so instructive to do so, the colour-bar signals are described in this chapter as though they were produced from cameras exposed to the given light information. Since electronically generated signals are designed to test the performance of the system, they impose upon it stringent demands and in fact the saturation and amplitude of the colours simulated by the generator are seldom reached in normal operation.

Method of studying colour-bar signals

Each bar is treated in turn. The luminance and chrominance signal amplitudes are calculated and the composite video signal is then deduced by adding these two components to the line blanking period waveform. Having found the form of the video signal for one line period, the effect of negatively modulating the vision carrier with this signal may then be considered.

Since relative amplitudes are to be studied it is convenient to label black level as zero and let the distance between black level and peak-white be unity. To the same scale the tips of the sync. pulses then rest at a distance of 0·43 on the other side of black level. The video signal may be drawn 'either way up'. In the first examples studied, the sync. pulses are 'pointing upwards' so that the appearance of the upper half of a negatively modulated vision carrier may then be visualized more easily.

It should be noted that standard specifications of colour-bar signals are sometimes scaled as unity overall (i.e., from sync. pulse tips to peak-white), in which event the distance from black level to peak-white is 0·7 instead of 1·0, and from black level to sync. level, 0·3 instead of 0·43.

Quadrature amplitude modulation (Q.A.M.)

NTSC and PAL systems both employ quadrature amplitude modulation (Q.A.M.) of the chrominance signal. The theory of such signals and the way in which PAL differs from NTSC are subjects which are studied in detail in chapters 8 and 9.

For the purpose of this chapter it is sufficient to state that a Q.A.M. chrominance signal may be resolved into two sine-waves of sub-carrier frequency at 90° to one another (i.e., in quadrature). One of these is proportional in amplitude to the $(R' - Y')$ colour-difference signal and the other to $(B' - Y')$.

It has been seen in the last chapter that each of the colour-difference signals may be either positive or negative. The sub-carrier sine waves which represent $(R' - Y')$ and $(B' - Y')$ have to indicate what polarity these signals have as well as showing their amplitudes. This is achieved by making the polarity reversals of colour-difference signals cause the sine waves representing these signals to be inverted (i.e., to change phase by 180°).

Hence each sine wave may have one of two possible phases. The phase of the sine wave representing $+(B' - Y')$ is taken as the reference phase of 0°; and this sine wave switches to a phase of $+180°$ when $(B' - Y')$ is negative. The other sine wave is at $+90°$ when $(R' - Y')$ is positive and $+270°$ (i.e., $-90°$) when $(R' - Y')$ is negative. This may be illustrated by a phasor (i.e., vector) diagram on which each of the sub-carrier frequency signals is represented as a phasor (see Fig. 3.1). The direction in which each phasor points and its length give a direct indication of the polarity and amplitude respectively of the colour-difference signal the sine wave represents.

The chrominance signal is formed by adding the two sine-wave components. When two sine-waves of equal frequency but different phase are added the resulting waveform is itself a sine-wave. The amplitude and phase of the chrominance signal sine wave may be determined by drawing the two individual phasors and completing a parallelogram. The resultant phasor represents the chrominance signal. Its amplitude and direction may be read off directly if the diagram is drawn to scale, or calculated by simple trigonometry if a dimensioned sketch is drawn.

It may be wondered how the two original sine-waves (or the information about polarity and amplitude which they both carry), can be recovered at the receiver from the chrominance signal. Although, during the transmission of an unchanging colour, it is true that the chrominance signal is a simple sine wave, nonetheless by its phase and amplitude it bears evidence of the polarities and amplitudes of the two separate signals from which it is formed. This subject is treated fully in chapters 8 and 9.

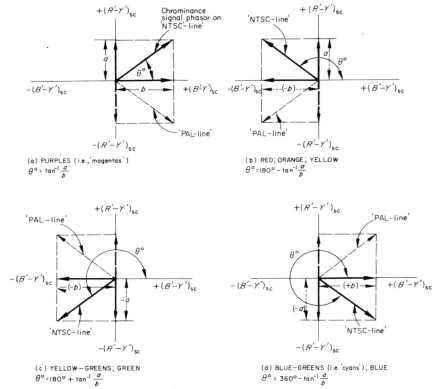

Fig. 3.1 *Chrominance signal phasor diagrams (see Table 3.1)*

Note:

(a) The labels $(B' - Y')_{sc}$ and $(R' - Y')_{sc}$ on the x and y axes refer to the chrominance signal sub-carrier components. These have amplitudes which are directly proportional to the $(B' - Y')$ and $(R' - Y')$ colour-difference signal amplitudes respectively.

(b) The chrominance signal has an amplitude given by: $C_h = \sqrt{a^2 + b^2}$ where a and b are the amplitudes of the $(R' - Y')$ and $(B' - Y')$ sub-carrier components respectively.

(c) The expression $\theta° = \tan^{-1}(a/b)$ is simply a 'short-hand' way of writing that $\theta°$ is the angle of which the tangent is (a/b).

Finally, with the PAL signal, the sub-carrier sine wave representing $(R' - Y')$ is phase inverted on alternate lines. Suppose, for a particular hue (e.g., red), that in the NTSC signal the $(R' - Y')$ component has a phase of $+90°$. In a PAL signal one line is identical to the NTSC signal but on the next the phase of this component is switched to $+270°$; returning again to $90°$ on the following line etc. This Phase Alternation Line-by-Line of the $(R' - Y')$ component gives the system its name of PAL.[1]

---

[1] In a true NTSC signal, the two sine waves which are added to form the chrominance signal are each representative of *both* $(R' - Y')$ *and* $(B' - Y')$ information. These two components are known as the I and Q signals and from them, at the receiver, $(R' - Y')$, $(B' - Y')$, and hence $(G' - Y')$ information

42

The chrominance phasor may rest in any of the four quadrants of a circle because there are four possible combinations of polarity of its two components. Also, when the $(R' - Y')$ component is inverted on alternate lines in the PAL signal, the effect is to cause the chrominance phasor to switch across the 'x', i.e., $(B' - Y')$ axis to the quadrant adjacent to the one it occupies on its normal NTSC phase.

These facts are summarized in Table 3.1 and the form of the corresponding chrominance signal phasor diagrams are shown in Fig. 3.1. Note that if a and b are the amplitudes of the sub-carrier frequency sine-waves bearing $(R' - Y')$ and $(B' - Y')$ colour-difference signal information respectively, then the amplitude C_h of the chrominance signal is given by:

$$C_h = \sqrt{a^2 + b^2}$$

It is stressed that the above introduction to the theory of NTSC and PAL chrominance signals is necessarily brief at this stage. A much more detailed study of the nature of these signals is made in chapters 8, 9, and 10.

Table 3.1 Showing the four possible combinations of colour-difference signal polarities, the phases of the corresponding two sub-carrier frequency sine-wave components and the quadrant position of the chrominance signal phasor which represents the sum of these two components. (See Fig. 3.1 for the phasor diagrams)

Hues	Colour-difference signal polarities		Sub-carrier phases		Chrominance signal	
	$(B' - Y')$	$(R' - Y')$	$(B' - Y')$ sine wave	$(R' - Y')$ sine wave	Quadrant in which phasor lies	Appearance of phasor diagrams
Purples	+	+ (−)	0°	90° (270°)	1st (4th)	see Fig. 3.1(a)
Red, orange, yellow	−	+ (−)	180°	90° (270°)	2nd (3rd)	see Fig. 3.1(b)
Yellow-greens, green	−	− (+)	180°	270° (90°)	3rd (2nd)	see Fig. 3.1(c)
Blue-greens, blue	+	− (+)	0°	270° (90°)	4th (1st)	see Fig. 3.1(d)

(a) The figures in brackets show the polarities and the angles on the alternate 'PAL-lines'.

(b) Purples are often called magentas and blue-greens called cyans. In this textbook magenta is used only for the specific purple which is formed by equal parts of red and blue, whilst cyan is used for the blue-green which contains equal parts of blue and green. The words magenta and cyan, then, always (in this book) imply certain specific chrominance signal phase angles (i.e., 61° and 283° respectively).

---

is recovered. It would only confuse the reader to discuss this complication at this point. For the purpose of developing an understanding of the PAL system, unless otherwise stated, I and Q signals (which are not used in the PAL system) are ignored. Whenever an NTSC-type signal (or 'NTSC-line') is mentioned in the text, the author implies a simplified NTSC system in which straightforward $(R' - Y')$ and $(B' - Y')$ modulation is employed. Finally, in an appendix at the end of the book, the I and Q signals are described so that a more complete comparison between the original NTSC system and the now widely used PAL development of it, is possible.

Saturation and amplitude

These are the two parameters used to describe colour-bar signals (e.g., 100% sat., 100% amp.; 95% sat., 100% amp.; 100% sat., 75% amp., etc.).

The description 100% saturation indicates that each of the colour-bars is a pure hue, undiluted by white light; 95% saturation implies that each colour-bar consists of 95% of the given hue together with 5% of white light. It is important to note that the figures refer to *light levels*. Camera output voltages *before gamma-correction* represent these light levels.

The term 100% amplitude indicates that one (at least) of the three cameras is giving maximum output (e.g., 1 V). It can refer to saturated or desaturated colours. 100% amplitude infers that the colour described, *at its existing degree of saturation*, cannot have a greater amplitude, e.g., $R = 1.0$, $B = 1.0$, $G = 0.2$ is 100% amp., 80% sat. magenta.[1]

100% saturated, 100% amplitude colour-bar signal (unweighted)

(a) WHITE BAR. Here $R = 1.0$; $G = 1.0$; $B = 1.0$, therefore

$$R' = (R)^{1/\gamma} = (1.0)^{1/2.2} = 1.0; \quad G' = 1.0; \quad B' = 1.0$$

(i) *Luminance signal*

$$Y' = 0.30R' + 0.59G' + 0.11B' = 0.30 + 0.59 + 0.11 = \mathbf{1.0}$$

(ii) *Colour-difference signals.* These are zero on white, e.g.

$$(R' - Y') = (1 - 1) = 0$$

(iii) *Chrominance signal.* With NTSC and PAL, the nature of the Q.A.M. system of modulation used is such that when the colour-difference signals equal zero, the 'r.f.' chrominance signal disappears altogether.

(b) YELLOW BAR. Here $R = 1.0$; $G = 1.0$; $B = 0$
$R' = 1.0$; $G' = 1.0$; $B' = 0$

(i) *Luminance signal*

$$Y' = 0.30R' + 0.59G' + 0.11B' = 0.30 + 0.59 = \mathbf{0.89}$$

(ii) *Colour-difference signals*

$$(R' - Y') = (1 - 0.89) = +0.11$$
$$(B' - Y') = (0 - 0.89) = -0.89$$

---

[1] In this book the figures for percentage amplitude refer to camera output voltages *before* gamma-correction. In some literature, however, figures for percentage amplitude refer to gamma-corrected levels. This makes no difference at 100% amplitude but it does for anything less than 100%, e.g., consider red and let $R = 0.22$, $B = 0$, $G = 0$. This is 22% amplitude, 100% saturated red, if referred to camera voltages. But $R' = 0.5$, $B = 0$, $G' = 0$ and the gamma-corrected signal is therefore of 50% amplitude.

44

(iii) *The Q.A.M. chrominance signal.* Since $(R' - Y')$ is positive, the sub-carrier frequency sine-wave representing it has a phase of $+90°$ on 'NTSC-lines' alternating to $+270°$ on 'PAL-lines'. Meanwhile $(B' - Y')$ is negative so that the $(B' - Y')$ sub-carrier sine-wave has a phase of $180°$.

The resulting chrominance phasor which represents the vector sum of these two sine-wave components lies in the second quadrant on NTSC-lines, switching over to the third quadrant on the alternate 'PAL-lines', i.e., it is of the form shown in Fig. 3.1(b).

The amplitude of the chrominance signal is given by:

$$C_\text{h} = \sqrt{(B' - Y')^2_\text{sc} + (R' - Y')^2_\text{sc}} = \sqrt{(-0{\cdot}89)^2 + (+0{\cdot}11)^2}$$
$$= \sqrt{0{\cdot}7921 + 0{\cdot}0121} = \sqrt{0{\cdot}8042} = \textbf{0·9}$$

(c) CYAN BAR. Here $R = 0; \quad G = 1{\cdot}0; \quad B = 1{\cdot}0$
$$R' = 0; \quad G' = 1{\cdot}0; \quad B' = 1{\cdot}0$$

(i) *Luminance signal*

$$Y' = 0{\cdot}3R' + 0{\cdot}59G' + 0{\cdot}11B' = 0 + 0{\cdot}59 + 0{\cdot}11 = \textbf{0·7}$$

(ii) *Colour-difference signals*

$$(R' - Y') = (0 - 0{\cdot}7) = -0{\cdot}7$$
$$(B' - Y') = (1 - 0{\cdot}7) = +0{\cdot}3$$

(iii) *Chrominance signal*

$$C_\text{h} = \sqrt{(B' - Y')^2_\text{sc} + (R' - Y')^2_\text{sc}} = \sqrt{(-0{\cdot}7)^2_\text{sc} + (0{\cdot}3)^2_\text{sc}} = \textbf{0·76}$$

Because $(R' - Y')$ is negative and $(B' - Y')$ is positive, the chrominance phasor lies in the fourth quadrant on NTSC-lines, switching to the first quadrant on PAL-lines, e.g., it has the form shown in Fig. 3.1(d).

Proceeding in this way for the remaining colour-bars, yields the results shown in Table 3.2. Actual chrominance signal phase angles are not considered at the moment because, for reasons discussed below, the signal is not acceptable in the form summarized in Table 3.2 and angles deduced from this information would not be those of the actual radiated signal.

Figure 3.2 shows the corresponding signals for one video line. At (a) is the luminance signal together with the line blanking period waveform. The chrominance signal is at (b), and (c) shows the composite video signal formed by adding (b) to (a).

Necessity for weighting factors

At (c) relative amplitudes of the video signal are shown by the y axis scale to the right of the waveform. To the left are shown modulation levels for a negatively modulated vision carrier. It is clear that this particular video waveform is unacceptable because it would cause severe overmodulation.

Table 3.2 Showing the theoretical amplitudes for a 100% saturated, 100% amplitude colour-bar signal. As shown in Fig. 3.2 the signal is unacceptable because it would cause severe overmodulation of the vision carrier. To prevent this, the sub-carrier frequency sine-waves representing the two colour-difference signals, are reduced in amplitude by the use of 'weighting factors'

Colour-bar	R'	G'	B'	Y'	$(B' - Y')$	$(R' - Y')$	Chrominance signal $C_h = \sqrt{(B' - Y')^2_{sc} + (R' - Y')^2_{sc}}$
White	1	1	1	1·0	0	0	0
Yellow	1	1	0	0·89	−0·89	+0·11	0·90
Cyan	0	1	1	0·70	+0·30	−0·70	0·76
Green	0	1	0	0·59	−0·59	−0·59	0·83
Magenta	1	0	1	0·41	+0·59	+0·59	0·83
Red	1	0	0	0·30	−0·3	+0·70	0·76
Blue	0	0	1	0·11	+0·89	−0·11	0·90
Black	0	0	0	0	0	0	0

To overcome this it is necessary to restrict the peak amplitude of the chrominance signal so that it does not take the vision carrier beyond certain prescribed limits.

If the distance from black to peak-white levels is taken as 1·0, it is stipulated that on a 100% saturated 100% amplitude colour-bar signal the maximum excursion of the vision signal shall not exceed 0·33 beyond peak-white or black levels. This may be said to represent 33% overmodulation during the active line and it confines the peak excursions of the chrominance signal to the limits of −0·33 and +1·33 shown by the dotted lines XX' across the waveform at (c). (*N.B.* For convenience the scale on the picture-content side of black-level is in positive units, and the sync. pulse tips are then at −0·43.)

To achieve this restriction the $(R' - Y')$ and $(B' - Y')$ sub-carrier components in the chrominance signal are scaled down by multiplying them by 'weighting factors'. Those used are 0·877 for the $(R' - Y')$ component and 0·493 for $(B' - Y')$. For brevity, the weighted signals are then referred to as the V and U components of the chrominance signal, where:

$$V = 0.877 (R' - Y')$$
$$U = 0.493 (B' - Y')$$

Calculation of weighting factors

The validity of the chosen values for the weighting factors may be checked as follows:
(a) Choose two colour-bars which extend beyond the prescribed limits in Fig. 3.2(c).

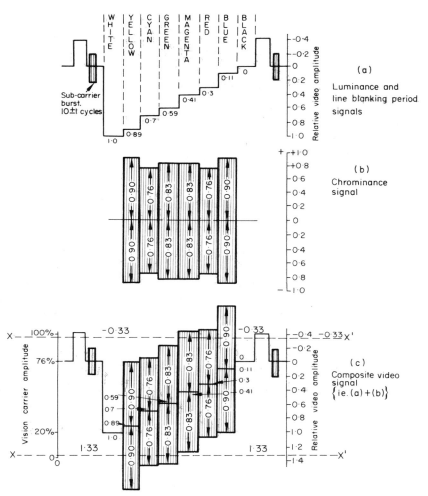

Fig. 3.2 *Showing luminance, chrominance, and composite video signals for a theoretical 100% saturated, 100% amplitude colour-bar signal (see Table 3.2)*

As seen from the vision carrier amplitude scale on the left at (c), this composite video signal would grossly over-modulate the transmitter. In practice the colour-difference signals are reduced by weighting factors to limit the maximum excursions of the signal to the levels shown by the broken lines marked XX'.

These must not be colours which are complementary to one another since the equations formed from such a pair are numerically equal and cannot be used in the way described below.

(b) Measure the distance from the luminance levels of these two chosen colour-bars, to the limiting level which it crosses in the diagram (e.g., for RED this distance is 0·63 and for BLUE it is 0·44). These distances represent the maximum permitted amplitudes for the chrominance signal on red and blue.

47

(c) Writing say w and z for the unknown $(B' - Y')$ and $(R' - Y')$ weighting factors respectively, form two simultaneous equations by equating the expression for the chrominance signal amplitude against the maximum values found under (b).

(d) Solving these equations for w and z yields the required weighting factor values. The method is outlined below, using the red and blue bars.

$$C_{\mathrm{h}} = \sqrt{\{w(B' - Y')\}^2 + \{z(R' - Y')\}^2}$$

ON RED

$$0\cdot63 = \sqrt{\{w(-0\cdot3)\}^2 + \{z(0\cdot7)\}^2}$$

$$(0\cdot63)^2 = w^2(-0\cdot3)^2 + z^2(0\cdot7)^2$$

$$(0\cdot63)^2 = 0\cdot09w^2 + 0\cdot49z^2 \tag{1}$$

ON BLUE

$$0\cdot44 = \sqrt{\{w(0\cdot89)\}^2 + \{z(-0\cdot11)\}^2}$$

$$(0\cdot44)^2 = 0\cdot7921w^2 + 0\cdot0121z^2 \tag{2}$$

Solving the simultaneous equations (1) and (2) yields values for w and z which are very close to the correct ones of $0\cdot493$ and $0\cdot877$ respectively.[1] To achieve these values exactly, it is necessary to express the luminance equation correct to three decimal places instead of two (i.e., to use $Y' = (0\cdot299R' + 0\cdot587G' + 0\cdot114B')$ instead of $Y' = (0\cdot30R' + 0\cdot59G' + 0\cdot11B')$, in the computation of the amplitudes of the colour-difference signals.

100% saturated, 100% amplitude colour-bar signal (weighted)

The following example shows how the amplitude and phase angle of the chrominance signal may be deduced for each colour-bar:

(a) YELLOW BAR. $R = 1\cdot0$, $G = 1\cdot0$, $B = 0$; $R' = 1\cdot0, G' = 1\cdot0$, $B' = 0$
   (i) *Luminance signal.* As before,

$$Y' = 0\cdot30 + 0\cdot59 = 0\cdot89$$

[1] Solution of (1) and (2). The ratio of the coefficients of w in (2) and (1) is $0\cdot7921/0\cdot09 = \mathbf{8\cdot8}$. Hence:

(1) $\times$ 8·8 yields

$$8\cdot8 \times 0\cdot3969 = 8\cdot8 \times 0\cdot09w^2 + 8\cdot8 \times 0\cdot49z^2$$

$$3\cdot4930 = 0\cdot7921w^2 + 4\cdot312z^2 \tag{3}$$

$$0\cdot1936 = 0\cdot7921w^2 + 0\cdot0121z^2 \tag{2}$$

(3) − (2)

$$3\cdot2994 = 4\cdot3009z^2$$

therefore

$$z^2 = \frac{3\cdot2996}{4\cdot3009} \quad \text{and} \quad z = \sqrt{\frac{3\cdot2994}{4\cdot3009}} = \mathbf{0\cdot876}$$

Also, from (1)

$$w^2 = \frac{0\cdot3969 - 0\cdot49z^2}{0\cdot09} = \frac{0\cdot3969 - 0\cdot3758}{0\cdot09} = 0\cdot2344$$

therefore

$$w = \sqrt{0\cdot2344} = \mathbf{0\cdot485}$$

(ii) *Colour-difference signals.* As before,

$$(R' - Y') = (1.0 - 0.89) = 0.11$$
$$(B' - Y') = (0 - 0.89) = -0.89$$

(iii) *Weighted colour-difference signals*

$$U = 0.493(B' - Y') = 0.493(-0.89) = -\mathbf{0.4387}$$
$$V = 0.877(R' - Y') = 0.877(+0.11) = +\mathbf{0.0965}$$

(iv) *Chrominance signal amplitude*

$$C_h = \sqrt{U^2 + V^2}$$
$$= \sqrt{(-0.4387)^2 + (0.0965)^2}$$
$$= \mathbf{0.44}$$

(v) *Chrominance signal phase angle.* The phase angle of a hue is always expressed in terms of the 'NTSC-line'. To determine the quadrant a sketch should be made of the form described in Fig. 3.1. The axes may be labelled $\pm U$ and $\pm V$. In the example U is negative and V positive, which places the chrominance signal phasor in the second quadrant. By employing the expression shown under Fig. 3.1(b) (but substituting U for a and V for b), the phase angle may now be calculated.

For yellow, on 'NTSC-lines', the phase angle is given by:

$$\theta = 180° - \tan^{-1}\frac{V}{U} = 180° - \tan^{-1}\frac{0.0965}{0.4387}$$
$$= 180° - 13° = \mathbf{167°}$$

In the PAL system, the chrominance signal phase angle on the alternate lines is deduced, as explained in Fig. 3.1, by switching the 'NTSC-line' phasor across the U axis to its mirror-image position in the adjacent quadrant. For yellow, the angle on 'PAL-lines' is therefore:

$$\theta = 180° + 13° = \mathbf{193°}$$

Proceeding in this way for the remaining colour-bars yields the results shown in Table 3.3. The reader is advised to work through some of these. Reference back to Fig. 3.1 shows that the angles for the four quadrants are given by the following expressions:

First quadrant: $\qquad \theta = \tan^{-1}\dfrac{V}{U}$

Second quadrant: $\qquad \theta = 180° - \tan^{-1}\dfrac{V}{U}$

Third quadrant: $\qquad \theta = 180° + \tan^{-1}\dfrac{V}{U}$

Fourth quadrant: $\qquad \theta = 360° - \tan^{-1}\dfrac{V}{U}$

Figure 3.3 shows the composite video signal for the 100% amplitude 100% saturated weighted colour-bar signal and the corresponding vision carrier modulation levels are shown to the left of the diagram.

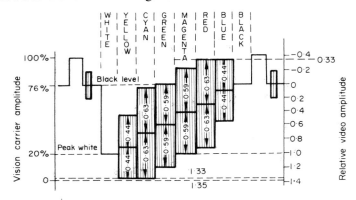

Fig. 3.3 *100% saturated, 100% amplitude colour-bar signal in which the colour-difference signals are reduced by weighting factors to restrict the chrominance signal excursions to 0·33 beyond black and peak-white levels*

This limits the maximum possible excursions beyond monochrome black and peak-white levels to 33% of the picture amplitude (i.e., of the blanking to peak-white level amplitude). The weighting factors used are 0·493 for $(B' - Y')$ and 0·877 for $(R' - Y')$.

Table 3.3 Details of a 100% amplitude, 100% saturated colour-bar signal when colour-difference signal weighting factors are employed

Colour-bar	Y'	$(B' - Y')$	$(R' - Y')$	$U =$ $0·493(B' - Y')$	$V =$ $0·877(R' - Y')$	Chrom. amp $= \sqrt{U^2 + V^2}$	Chrom. phase angle ('NTSC-line')
White	1·0	0	0	0	0	0	—
Yellow	0·89	−0·89	+0·11	−0·4388	0·0965	0·44	167°
Cyan	0·7	+0·3	−0·7	+0·1479	−0·6139	0·63	283°
Green	0·59	−0·59	−0·59	−0·2909	−0·5174	0·59	241°
Magenta	0·41	+0·59	+0·59	+0·2909	+0·5174	0·59	61°
Red	0·3	−0·3	+0·7	−0·1479	+0·6139	0·63	103°
Blue	0·11	+0·89	−0·11	+0·4388	−0·0965	0·44	347°
Black	0	0	0	0	0	0	—

Colour phase angle chart

Using the information in Table 3.3 a diagram may be drawn showing the chrominance phasor positions for the primary and complementary colours. This is shown in Fig. 3.4.

Note the following points:

(a) Each complementary hue is diametrically opposite its associated primary (e.g., yellow is opposite blue).

50

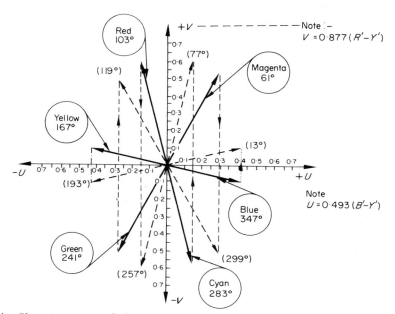

Fig. 3.4 *Chrominance signal phasor positions for the primary and complementary colours*

The relative amplitudes are those of a 100% saturated, 100% amplitude signal, the details of which are shown in Table 3.3. The dotted phasors correspond to 'PAL-lines'; e.g., for BLUE the phasor on 'PAL-lines' is at 13°. The vertical dotted lines illustrate the fact that the phasor *switches* between the pairs of phase angles (on a line-by-line basis) and does *not* swing through an arc.

(b) The amplitudes of these opposite pairs of phasors are equal. This is logical since they are both of equal saturation (in this case 100%) and the algebraic sum of them must be zero since together they make white. This is not to imply that they are in fact both present on white; since both colour-difference signals are zero on white. Suppose, however, that yellow is present on its own at 100% saturation. If blue is added the yellow desaturates and the chrominance phasor gets shorter. As far as the diagram is concerned, the effect on the yellow phasor may be imagined to be caused by the presence of a diametrically opposite blue phasor which reduces the net amplitude of the yellow phasor. In reality of course, only one chrominance phasor can be present at any one time. The desaturation affects the colour-difference signals before the chrominance signal is built.

(c) Projection from a given phasor to the U and V axes shows the relative amplitudes of the weighted $(B' - Y')$ and $(R' - Y')$ sub-carrier signals which together form the chrominance signal. Red does not lie on the $(R' - Y')$ axis nor blue on the $(B' - Y')$ axis. It is a common fallacy to think—for example—that on red $(B' - Y')$ must be zero and $(R' - Y')$ maximum. What *is* true is that on reds $(R' - Y')$ is large and $(B' - Y')$ small; and vice versa on blue.

(d) The positions of the phasors on 'PAL-lines' may be found simply by switching

51

the phasor to the opposite side of the U axis; i.e., PAL-line phasors are the mirror image (in the U axis) of NTSC-line phasors.
(e) It is useful to memorize the chrominance signal phase angles for the three primaries (i.e., red = 103°, green = 241°, blue = 347°). The complementary angles are each deduced by adding 180° to the appropriate 'opposite' primary (e.g., red = 103°; hence cyan = 103° + 180° = 283°).

95% saturated; 100% amplitude colour-bar signal

This is the signal transmitted as one of the test signals, by the BBC. It is also present at the very top of Test Card F. (For ITA and EBU colour-bar signals, see chapter 16.)

The sequence of calculations for deducing the form of this signal is outlined below. In Fig. 3.5 each step in the production of the signal at the transmitter is illustrated. Working through this sequence is very instructive. Having done so it is interesting to note that if the diagrams are read in reverse from bottom to top, the receiver process is portrayed. Thus the colour-bar signal shown at (r) represents the composite video signal recovered at the main vision detector and the diagrams above this illustrate the successive steps in the recovery of the three gamma-corrected voltages R', G', and B'. Finally, R, G, and B represent the relative amplitudes of the red, green, and blue lights emitted by the c.r.t.

To show how the various waveforms are arrived at, the successive steps in building them (at the transmitter) are outlined below for yellow. These steps are labelled (a), (b), (c), etc., to correspond to the appropriate diagrams in Fig. 3.5.

(a) *Position of colours*

This shows the position of the colours along a raster line.

(b), (c), and (d) *Camera outputs; before gamma-correction*

95% saturation 100% amplitude is specified. The description 100% amplitude indicates that the two hues forming yellow, i.e., red and green, are at maximum amplitude. Hence $R = 1.0$ and $G = 1.0$. But the description 95% saturation indicates that 5% of white light is present and white light is produced by equal quantities (in T-units) of red, green, and blue. 5% of white is equivalent to $0.05R$, $0.05G$, and $0.05B$. Hence of the total amount of red and green present, $0.05R$ and $0.05G$ represent the white content of the desaturated yellow, and $0.95R$ with $0.95G$ represents the yellow. The three camera outputs are therefore $R = 1.0$, $G = 1.0$, $B = 0.05$.

(e), (f), and (g) *Gamma-corrected camera voltages*

These are found by applying the values for R, G, and B to the transmitter gamma curve shown in Fig. 2.1. From this, $R' = 1.0$, $G' = 1.0$, and $B' = 0.25$.

Note that the very small voltage representing blue is substantially increased by gamma-correction; e.g., if $B = 0.05$ V $= 50$ mV, $B' = 0.05^{1/2.2}$ V $= 0.25$ V $= 250$ mV. Hence, very small amounts of desaturation have a marked effect upon all

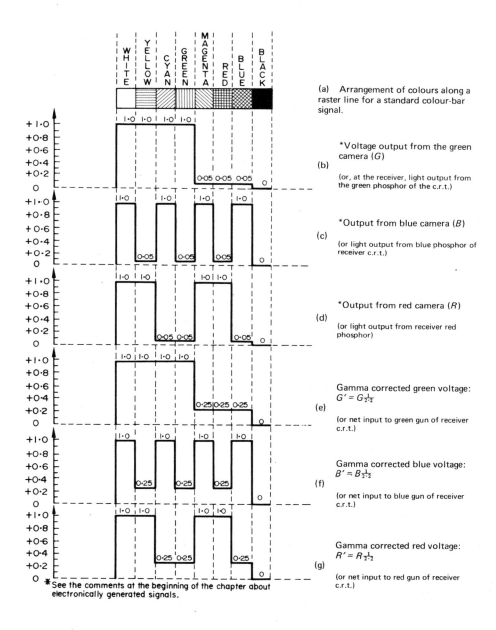

(a) Arrangement of colours along a raster line for a standard colour-bar signal.

(b) *Voltage output from the green camera (G)

(or, at the receiver, light output from the green phosphor of the c.r.t.)

(c) *Output from blue camera (B)

(or light output from blue phosphor of receiver c.r.t.)

(d) *Output from red camera (R)

(or light output from receiver red phosphor)

(e) Gamma corrected green voltage: $G' = G_{\frac{1}{2 \cdot 2}}$

(or net input to green gun of receiver c.r.t.)

(f) Gamma corrected blue voltage: $B' = B_{\frac{1}{2 \cdot 2}}$

(or net input to blue gun of receiver c.r.t.)

(g) Gamma corrected red voltage: $R' = R_{\frac{1}{2 \cdot 2}}$

(or net input to red gun of receiver c.r.t.)

*See the comments at the beginning of the chapter about electronically generated signals.

Fig. 3.5 *(continued on next page)*

53

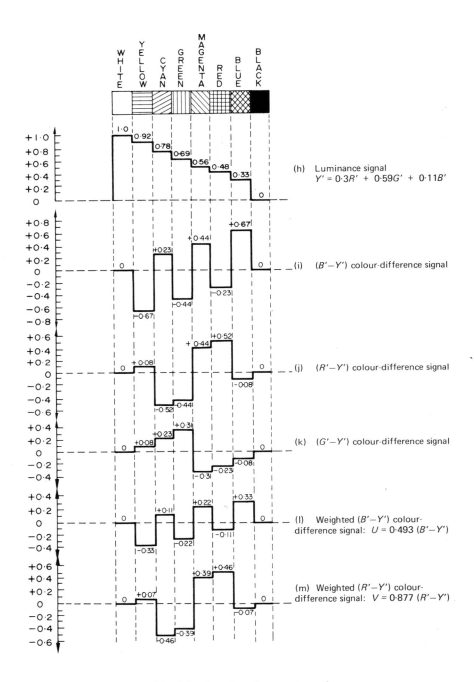

(h) Luminance signal
$Y' = 0.3R' + 0.59G' + 0.11B'$

(i) $(B'-Y')$ colour-difference signal

(j) $(R'-Y')$ colour-difference signal

(k) $(G'-Y')$ colour-difference signal

(l) Weighted $(B'-Y')$ colour-difference signal: $U = 0.493 (B'-Y')$

(m) Weighted $(R'-Y')$ colour-difference signal: $V = 0.877 (R'-Y')$

Fig. 3.5 *(continued on next page)*

54

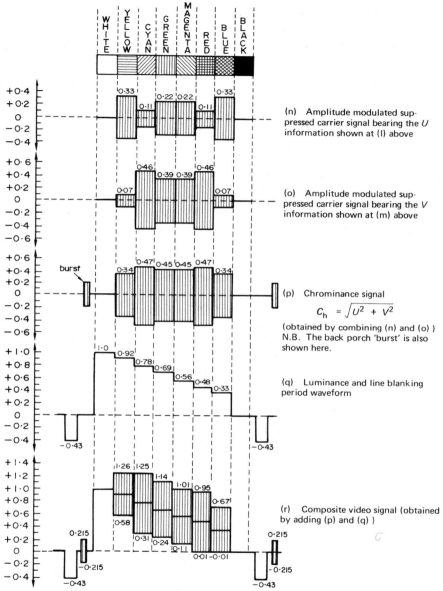

Fig. 3.5 *95% Saturated, 100% amplitude colour-bar signal*

Note:

(a) Reading the diagrams downwards from (a) to (r) but omitting (k), shows the progressive development of the composite video signal at the source.

(b) Reading the diagrams upwards from (r) to (a) shows the reverse process in a PAL-D receiver. (*N.B.* The $(G' - Y')$ signal at (k) is obtained by matrixing (i) and (j).)

55

subsequent signal amplitudes. Thus, on 100% sat. yellow, $R' = 1.0$, $G' = 1.0$, and $B' = 0$. Desaturating by only 5% makes B' change from zero to 25% of R' and G'. This compensates for the very low sensitivity at the foot of the receiver c.r.t.'s I_a/V_g characteristic.

(h) *Luminance signal*

$$Y' = 0.30R' + 0.59G' + 0.11B'$$

On yellow,
$$Y' = 0.30(1) + 0.59(1) + 0.11(0.25)$$
$$= 0.30 \quad + 0.59 \quad + 0.0275$$
$$= 0.9175 \approx 0.92$$

N.B. The introduction of 5% of white raises the luminance level from its value of 0.89 on 100% sat. yellow, to 0.92 on 95% sat. yellow.

(i) $(B' - Y')$ *colour-difference signal*

On yellow, $(B' - Y') = (0.25 - 0.92) = -0.67$

(j) $(R' - Y')$ *colour-difference signal*

On yellow, $(R' - Y') = (1.0 - 0.92) = +0.08$

(k) $(G' - Y')$ *colour-difference signal*

This is not produced at the transmitter but it is instructive to compute its value, especially as the diagrams used in reverse order are useful for receiver studies. On yellow,

$$(G' - Y') = (1.0 - 0.92) = +0.08$$

(l) *Weighted* $(B' - Y')$ *colour-difference signal: U*

This is formed by multiplying the $(B' - Y')$ colour-difference signal at (i) by the amplitude reducing factor of 0.493, i.e.,

$$U = 0.493(B' - Y')$$

On yellow $\quad U = 0.493 \times -0.67 = -0.33$

(m) *Weighted* $(R' - Y')$ *colour-difference signal: V*

Similarly, this is formed by multiplying the $(R' - Y')$ signal at (j) by the reduction factor of 0.877, i.e.,

$$V = 0.877(R' - Y')$$

On yellow $\quad V = 0.877 \times 0.08 = 0.07$

(n) *The U modulation-product*

This is the amplitude modulated suppressed carrier signal produced by a double-balanced modulator to which the sub-carrier frequency ($f_{sc} = 4.43361875$ MHz) and the U colour-difference signal are applied.

(o) *The V modulation-product*

Similarly this is the a.m. suppressed carrier signal produced by the *V* balanced modulator.

(p) *The chrominance signal*

This r.f. signal is simply the vector sum of the two r.f. signals shown at (n) and (o). These two r.f. sine-wave signals are mutually in quadrature and have amplitudes of *U* and *V*. The amplitude of the chrominance signal at (p) is therefore given by:

$$C_h = \sqrt{U^2 + V^2}$$

e.g., on yellow,

$$C_h = \sqrt{0.33^2 + 0.07^2} \approx 0.337$$

N.B. The sub-carrier burst is also shown on the waveform at (p). This is actually produced in PAL coders by pulsing the *U* and *V* modulators during the back-porch of the line blanking period. As shown in the PAL-coder described in the next chapter, both modulators yield a burst and the radiated burst is the vector sum of these two components, which is produced by the chrominance signal adder circuit. In such a coder, therefore, the waveforms at (l), (m), (n), and (o) would also show burst components.

(q) *Luminance signal and line blanking period waveform*

This diagram shows the luminance signal combined with the line blanking period waveform.

(r) *Composite video signal*

This is formed by adding the chrominance signal of (p) to the luminance part of the waveform at (q).

The corresponding figures for the remainder of the colour-bars are summarized in Table 3.4 below, together with the appropriate phase angles.

Table 3.4 Details of 95% saturated, 100% amplitude colour-bar signal. This signal is shown built up step-by-step in Fig. 3.5

Colour-bar	R	G	B	R'	G'	B'	Y'	(B'−Y')	(R'−Y')	U	V	Chrominance signal	
												Amp.	Phase angle
White	1·0	1·0	1·0	1·0	1·0	1·0	1·0	0	0	0	0	0	—
Yellow	·1·0	1·0	0·05	1·0	1·0	0·25	0·92	−0·67	+0·08	−0·33	+0·07	0·34	167° (193°)*
Cyan	0·05	1·0	1·0	0·25	1·0	1·0	0·78	+0·23	−0·53	+0·11	−0·46	0·47	283° (77°)
Green	0·05	1·0	0·05	0·25	1·0	0·25	0·69	−0·44	−0·44	−0·22	−0·39	0·45	241° (119°)
Magenta	1·0	0·05	1·0	1·0	0·25	1·0	0·56	+0·44	+0·44	+0·22	+0·39	0·45	61° (299°)
Red	1·0	0·05	0·05	1·0	0·25	0·25	0·48	−0·23	+0·52	−0·11	+0·46	0·47	103° (257°)
Blue	0·05	0·05	1·0	0·25	0·25	1·0	0·33	+0·67	−0·08	+0·33	−0·07	0·34	347° (13°)
Black	0	0	0	0	0	0	0	0	0	0	0	0	—

* The figures in brackets show the phase angles on 'PAL-lines'. $U = 0.493(B' - Y')$, $V = 0.877(R' - Y')$.

The following further points should be noted about Fig. 3.5 and the data in Table 3.4:

(a) Comparing the results with those for the 100% sat., 100% amp. weighted signal, it will be seen that the effect of desaturation to 95% is to increase the luminance levels and decrease the amplitude of the chrominance signal. This is what would be expected for a 'whiter' signal.

(b) The phase angles for primary and complementary hues remain the same as for the 100% sat., 100% amp. weighted signal.

(c) Examination of the three colour-difference signals shows that $(G' - Y')$ has the smallest peak-to-peak amplitude. It is never more than equal to the smaller one of the other two colour-difference signals.

(d) When considering a receiver, the colour-difference and luminance signals must be added to show the net R', G', and B' inputs to the colour receiver c.r.t., e.g., on yellow:

$$(R' - Y') = +0.08; \quad (G' - Y') = +0.08;$$
$$(B' - Y') = -0.67 \quad \text{and} \quad Y' \quad = +0.92.$$

Thus:

$$R' = (R' - Y') + Y' = +0.08 + 0.92 = 1.0$$
$$G' = (G' - Y') + Y' = +0.08 + 0.92 = 1.0$$
$$B' = (B' - Y') + Y' \times -0.67 + 0.92 = 0.25$$

The corresponding light outputs are shown at (a), (b), and (c). These could be deduced by applying the values for R', G', and B' to the receiver gamma curve of Fig. 2.1. Expressed algebraically, the light outputs (assuming $\gamma = 2.2$ for the receiver tube) are given by:

$$R = (R')^\gamma = (1.0)^{2.2} = 1.0$$
$$G = (G')^\gamma = (1.0)^{2.2} = 1.0$$
$$B = (B')^\gamma = (0.25)^{2.2} = 0.05$$

It is recommended that these waveforms are looked at again when receiver colour-difference amplifiers and c.r.t. drive systems are being studied.

Phase angles of arbitrary hues

The phase angles of primaries or complementaries remain constant irrespective of the degree of saturation. This is obviously true for magenta, where:

$$\theta = \tan^{-1} \frac{V}{U} = \tan^{-1} \frac{0.877(R' - Y')}{0.493(B' - Y')}$$

but $R' = B'$ on magenta, hence

$$\theta = \tan^{-1} \frac{0.877}{0.493} = 61°$$

at all levels of saturation.

The constancy of phase angles on primaries and complementaries arises because two of the three primaries are always numerically equal at all levels of saturation, and it can be shown that this makes the ratio $(R' - Y')$ to $(B' - Y')$ constant in these six cases.

On arbitrary hues, however, the three primaries are all at different magnitudes and the ratio $(R' - Y')$ to $(B' - Y')$ is no longer constant, but changes with saturation levels. Hence the phase angle θ also changes.

The point does not affect the practical performance of a properly adjusted colour television system. However, care must be taken in superimposing chrominance signal phase angles on chromaticity diagrams. It is permissible to mark the phase angles of the primaries and complementaries on the perimeter of the colour chart. Straight lines joining these points to the white point pass through all points of constant hue *and* constant phase angle. If however, the phase angle of an arbitrary hue at full saturation is marked on the perimeter of the colour chart, a straight line joining this point to the white point, although showing all points of constant hue, no longer represents points of constant phase angle. All points along this line have phase angles which differ from the one shown on the perimeter.

The following list gives an example of an arbitrary hue at different levels of saturation.

A purple hue is chosen in which the ratio of R to B is held constant at $2:1$ at all the listed levels of saturation.

The figures in brackets by the R and B values show the portion of these primaries which remains when the white content (as indicated by the G amplitude) is deducted. These portions remain in the ratio $2:1$. As will be seen, the phase angle changes slightly with saturation.

Table 3.5 Showing the chrominance signal phase angle for an arbitrary purple hue at various levels of saturation

Camera voltages before gamma-correction			Sat. %	Amp. %	Phase angle (NTSC-Lines)
R	G	B			
1·0 (0·9)	0·1	0·55 (0·45)	90	100	76° 54′
1·0 (0·8)	0·2	0·6 (0·4)	80	100	78° 27′
1·0 (0·7)	0·3	0·65 (0·35)	70	100	79° 35′
1·0 (0·6)	0·4	0·7 (0·3)	60	100	80° 9′

Chrominance signal amplitude

It is a common fallacy to think that the amplitude of the chrominance signal depends only upon saturation. This is not so; it depends both upon the saturation and amplitude of the colour it represents. This is demonstrated below, by showing that the same chrominance phasor can represent two quite different levels of saturation of a

59

given hue. Magenta is chosen because this makes the colour-difference signals equal and simplifies calculations.

EXAMPLE 1. 100% amplitude, 78% saturated, magenta. Here
$$R = 1\cdot0, \quad B = 1\cdot0, \quad G = 0\cdot22; \quad (N.B. \ 22\% \text{ of white})$$
therefore $R' = 1\cdot0, \quad B' = 1\cdot0, \quad G' = 0\cdot22^{1/\gamma} = 0\cdot5$ (using the gamma-curves in Fig. 2.1)

(a) *Luminance signal*
$$Y' = 0\cdot3R' + 0\cdot59G' + 0\cdot11B'$$
therefore $Y' = 0\cdot3(1\cdot0) + 0\cdot59(0\cdot5) + 0\cdot11(1\cdot0)$
therefore $Y' = 0\cdot3 + 0\cdot295 + 0\cdot11 = \mathbf{0\cdot705}$

(b) *Colour-difference signals*
$$(R' - Y') = (1\cdot0 - 0\cdot705) = 0\cdot295$$
and, since $B' = R'$,
$$(B' - Y') = (R' - Y') = 0\cdot295$$

(c) *Chrominance signal*
$$\text{Amplitude} = C_h = \sqrt{U^2 + V^2}$$
therefore $C_h = \sqrt{\{0\cdot493(B' - Y')\}^2 + \{0\cdot877(R' - Y')\}^2}$
$$= \sqrt{(0\cdot493 \times 0\cdot295)^2 + (0\cdot877 \times 0\cdot295)^2} \quad \approx 0\cdot3$$

Phase angle
$$\theta = \tan^{-1}\left(\frac{V}{U}\right) = \tan^{-1}\left\{\frac{0\cdot877(R' - Y')}{0\cdot493(B' - Y')}\right\} = \tan^{-1}\left(\frac{0\cdot877}{0\cdot493}\right) = \mathbf{61°}$$

EXAMPLE 2. 22% amplitude, 100% saturated, magenta. Here
$$R = 0\cdot22, \qquad\qquad B = 0\cdot22, \qquad\qquad G = 0$$
therefore $R' = (0\cdot22)^{1/\gamma} = 0\cdot5, \quad B' = (0\cdot22)^{1/\gamma} = 0\cdot5, \quad G' = 0$

(a) *Luminance signal*
$$Y' = 0\cdot3(R') + 0\cdot59(G') + 0\cdot11B'$$
$$= 0\cdot3(0\cdot5) + 0\cdot3(0) + 0\cdot11(0\cdot5)$$
$$= 0\cdot15 + 0 + 0\cdot055 = \mathbf{0\cdot205}$$

(b) *Colour-difference signals*
$$(R' - Y') = (0\cdot5 - 0\cdot205) = +0\cdot295$$
and since $B' = R'$,
$$(B' - Y') = (R' - Y') = +0\cdot295$$

60

These values are the same as in (b) for example 1, so that the chrominance signal has the same amplitude and phase angle in the two cases; the values being those shown at (c) for example 1.

The fact that the same chrominance signal can describe two different levels of saturation does not imply any ambiguity in the system. The luminance signal is not the same in the two cases above and by pursuing the matter a little further it will be seen that the correct display appears on the receiver screen.

The net inputs of R', G', and B' to the c.r.t. are:

EXAMPLE 1

$$R' = (R' - Y') + Y' = 0.295 + 0.705 = 1.0$$
$$B' = (B' - Y') + Y' = 0.295 + 0.705 = 1.0$$
$$G' = (G' - Y') + Y' = (0.5 - 0.705) + 0.705 = 0.5$$

EXAMPLE 2

$$R' = (R' - Y') + Y' = 0.295 + 0.205 = 0.5$$
$$B' = (B' - Y') + Y' = 0.295 + 0.205 = 0.5$$
$$G' = (G' - Y') + Y' = (0 - 0.205) + 0.205 = 0$$

The light outputs for the two examples may be found by applying the above values of R', G', and B' to the receiver gamma curve of Fig. 2.1.

EXAMPLE 1

$$\text{Red light} \quad \propto (1.0)^{2.2} \propto 1.0$$
$$\text{Blue light} \quad \propto (1.0)^{2.2} \propto 1.0$$
$$\text{Green light} \propto (0.5)^{2.2} \propto 0.22$$

This represents the original 78% saturated, 100% amplitude magenta.

EXAMPLE 2

$$\text{Red light} \quad \propto (0.5)^{2.2} \propto 0.22$$
$$\text{Blue light} \quad \propto (0.5)^{2.2} \propto 0.22$$
$$\text{Green light} \propto 0$$

This represents the original 100% saturated, 22% amplitude magenta.

Alternative colour-bar nomenclature

A system of describing colour-bar signals by a four-figure code (e.g., 100/0/100/25), is described in chapter 16. It refers to *gamma-corrected* rather than *pre-gamma-corrected* signals. Since the latter are directly representative of *light levels*, the original system appears more fundamental and meaningful.

4

Basic PAL Coder, Transmitter, and Receiver Arrangements

Comparison of colour television systems

The main world systems are NTSC, PAL, and SECAM. All of these describe the picture in terms of luminance and colour-difference signals. It is the way in which the chrominance signal is modulated by the colour-difference signals which constitutes the main differences between these systems.

Figures 4.1 and 4.2 show generalized block diagrams of colour-television transmitters and receivers respectively. These diagrams could form the basis of a study of any one of the systems. The areas where differences lie are enclosed by dotted lines.

NTSC and PAL are alike in employing Q.A.M. of the chrominance signal. PAL uses simple weighted $(R' - Y')$ and $(B' - Y')$ colour-difference signals of equal bandwidth to modulate the two quadrature phase (but equal frequency) sub-carriers

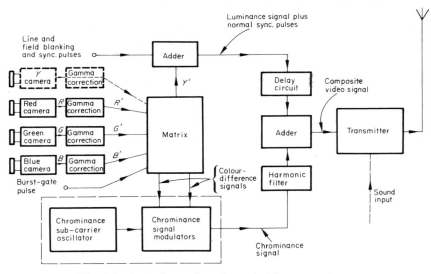

Fig. 4.1 *Basic form of a colour television transmitter*

to form the two components which when added yield the chrominance signal. In NTSC the more complex I and Q colour-difference signals are used. These have unequal bandwidths; the I being some three times broader than the Q.

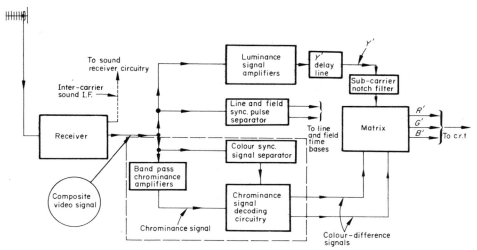

Fig. 4.2 *Basic form of a colour television receiver*

In SECAM it is again the simpler $(R' - Y')$ and $(B' - Y')$ colour-difference signals which are used but here the method of modulation is entirely different. Frequency modulation of the sub-carrier is used and instead of both $(R' - Y')$ and $(B' - Y')$ information being present in the chrominance signal simultaneously (as is the case with NTSC and PAL), the sub-carrier is modulated by $(R' - Y')$ on one line and $(B' - Y')$ on the next.

Since this book is primarily concerned with PAL, the work which now follows in this chapter is confined to an introduction to the main features of this system. However, PAL is a direct development of NTSC. For the benefit of those who wish to gain a more adequate understanding of the differences between these two systems, further information is given about NTSC in Appendix A at the end of the book.

The basic PAL coding process

A 95% saturated, 100% amplitude colour-bar signal was built up step-by-step in Fig. 3.5.

A basic PAL coder arrangement showing how such a composite video signal may be built up, is shown in Fig. 4.3. The letters in the waveform 'balloons' refer back to Fig. 3.5 where these waveforms are more clearly drawn.

The gamma-corrected R', G', and B' inputs to the matrix, give rise to $Y', (R' - Y')$, and $(B' - Y')$ outputs. Because the colour-difference signals are bandwidth restricted by filters which pass the range 0 to 1 MHz, they suffer a small delay relative to the Y' signal which has a broader bandwidth of 5·5 MHz. To bring the Y' and chrominance signals into step at the point where they are added, it is necessary to insert a compensating delay into the Y' path.

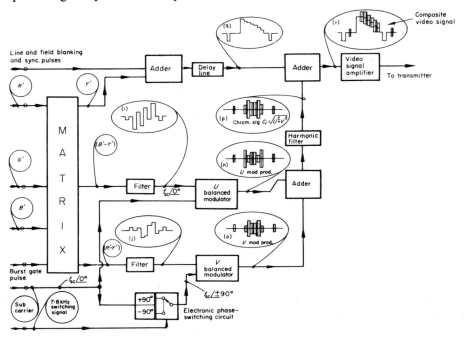

Fig. 4.3 *Basic organization of a PAL coder*

(*N.B.* The waveforms correspond to those in Fig. 3.5.)

The $(R' - Y')$ and $(B' - Y')$ signals pass to balanced modulators together with sub-carrier inputs at appropriate phases. The principle of the balanced modulators is discussed in chapter 8. In the sub-carrier path to the V modulator is a phase-switching circuit which passes to the modulator a sub-carrier having a phase of 90° on one line but 270° on alternate lines. Since one switching cycle takes two lines, the square-wave switching signal to the phase switch is of half-line frequency, i.e., approximately 7·8 kHz.

The double-sideband suppressed carrier signals from the modulators are added to yield the Q.A.M. chrominance signal. This passes through a filter (which removes harmonics of the sub-carrier frequency) and on to an adding circuit where it is combined with the luminance and blanking signals to form a composite video signal. This goes forward to the transmitter to modulate the vision carrier in the normal way.[1]

[1] See 'The Vision Transmitter' in Chapter 2 of *Television Receiver Theory*: Part 1, by G. H. Hutson, published by Arnolds of London.

In this diagram the weighting operation is assumed to be carried out in the modulator 'boxes', e.g., by attenuating the $(B' - Y')$ and $(R' - Y')$ inputs, or by corresponding adjustments of the modulator outputs.

This weighting operation may be carried out in the main 'matrix' which will then deliver colour-difference signals of amplitudes $U = 0.493(B' - Y')$ and $V = 0.877(R' - Y')$.

The end product is the same, i.e., the chrominance signal sub-carrier frequency sine-wave components have amplitudes in the ratio $U:V$, not $(B' - Y'):(R' - Y')$.

The instantaneous amplitude of the composite video signal (i.e., of the modulating information) during the active part (i.e., the picture detail) of raster lines may be written as:

$$M = Y' + U' \sin \omega t \pm V' \cos \omega t^{1}$$

The full significance of this expression will be apparent after reading chapters 8 and 9.

PAL video and vision signals

Figure 4.4 shows the modulation levels for the negatively modulated 625-line vision carrier when bearing a 95% sat., 100% amp., colour-bar signal. For convenience, the luminance and chrominance amplitudes are repeated under the diagram. As before these are based upon a scale of 0 to 1·0 from black to peak-white levels.

Since the chrominance signal consists of two suppressed carrier signals, a replacement carrier has to be generated at the receiver. For the purpose of locking the frequency and phase of the re-inserted sub-carrier generated by the receiver's 'reference oscillator' a burst of sub-carrier is transmitted during the back porch in the line-blanking period.

This consists of 10 ± 1 cycles. In an NTSC signal the burst phase is 180°. With PAL, however, the burst phase angle is switched on a line-by-line basis from 135° on 'NTSC-lines', to 225° on the alternate 'PAL-lines'. This is done to allow the receiver to identify NTSC and PAL lines. The reason for this and the way in which the 'swinging-burst' is utilized to achieve synchronism is discussed fully in later chapters. In the PAL signal, since the burst switches in phase by $\pm 45°$ line-by-line, about 180°, its average phase is still 180° which is the same as that in the original NTSC system. This phase angle was chosen to give minimum interference during the line fly-back stroke in colour receivers. Although under normal operation the burst is

[1] (a) In most literature the letter E is used in each term to indicate that voltages are being considered and appropriate suffixes to each E identify the information represented by the term. Thus:

$$E_m = E'_Y + E'_U \sin \omega t \pm E'_V \cos \omega t$$

(b) Note that since a sine-wave and a cosine-wave of equal frequency are mutually at 90°, the quadrature relationship between the U and V parts is shown by writing the expression in these terms. The $\pm$ signs in front of $E'_v \cos \omega t$ indicates the line-by-line inversion of this component of the PAL chrominance information.

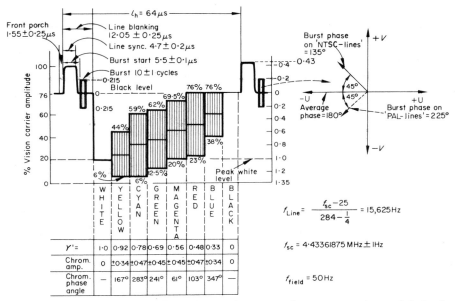

Fig. 4.4 *Showing the video signal waveform and corresponding vision carrier modulation levels for a 95% saturated, 100% amplitude colour-bar signal*

gated out of the signal path to the chrominance demodulators and directed only to that part of the receiver where it is required (i.e., to the reference oscillator's automatic frequency and phase-controlling circuit), it is possible under fault conditions for the burst to get through to the demodulators. This gives rise to an output voltage which modulates the beam current during line fly-back and causes interference. The choice of a burst phase angle of 180° reduces this interference to a minimum. It shows up as a very low amplitude green pattern (vertical striations) towards the left of the screen.

It will be noted on Fig. 4.4 that the line frequency f_h is stated in terms of the sub-carrier frequency f_{sc}. At the signal source f_{sc} is the standard frequency and f_h is derived from f_{sc} by count-down circuits so that the correct numerical relationship between f_{sc} and f_h is maintained at all times.

Although the field frequency f_v is equal to the nominal mains frequency of 50 Hz, it is not locked to the mains. The mains frequency varies slightly with loading and this would cause errors in the relationship between f_{sc}, f_h, and f_v, if f_v were mains-locked. To obviate this the field frequency is maintained accurately at 50 Hz independently of the mains. Since the system is not mains-synchronized it is said to be asynchronous. A result of this is that any mains hum pattern on the screen (e.g., due to a fault condition) is no longer stationary but drifts at a rate determined by the difference between the field and mains frequencies.

In Fig. 4.5 the video waveform during the field blanking period is shown. The

66

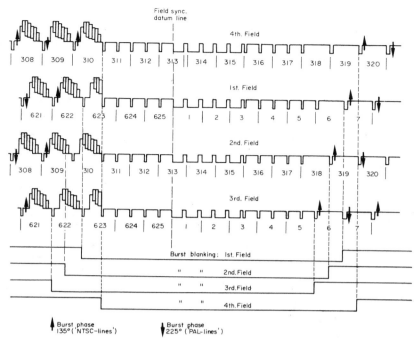

Fig. 4.5 *Showing the waveform of the 625-line PAL video signal during the field blanking period*

burst is gated out of the transmitted signal during this interval. In the PAL signal, in order to make the burst phase start and stop in identical directions at the beginning and end of each field, the burst blanking pulse is shifted as shown, so that it follows a four-field cycle. If the burst blanking pulse were not staggered in this way but repeated at regular intervals of $\frac{1}{50}$ s (i.e., at intervals of $312\frac{1}{2}$ lines precisely), the burst phases at the end of each field and the start of the next would be in one direction for fields 1 and 4, but the opposite for fields 2 and 3. This may be seen by applying the same field blanking pulse, say the third at the foot of Fig. 4.5, to the four fields shown above. In some receiver circuits, it was found that these different start and stop phase sequences caused a flicker disturbance at the top of the screen when colours of high saturation were present there.

Basic PAL transmitter arrangements

To summarize the basic principles of the production of a PAL colour television signal, a simplified diagram of a transmission system is shown in Fig. 4.6.

It should be emphasized that at this point in the study of the subject the aim is to gain an outline mental picture of the general idea of the system. Subsequent detailed studies of the nature of Q.A.M. signals will lead to a full appreciation of the formation of the chrominance signal and of its interesting properties.

It is intended that the reader shall refer back to Figs. 4.3, 4.6, and 4.7 at various times during the reading of this book, as appropriate subjects are dealt with in successive chapters.

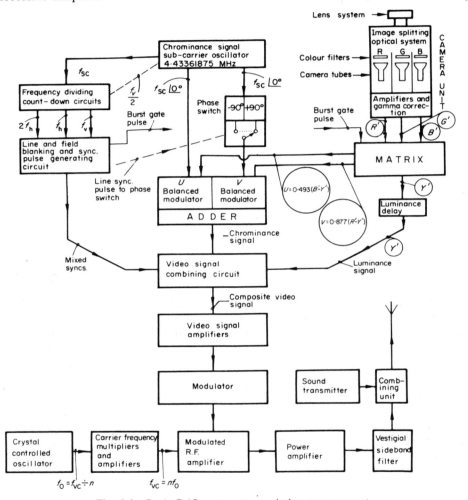

Fig. 4.6 *Basic PAL-system transmission arrangement*

It will be noticed on both Fig. 4.3 and Fig. 4.6 that one of the inputs to the matrix is labelled 'burst gating signal'. This is a square type pulse at line frequency, timed to appear during the back-porch period. For its duration the matrix delivers to the two modulators inputs such that the $(B' - Y')$ modulator yields a sub-carrier burst at

180° whilst the $(R' - Y')$ circuit gives a burst of the same amplitude but having a phase of 90° on one line and 270° on the next. The adder yields an output which is the vector sum of the two inputs, i.e., it delivers a sub-carrier frequency sine-wave at 135° on one line and 225° on the next.

The matrix following the camera unit delivers the weighted colour-difference signals $U = 0.493(B' - Y')$ and $V = 0.877(R' - Y')$ to the U and V modulators, and the luminance signal Y' is passed via a luminance delay circuit to the video signal combining unit.

In the simplified block diagram Fig. 4.6, the sub-carrier is shown as being directly generated at 4·43361875 MHz and this is shown as passing to 'countdown' circuits to produce the required synchronizing frequencies of $2f_h$, f_h, and f_v. (Note that a frequency of $2f_h$ is needed because this is the repetition rate of the *half-line* and *equalizing* pulses in the field blanking period.)

The numerical relationships are in fact such that it is easier to start off with a 'master-frequency' of 4·43361875 MHz − 25 Hz = 4·43359375 MHz. This frequency is $(1135/4 \times f_h)$ and may conveniently be counted down to yield $2f_h$, f_h, and f_v. Finally a component at $f_v/2 = 25$ Hz is derived and this is then added to the generated 'master-frequency' to give the required chrominance sub-carrier frequency of 4·43361875 MHz. In this sense f_{sc} is itself a 'derived frequency', with the standard frequency controlling the system being 4·43359375 MHz.

It will be realized by reference back to the section on dot-patterns at the end of chapter 2, that the complication arises from the addition of the extra 25 Hz to the *quarter-line offset* sub-carrier, since its presence means that f_{sc}, f_h, and f_v are not related by factors which are integers.

There are other methods of deriving f_{sc}, $2f_h$, f_h, and f_v from crystal oscillators which form the master-control for the system standards, but a study of these falls outside of the scope of this textbook.

Basic PAL receiver arrangement

In a similar way, Fig. 4.7 shows the basic form of a PAL receiver. Once again it is emphasized that each section of this is later studied in detail and to avoid repetition little need be said about the diagram at this stage. The general pattern should, however, be noted. It will be observed that the composite video signal obtained from the vision demodulator, passes, after some initial amplification, to four different sections of the circuit. These are:

(a) The luminance amplifier, which includes a delay circuit to compensate for the short delay which is introduced in the narrower bandwidth chrominance amplifier circuit path. Also present is a 'notch filter' to remove the chrominance signal.

(b) A sync. separator which feeds locking pulses to the line and field timebases. These latter now have an additional function to perform. Apart from providing the normal line and field scanning currents in the deflector coils, they have to provide the dynamic convergence waveforms described in chapters 6 and 7.

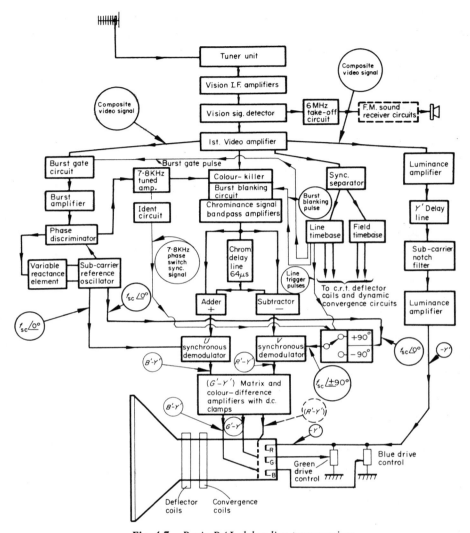

Fig. 4.7   Basic PAL delay-line type receiver

(c) A chrominance signal path which includes bandpass amplifiers and synchronous demodulators designed to accept the chrominance signal which is really an r.f. signal of 2 MHz bandwidth centred on the sub-carrier frequency of 4·433 MHz.

This path is shut down by a burst blanking circuit at the end of each active line so that the burst does not get through. The burst blanking circuit is driven by a pulse from the line timebase. This is suitably timed to open-circuit the chrominance signal path during the back-porch period when the burst is present.

A colour-killer circuit shuts down the chrominance amplifier during monochrome transmissions. This prevents random information in the luminance signal, which happens to fall within the bandwidth of the chrominance amplifiers, from getting through to the demodulators and causing coloured interference on the screen. In effect the colour-killer acts as an electronic switch which is closed during colour transmissions and opened during monochrome programmes. The switch is activated by a voltage which is only present when the burst is present. In the diagram it is driven by the 7·8 kHz component which is present in the 'swinging-burst' of a PAL signal. (The derivation of the 7·8 kHz component and its applications, are discussed in chapters 13, 14, and 15.)

The chrominance delay-line and associated circuitry serves to separate the U and V r.f. components from the combined Q.A.M. chrominance signals. These components then go forward to synchronous demodulators from which the two colour-difference signals $(B' - Y')$ and $(R' - Y')$ are recovered. These in turn go forward to a matrix from which the missing $(G' - Y')$ colour-difference signal is derived.

(d) Finally the fourth branch of the circuit accepts only the gated-out burst component of the composite video signal and uses this as a standard against which to lock-in the sub-carrier reference oscillator from which suitably phased outputs are fed to the two demodulators.

The end product of the receiver circuitry must be the three voltages R', G', and B' to modulate the three beams of the c.r.t. As will be seen in chapter 16 the colour-difference signals are often fed to the grids of the c.r.t. with a luminance signal of negative-going polarity (i.e., $-Y'$) passing to the cathodes. By suitable adjustment of the relative amplitudes to take account of the different grid and cathode sensitivities this makes the c.r.t. itself perform the matrixing operation mentioned briefly in chapter 2. Alternatively, the Y' and colour-difference signals are all fed to a matrix and the tube then receives straightforward R', G', and B' inputs. This was pre-supposed to be the method in the simplified generalized receiver diagram of Fig. 4.2.

5

Receiver Display Devices

At the time of writing, colour and monochrome receivers use cathode ray tubes as the display devices. Meanwhile research scientists continue to look for alternatives and it is possible that devices employing entirely different techniques may be developed.

Colour television cathode ray tubes; basic requirements

A colour television cathode ray tube screen has to be coated with three different phosphors, one for each of the chosen red, green, and blue primaries. These must be separated physically from one another and each energized by an electron beam of intensity proportional to the appropriate colour voltages R', G', or B'. The object is to produce three coincident rasters which reproduce the red, green, and blue content of the transmitted picture. Seen from a normal viewing distance the eye records at each part of the picture the hue corresponding to the addition of the light outputs of the three primary colours radiated from that part of the screen.

The phosphors may be arranged in dots as in shadow-mask tubes; in horizontal strips as in chromatron (i.e., Lawrence) tubes or in vertical strips as in trinitron tubes.

Excitation may be by:

(a) Three separate guns; one for each phosphor. This method is used in shadow-mask tubes.

(b) A single beam the modulation of which is switched in sequence between the three colour voltages as the beam moves from phosphor to phosphor. Chromatron tubes employ this method.

(c) A single gun which develops three simultaneously projected beams each separately modulated, one for each phosphor. This principle is used in the trinitron tube but the gun itself could equally well be employed in shadow-mask tubes.

Shadow-mask tubes (see Fig. 5.1)

Basic principles

In the shadow-mask tube, developed in America by R.C.A., the phosphor dots on the screen are arranged in threes. Each group forms an equilateral triangle with

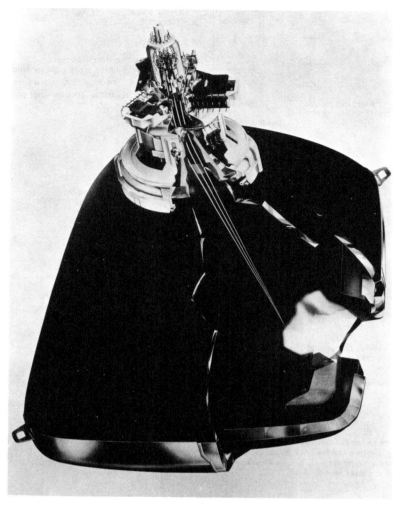

Fig. 5.1 *Cutaway view of a shadow-mask tube, showing how the three beams converge on one hole in the mask*

(Photograph reproduced by kind permission of Mullard Limited)

a red-light-emitting phosphor dot in one corner, green in the second, and blue in the third. In a typical tube there are some 440,000 of these *triads* which together form a closely interwoven pattern covering the screen.

Situated about 1 cm behind the screen is the metal shadow-mask. In appearance this is rather like a piece of gauze, with one hole for every screen phosphor dot triad. The purpose of the mask is to ensure that all phosphor dots are bombarded only by electrons from from their associated beam (see Fig. 5.2).

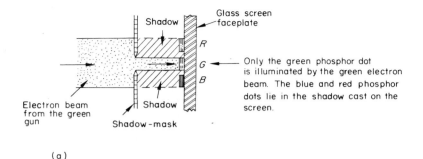

Only the green phosphor dot is illuminated by the green electron beam. The blue and red phosphor dots lie in the shadow cast on the screen.

(a)

Glass faceplate

Triad of phosphor dots

Shadow-mask

Axis of blue beam

Axis of green beam

Blue colour and deflection centre

Axis of red beam

Green colour centre

Red colour centre

(b)

Fig. 5.2 *Illustrating the action of the shadow-mask*

(a) Shows how electrons from a given beam only strike one of the three phosphor dots in each triad; the other two dots lie in the 'electron shadow' cast by the mask.

(b) Shows how a particular hole is associated with one phosphor triad and that a given phosphor dot can only be hit by one of the three beams.

The shadow mask is made from a mild-steel sheet some 0·15 mm thick. During manufacture, the sheet is coated on both sides with a photo-resist chemical and covered (again on both sides) by photographic negatives bearing black dots where holes are required. On exposure to ultraviolet light the coating hardens between the dots and becomes impervious to the ferric chloride etching solution which (after the sheet has been washed to remove the dots of unhardened chemical) is finally sprayed on both sides of the sheet to etch away the holes. This method produces holes having a profile similar to that shown in Fig. 5.3. As illustrated in the diagram this shape reduces the scatter of electrons from the hole's edge, since the thickness of the edge is minimized.

The shadow mask is then used as a template in the processes by which the three types of phosphor dots are laid down and a given mask becomes uniquely identified with a particular screen plate.

As in monochrome tubes, the screen is aluminized and this coating, together with the shadow mask, is held at final anode potential.

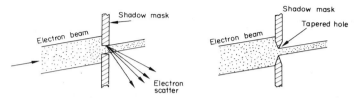

Fig. 5.3 *Showing how electron scatter from the edge of a shadow-mask hole is much reduced by giving the hole a tapered profile*

The three guns in the tube are equally spaced at 120° around the tube axis. This gives three separate electron beams which are deflected by the same line and field deflection fields. When operating correctly, at the screen these three beams appear to emanate from three separate points spaced at 120° intervals on a plane at the centre of the deflection field. These points are referred to as *colour centres*. In manufacture, ultraviolet light is shone through the shadow mask from each of these centres in turn, as part of a series of processes during which the phosphor dots are being formed. Since the *colour centres* are precisely defined in the manufacturing process, but the *deflection centres* are on a plane determined by the position of the deflector coils along the tube neck, it follows that it is important so to position the coils that the deflection and colour centres lie in the same plane. This forms part of the 'purity' adjustments described later.

If these adjustments are properly carried out, the electron beam from any one gun is so directed at the shadow mask that the electrons which pass through a given hole are only able to hit one of the three phosphor dots in the associated triad. This

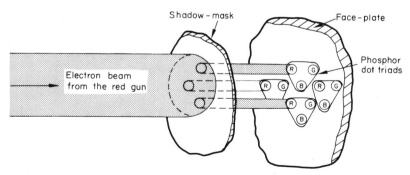

Fig. 5.4 *Showing how a given electron beam may straddle a small group of shadow-mask holes, but (assuming correct purity adjustments have been made) only the appropriate colour phosphor dot in each triad is bombarded*

75

is illustrated in Fig. 5.2(b) and 5.4. Electron beams may be treated as light beams for this purpose, travelling in straight lines from the deflection centres to the shadow mask and through the holes to the screen. Each electron beam may straddle some three or four holes at a time, but a particular beam only hits its own phosphor dots. The other two dots in each triad lie in the shadow cast by the mask.

The ratio of electrons passing through the holes to those hitting the shadow mask is determined by the ratio of the total areas of the holes to the area of the mask between them. In practice only some 15% to 20% of the electrons actually activate the phosphors. Over 80% of the total beam current energy is dissipated as a heat loss in the shadow mask. To give adequate maximum brightness the current reaching the screen has to be of the order of 300 μA and to achieve this a total maximum beam current in the region of 1·5 mA is necessary.

Operating conditions: voltages

Table 5.1 shows typical operating conditions for a shadow-mask tube. Independent adjustment of the first anode voltage on each of the three guns is necessary (together with adjustments of the relative luminance signal drive), in order to establish the correct proportions of R, G, and B beam currents to yield the chosen white (i.e., Illum. D_{6500}). The voltages shown for V_{a1} indicate the maximum range likely to be necessary to achieve extinction of all three beams when the grids are held constant at -105 V relative to the cathodes. This matter is further discussed under grey-scale tracking.

Table 5.1 Typical operating conditions for a shadow-mask tube

Electrode	Voltages relative to:	
	Cathode	*H.T. negative*
Third and fourth anodes ($V_{a3}:V_{a4}$)	25 kV	25 kV
Second (i.e., focus) anode (V_{a2})	4·2 to 5·0 kV	4·2 to 5·0 kV
First anode (i.e., 'screen') V_{a1}	210 to 495 V	340 to 730 V
Grid	-65 to -135 V	$+95$*
Cathode	0	$+130$ to $+235$*

* It is usual to hold the 'no-signal' grid voltage constant and vary the bias (hence the brightness level) by varying the 'black level' voltage on the cathodes (see chapter 16).

Total beam current

To produce white (C.I.E. co-ordinates $x = 0·3127$; $y = 0·3290$, i.e., Illuminant D_{6500}) with a light output from the screen centre of the order 60 to 70 cd/m^2 a total e.h.t. current ($I_{a3} + I_{a4}$) of some 800 μA is required. On maximum brightness the total e.h.t. current may rise to 1·5 mA.

Ratio of gun currents

The efficiencies of the three phosphors are different. To produce white, unequal beam currents are needed. Typically, the proportions of the total e.h.t. current from each gun to give white are:

red 42%; blue 28%; green 30%

Since the red phosphor requires the greatest current it is normal to express the ratio of the red gun current to the green and blue gun currents in turn. These ratios vary from tube to tube, especially after substantial use. Table 5.2 indicates what order the ratios may have.

Table 5.2 Ratios of shadow-mask tube cathode currents to produce white

Ratio	Min.	Av.*	Max.
Red gun to blue gun	1·0	1·5	2·0
Red gun to green gun	1·0	1·4	1·8

* The average figures correspond to the percentages quoted above; i.e., the ratios are:

Red to blue = 42%:28% = 6:4 = 1·5:1
Red to green = 42%:30% = 7:5 = 1·4:1

Degaussing

To minimize the effect of the earth's magnetic field and stray fields on the deflection of the three beams (and therefore on purity as well as the accuracy with which they track one another), a magnetic shield is fixed over part of the tube cone. This is made of cold-rolled steel of about 0·5 mm thickness.

In addition, the shadow mask itself—together with other steel fittings near the tube face, including the guard-rim—must be de-magnetized or again purity and convergence are degraded. This degaussing is achieved in two ways. When the receiver is first installed an external degaussing coil is usually used. This consists of a coil with sufficient turns to establish a field of some 1000 ampere-turns when connected direct to the a.c. mains. The coil is held parallel to the screen face, and moved slowly about in circular motions over the screen and around the front edges of the cabinet, after which it is slowly moved away from the face of the tube, turned face downwards and finally switched off when it is some 6 ft to 10 ft away from the receiver. This operation carries the steel parts through successive cycles of magnetization and as the coil moves away the strength of the field gradually diminishes so that when the coil is switched off the shadow mask and other steel parts are left with a small residual magnetization which opposes the earth's magnetic field, leaving the space within the tube virtually 'field-free'. When subjected to degaussing, steel situated in an environment where there is a static magnetic field (such as the earth's field) is left weakly magnetized with a polarity which opposes the static field.

Also a degaussing coil is fitted in the receiver itself. This is so arranged that when the receiver is first switched on a strong mains current passes through the coil and this then dies away to an insignificant level after a few moments. In this way the effects of day-to-day extraneous fields (e.g., from magnetic toys and domestic apparatus, etc.) which may cause magnetization of the shadow mask and other steel parts are removed each time the receiver is used. Because of the use of electromagnetic solenoids in system-changing switching, some receivers are also designed so that the degaussing operation is carried out each time the 405–625 system switch is used.

A typical automatic degaussing system is shown in Figs. 5.5 and 5.6. Two degaussing coils in series are used. Both of these are arranged partly outside and partly underneath the magnetic shield which is mounted on the tube neck. The external parts are adjacent to the tube's steel reinforcing rim-band so that this and any other steel fittings near the tube face are demagnetized, as well as the shadow mask itself.

It is estimated that an initial switch-on field strength of the order of 500 ampere-turns is adequate to remove any magnetization likely to be induced in a normal domestic situation. This should decay away to a level of less than 0·3 ampere-turns so that the remaining field from the degaussing coil does not affect the tube beams. This is illustrated in Fig. 5.5(c).

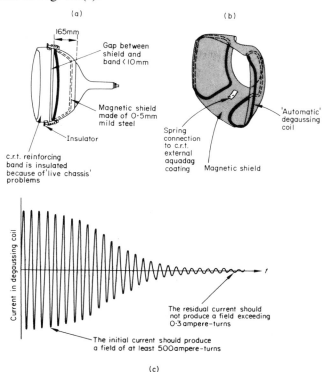

Fig. 5.5 *Automatic degaussing techniques*

(a) and (b) Show the way in which the two coils are arranged.
(c) Illustrates the variation of current in the coils from the moment of switching on.

78

In the circuit shown in Fig. 5.6, when first switching on, the series positive-temperature-coefficient resistor R_1 has a comparatively low resistance and the voltage across the degaussing coil, in series with the voltage-dependent resistor R_2, is high. The coil may typically be of 400 turns and 50 ohms resistance. The initial current through the coil is then about 1·25 A hence the field strength is approximately $400 \times 1·25 = 500$ ampere-turns. As the p.t.c. resistor R_1 warms up its resistance rises and the voltage across the v.d.r. R_2 and the coil, decreases. With the fall in voltage the resistance of R_2 rises and this reduces the current through the coil still further. The shunt resistor R_3 passes sufficient current to maintain the temperature of R_1, and the circuit settles down with a current of about 0·75 mA through the coil. The standing field during normal operation is then $400 \times 0·75 \times 10^{-3} = 0·3$ AT.

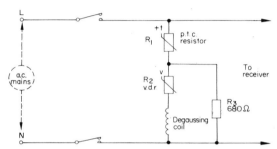

Fig. 5.6 *Example of an automatic degaussing circuit*

A variety of other circuits will be found. All must give an adequate initial field, decaying away to a negligible level after a few moments. In some circuits a switch is incorporated which finally switches off the current through the coils altogether.

Purity

It is essential that each of the three electron beams only bombards its own particular phosphor dots. With the green and blue beams off, the raster should be pure red. Similarly with red and blue beams off the raster should be pure green and pure blue when red and green are off.

The condition necessary to establish purity is that the deflection centres of the three beams must each coincide with the colour centres. Various measures have to be taken to establish this condition.

As explained earlier, the positions of the colour centres are precisely determined during the manufacture of the tube. Clearly, the plane of the deflection centres may be shifted along the tube neck until it coincides with the plane of the colour centres, simply by sliding the deflection coils up and down the tube neck.

However, it is also necessary to so direct the three beams along the tube neck that they each pass directly through the colour centres. To achieve this, two further adjustments are needed.

It must be possible to rotate the beams until they have the correct angular positions and also to move them inwards or outwards radially until they are the correct distance from the tube axis. The last two adjustments are facilitated by fitting a purity magnet assembly on the tube neck, positioned at a convenient point a little way along the tube from the base (see Fig. 5.7).

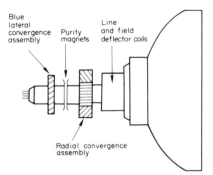

Fig. 5.7 Showing in outline form the various components mounted along the neck of a shadow-mask tube

This assembly is simply two annular rings, each of which is magnetized across a diameter. Each, on its own, would set up a transverse field in the tube neck. With both present, the net field is the resultant of the two fields and this has a maximum value of twice the strength of one field and a minimum value of zero.

Both the direction and the magnitude of the net field may be varied. Rotating the rings together, rotates this transverse field but leaves its strength unchanged. This causes all three beams to move circumferentially.

Rotating the rings in opposite directions, by equal amounts from their initial positions, leaves the direction of the net field unchanged but alters its strength. This causes all three beams to move transversely.

The rings are sometimes marked with notches, or bear marked tabs. When these marks are together the field strength is zero. Spreading them apart increases the field and makes the beams move in a transverse direction, whilst keeping the tabs or notches the same distance apart but moving them around the tube neck, imparts a circumferential motion to the three beams. Figure 5.8 illustrates the principle.

A systematic procedure is necessary to establish purity. To begin with, attention is focused on the central area of the screen where deflection is very small. The three guns are inclined by about 1° to the axis so that the beams are already approximately directed to converge correctly at the shadow mask in the central area. Small discrepancies in manufacture are now corrected by purity adjustments. A typical procedure is as follows:

(a) Switch off the green and blue beams. (Provision for blanking out each of the three beams is usually made by reducing the screen voltages to zero.)

(b) Slide the deflector coil assembly back towards the tube base as far as it will go.

The purity magnets are now rotated together, and the tabs (or grooves) moved

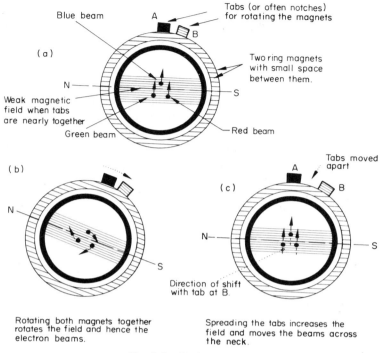

Blue beam

A

Tabs (or often notches)
for rotating the magnets

B

(a)

Two ring magnets
with small space
between them.

N

S

Weak magnetic
field when tabs
are nearly together

Green beam

Red beam

(b)

N

S

(c)

Tabs moved
apart

A

B

N

S

Direction of shift
with tab at B.

Rotating both magnets together
rotates the field and hence the
electron beams.

Spreading the tabs increases the
field and moves the beams across
the neck.

Fig. 5.8   *Purity magnets*

apart (either one way or the other, as found necessary) until a large red blob is produced in the central area of the screen. This will be a shapeless blob, not a perfectly circular one. No attention should be directed at areas away from the centre. Since the deflector coils are pulled back the deflection centres must of necessity be well away from the colour centres so that the adjustments being made are simply intended to make the three beams pass through the colour centres on their way to the screen. Clearly there is still deflection from the deflector coils and the beams are still being made to trace rasters. However, the deflection fields are minimum during the time the beams are in the central area of the screen and the accuracy of their landing (i.e., the purity) is entirely determined by the geometry of the tube itself, the position of the guns and the direction of the beams as modified by the fixed deflection caused by the permanent magnetic fields of the adjusted purity magnets.

(c) Having obtained the best possible purity in the central area, the deflector coils are now carefully moved along the tube neck until the best possible purity is achieved over the entire raster. This adjustment simply brings the plane of the deflection centres co-incident with the plane of the colour centres.

(d) With the red and blue beams off, green purity should now be looked at. Similarly with red and green beams off, blue purity is examined. It may be necessary to compromise slightly between red, green, and blue purity by slight re-adjustments of the purity magnets and of the deflector coil position to achieve the optimum overall result.

Grey scale tracking

The object of this procedure is to ensure that monochrome information at all contrast levels appears white, showing no colour tint at all. If the three guns were identical, having precisely the same cut-off points, with the same I_b/V_g characteristics, and if, in addition, the three phosphors had equal efficiencies, then a correct grey-scale would automatically be obtained. It has already been pointed out that the phosphor efficiencies differ and in addition the three guns do not have identical cut-off points or slopes. To compensate for these differences various adjustments have to be made. Again a systematic procedure is called for. In practice this amounts to two distinct steps.

(a) ADJUSTMENT OF LOWLIGHTS. Figure 5.9 shows (in exaggerated form) how the three I_b/V_g curves may differ. It is assumed that each gun has exactly the same voltages on all electrodes. It will be seen that the cut-off points are different and so are the slopes. A 'shaded raster' video signal input is shown applied to these three curves

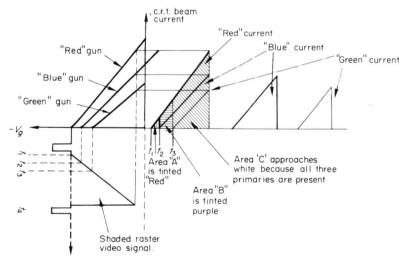

Fig. 5.9 *Illustrating the need for 'lowlight' grey-scale adjustments*

Note:
(a) All three guns are assumed to have equal first anode voltages.
(b) Each I_b/V_g curve has a different cut-off point and a different slope.
(c) The three guns do not start to produce beam currents at the same time (i.e., when they should do, at time t_1).
(d) From t_1 to t_2 instead of a very dark grey, a very dim reddish light is given off by the tube (see Area 'A').
(e) From t_2 to t_3 instead of a somewhat less dark grey, a dim purple is produced (see Area 'B').
(f) From t_3 there *is* a 'green' contribution and the hue, though not grey, is less tinted (see Area 'C').

82

simultaneously. The way in which the areas of low brightness (i.e., the lowlights), acquire a coloured 'tint' instead of being correctly reproduced as 'dark-greys', is illustrated.

To correct this it is necessary to bring the cut-off points into coincidence. This is achieved by making the screen (i.e., the first anode) voltages different from one another. It will be recalled that the width of the grid base of a pentode may be broadened or narrowed by increasing or decreasing the screen voltage. The same is true of the grid base of a c.r.t. One procedure sometimes used is to switch off the field deflection leaving just a central horizontal line on the screen. With the blue and green beams switched off the red screen voltage is adjusted until the red line just disappears. Then, with the red and blue beams off the green screen voltage is adjusted until the green line just disappears. Finally, blue is adjusted in the same way with the red and green beams off. Since all three guns have the same grid and cathode voltages under these conditions, this sequence of adjustments has now brought all three guns to a common black level. All are on the threshold of producing a visible raster once a drive is applied to the tube. In effect the I_b/V_g curves have been moved along until their cut-off points are coincident. Figure 5.10 illustrates the principle. An example of typical screen voltage supply circuitry is shown in Fig. 5.11.

Since these screen voltage adjustments are concerned with black level equalization, a different procedure is often adopted. If a stepped grey scale signal is available, the

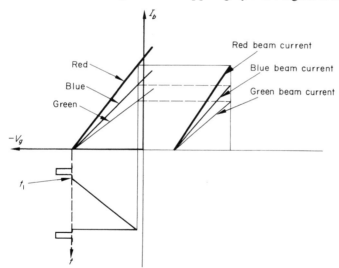

Fig. 5.10 *Showing the effect of correct 'lowlight' grey-scale adjustments*

Note:
(a) All three guns now have *different* first anode voltages. $V_{a_1(B)}$ has been increased, and $V_{a_1(G)}$ increased still more (c.f. Fig. 5.9) to widen the blue and green gun grid-bases so that all three guns begin to conduct together, i.e., at time t_1.
(b) Lowlights will now be true greys, but—due both to the different I_b/V_g slopes, and to the different phosphor characteristics—highlights will still be tinted.
(c) It remains to adjust the drives to the three guns so that highlights are not tinted.

three screen voltages may be adjusted to give a correct rendering (i.e., untinted) of the very dark columns in the stepped grey-scale. This is sometimes referred to as adjustment of the 'lowlights'. A 'shaded-raster' signal is equally suitable for this adjustment.

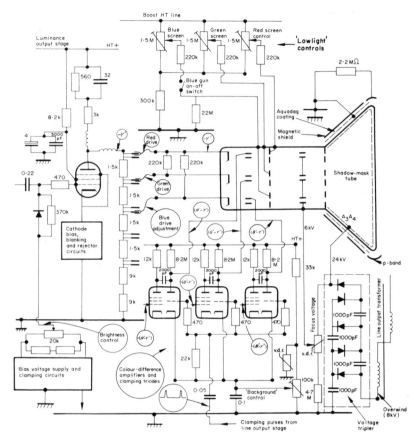

Fig. 5.11 *Shadow-mask tube supply voltage and signal drive circuits*
(Associated diagram: Fig. 16.3.)

(b) ADJUSTMENT OF HIGHLIGHTS. It remains to ensure that all other levels of white are correctly reproduced. This is sometimes referred to as adjustment of 'highlights'. The procedure must compensate for the slightly different slopes and also for the substantially different phosphor efficiencies. This is achieved by varying the video signal (i.e., luminance) drive to the three guns. Since the red phosphor has the lowest efficiency (in a new tube), it is usual to feed the maximum video signal to the red cathode. By the use of potentiometers the video signal amplitudes to the green and

84

blue guns may be reduced relative to the red drive. In practice this merely amounts to adjusting the green and blue drive controls until areas of high contrast in a monochrome picture, or the highly contrasted steps on a grey-scale signal, are reproduced as untinted white. Figure 5.11 illustrates a simple method using a resistor chain to give a stepped drive adjustment. More usually however, variable resistors are preferred because they allow a finer adjustment. Other circuits are studied in chapter 16.

After long use and ageing it is sometimes necessary for either the green or blue guns to receive the maximum available drive, whilst to preserve the correct white the red drive may then need to be relatively smaller.

The receiver circuit in Fig. 5.11 is of the type in which the luminance signal is fed to the cathodes and the colour-difference signals are applied to the respective grids. The diagram gives an overall introduction to the signal drive and the supply voltage circuitry associated with a shadow-mask tube. The theory of luminance and colour-difference amplifiers is studied in chapter 16 whilst the action of e.h.t. voltage triplers is described in chapter 17. At this time, however, it is worth noting that the colour-difference signals are a.c. coupled to the grids of the c.r.t., but in shunt with each grid is a triode d.c. clamping circuit which is pulsed at the end of each raster line to set the steady grid voltages at a suitable pre-determined level. This level is determined by the 'background control' the setting of which forms part of the grey-scale adjustment procedure. With the brightness control in its mid-position, the field scan collapsed and the screen controls set to maximum, the background control is adjusted to make the single remaining horizontal line just visible. The screen controls are then adjusted to just extinguish the line. With the field scan restored the brightness control is finally set to make the raster just visible.

For optimum accuracy, grey-scale adjustments are best made by a direct subjective comparison between the white and greys on the screen against a standard D_{6500} illuminant source with a suitable neutral stepped filter. Special apparatus is marketed for this purpose.

The in-line shadow-mask tube

The delta positioning of the three guns around the tube axis in a normal shadow-mask tube makes it difficult to achieve complete convergence of the three beams as they scan the screen. As will be seen in the next two chapters, quite complicated circuit arrangements are needed to maintain good convergence.

In the in-line shadow-mask tube the three guns are placed side by side and the phosphors in the screen triads are side by side. It is then relatively easy to deflect the two outer beams inwards slightly to converge with the central green beam. However, for a given tube neck diameter, the maximum physical size of the electron guns in an in-line tube is some 30% smaller than the guns may be in the corresponding delta tube. This means that the density of the electron beams is substantially less and this disadvantage must be set against the easier convergence. Even with the delta gun arrangement it is difficult to achieve adequate brightness.

Although, at the time of writing, the shadow-mask tube is by far the most widely used colour television cathode ray tube, other types of tubes, notably chromatron and trinitron tubes, are in commercial use; particularly in smaller screen portable type receivers. Before going on to study how convergence of the three beams is achieved in shadow-mask tubes, it is instructive to look at the basic principles of these other tubes.

The chromatron (or Lawrence) tube

The three phosphors in chromatron tubes are laid down in horizontal strips across the screen as shown in Fig. 5.12. These strips are arranged in the sequence red, green, and blue from top to bottom of the screen and there must be at least as many triads of strips as there are active lines in the raster of the system in use. Associated with each triad of strips are two colour grids. These take the form of wires positioned one behind the red and one behind the blue strips.

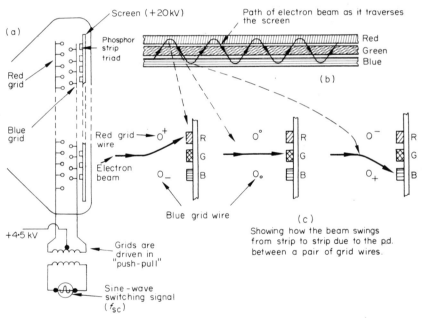

Fig. 5.12 *Diagrams illustrating the principle of a chromatron tube*

When the single electron beam is scanning one raster line it is concerned with one triad of strips. As the beam moves across the screen it is moved up and down vertically with a sinusoidal motion (sometimes referred to as a spot wobble) at a high frequency. It is convenient to use the sub-carrier frequency for this purpose. The vertical movement is achieved by applying a sinusoidal voltage in push-pull to the two grids. When the potential between the grids is zero the beam passes straight through and bombards the green phosphor. On one half-cycle the red grid is positive with respect to the blue and the beam is shifted upwards to hit the red phosphor. Similarly, on the alternate half-cycle the blue grid is positive with respect to the red and the beam is directed at the blue phosphor. In synchronism with this spot movement, the modulation of the beam is switched from one colour amplifier to another. These are referred to as gated amplifiers. It will be observed that the beam visits the green phosphor twice per cycle and it follows that the green amplifier has to be gated by a switching signal of twice the frequency of the voltage applied to the c.r.t. red and blue grids. Because the spot bombards the green strip twice as many times as the associated red and blue strips, it is necessary to adjust the modulation voltage from the green colour-amplifier to preserve the correct ratio between the red, green, and blue light outputs from the screen.

Chromatron tubes are in other respects similar to monochrome tubes. Since a single gun only is used, the neck diameter is much smaller than in a shadow-mask tube so that the required deflector coil currents are less. There is no need for purity and convergence assemblies and the line and field output stages are the same as in monochrome receivers.

There is a considerable capacitance between the red and blue grids and this results in an appreciable current demand upon the source of the r.f. voltage. The operation of gating the colour amplifiers also presents a problem not present with shadow-mask tubes. However, the demands upon the e.h.t. system are less since there is not the heavy loss of beam current which arises in the shadow-mask tube.

The mean potential of the red and blue grids is usually between 4 kV and 5 kV with respect to cathode, whilst the aluminized screen is some 15 kV positive to the grids or 20 kV positive to cathode. The peak r.f. voltage to the grids is of the order 100 to 400 volts.

The trinitron tube

The trinitron tube, developed by the Sony Corporation of Japan, represents a marked step forward in colour television cathode ray tube technology. The main disadvantages of the conventional delta gun shadow-mask tube may be summarized as follows:

(a) Convergence is difficult and calls for considerable circuit complexity and service adjustments.

(b) Using a tube neck of reasonable size the density of the electron beams (and hence the picture brightness) is limited because of the small size of the electron guns.

(c) The focus cannot be sharp over the entire screen because the focus and convergence planes cannot be co-incident for three beams emanating from guns positioned at 120° intervals around the tube axis.

(d) The electron transparency of the shadow-mask is very low. It intercepts over 80% of the beam current.

In the trinitron tube each one of these disadvantages has been attacked and successfully reduced.

The trinitron differs from the shadow-mask tube in the following respects:

(a) The phosphors are arranged in vertical strips. There are several hundred vertical phosphor-strip triads on the screen.

(b) The shadow mask is replaced by a metal aperture grille, with one vertical slot for each phosphor triad. The aperture grille has a greater electron transparency (about 30% greater) than the shadow mask and is no more difficult to manufacture.

(c) Instead of three separate guns producing beams spaced at 120° intervals around the axis, one single gun which produces three in-line beams is used.

The single gun employs three in-line cathodes. The three beams pass into a first weak electron lens which bends the two outer (red and blue) beams so that they and the axial green beam intersect at the centre of the second (and main) electron lens situated a little further along the tube neck. Because the three beams appear to emanate from the same point in the lens system, they have a common focus plane and for this reason a sharper image is obtained, with good focus over the entire picture area.

Since only one lens system is used the gun has a diameter which is about twice

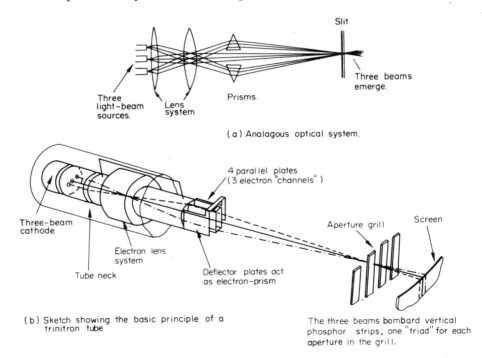

(a) Analogous optical system.

(b) Sketch showing the basic principle of a trinitron tube

The three beams bombard vertical phosphor strips; one "triad" for each aperture in the grill.

Fig. 5.13 *Diagrams illustrating the principle of a trinitron tube*

that of the individual guns in a delta-type shadow-mask tube having the same neck diameter. This in turn leads to the beam density being substantially greater and this fact—together with the greater electron transparency of the aperture grille—gives the trinitron a brightness which is approximately twice that of a shadow mask of comparable size.

As with the in-line shadow-mask tube, convergence is much simplified. In the trinitron, the red and blue beams pass between pairs of deflector plates.

The inner plates of these two pairs are held at the same potential so that the axial green beam passes undeflected between them. Convergence is achieved by applying parabolic waveforms at line frequency to the two pairs of plates. This has the effect of moving the red and blue beams inwards to converge with the green beam. Two adjustments only are needed. The comparative simplicity of this convergence arrangement will be appreciated when the next two chapters, which deal with shadow-mask tube convergence circuits, have been studied.

In Fig. 5.13(a) the principle of the trinitron electron gun assembly is represented by a simple analogous optical system with the electron beams replaced by light beams. The three beams are cathode modulated only so that receivers using trinitron tubes employ R', G', B' (or rather $-R'$, $-G'$, $-B'$) drives.

It is evident that since only one electron gun assembly has to be accommodated it is possible to make small colour television tubes for portable type receivers. A small neck diameter leads in turn to much reduced deflector coil currents which may be provided by low-power line and field output stages. This is not to suggest that the trinitron tube is essentially for small-screen receivers. Tubes of all required sizes may be made. Figure 5.14 shows a photograph of the trinitron electron gun assembly.

Fig. 5.14 *Trinitron electron gun assembly*
(Photograph reproduced by kind permission of the Sony Corporation of Japan)

6

Convergence: General Principles

For a perfect picture the red, green, and blue beams must track precisely to produce three exactly coincident rasters of the correct rectangular shape (i.e., of the correct aspect ratio). The technique of bringing the beams together so that they hit the same part of the screen at the same time is referred to as convergence and this is achieved by positional adjustments of the individual beams.

These corrective beam movements are brought about by passing the beams through individual deflecting fields. In delta-type shadow-mask tubes, all three beams are shifted by magnetic fields, but in the trinitron the red and blue beams are deflected by electrostatic fields. In the trinitron there is no need to shift the green beam since it lies along the tube's axis.

When the best possible convergence is obtained it is then usually true that the picture produced, though showing little or no sign of slip-out (i.e., colour-fringing due to the rasters not exactly coinciding) is not truly rectangular in shape but shows some pincushion distortion. This bowing inwards of the top, bottom, and two sides of the picture is then removed by the use of dynamic raster-shape correction techniques which affect the three beams equally and simultaneously.

It should be noted that purity may be perfect but convergence very bad. The adjustment of purity merely ensures that each beam can only bombard its own particular phosphor dots. However, as they scan the screen, the red, green, and blue spots may not always be coincident and if this is the case it is obvious that the red, green, and blue pictures will not fall on top of one another. The quality of convergence may conveniently be studied by using a signal which, when accurately reproduced, appears as a crosshatch pattern of white vertical and horizontal lines. Lack of convergence shows up very clearly on such a pattern. Often this is confined to the edges of the picture, e.g., if the blue beam fails to converge at the extreme right of the picture the vertical lines on this side appear yellow with blue 'slipped-out' lines alongside them.

It is difficult to obtain perfect convergence in the four corners of the screen and the white lines may in these areas open up into adjacent red, green, and blue lines.

Convergence in the shadow-mask tube (see Plate 3 inserted between pages 102–103.

The technique of correction of convergence in shadow-mask tubes falls into two parts referred to as static and dynamic convergence.

Static convergence involves the movement of the beams by permanent magnetic fields, which, once correctly set, bring the beams into convergence in the central area of the screen.

Convergence over the rest of the screen is achieved by continuously varying (i.e., dynamic) magnetic fields, the instantaneous strengths of which depend upon the positions of the spots on the screen. These fields are set up by electromagnets which carry currents at line and field frequencies.

The separate magnetic fields needed to allow the three beams to be shifted individually, are established in the tube by a convergence yoke assembly which slides over the tube neck. As shown in Fig. 6.1 the three yokes of this assembly are positioned opposite pole pieces within the tube neck. Internal magnetic screening shields divide the neck into three sectors in this region, so that each beam is isolated from the convergence fields of the other two beams. The magnetic fields established between the pole pieces operate upon the beams to move them radially; either inwards or outwards depending upon the direction of the field. In addition to this main convergence unit, there is a separate 'lateral blue' convergence assembly. Figure 6.2(a) shows a simple example of such a unit. The field from this affects only the blue beam and moves it sideways.

Modern blue lateral units usually carry both static and dynamic corrective fields. Often the unit is so designed that all three beams are affected. Figure 6.2(b) illustrates

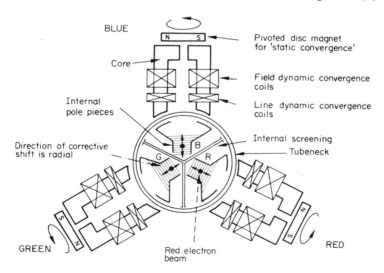

Fig. 6.1 *Showing the principle of a radial convergence assembly*

(*N.B.* The diagram is a 'back-view'. Viewed from the Rear the Red gun is on the Right when the blue gun is at the top.)

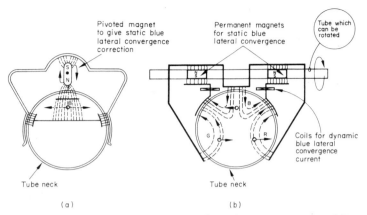

Fig. 6.2 *Showing the principle of blue lateral convergence assemblies*

(a) Shows a simple blue lateral static convergence arrangement.
(b) Includes provision for both static and dynamic lateral convergence correction.

the principle. The main field shifts the blue beam in one direction whilst secondary fields cause the red and green beams to move in the opposite direction. Although this could properly be described as a differential lateral shift unit it is often referred to simply as the blue lateral convergence assembly. As would be expected the current causing the dynamic field is derived from the line timebase.

Static convergence

In manufacture, the three gun assemblies are inclined towards the axis by an angle of the order of 1° to 1·5°. This so directs the three beams that they roughly converge at the screen centre. By the use of small permanent magnets, the beams are then shifted over a limited range to achieve perfect convergence in the central area of the screen.

Each of the three yokes on the main convergence unit carries a small magnet of this kind which may be moved in such a way that the field strength can be varied both in intensity and in direction. Often the magnets are in the form of pivoted discs. When positioned with the N and S poles directly over the two halves of the yoke, the magnetic field—and the resulting static beam shift in one direction—are maximum. Twisting the magnet reduces the field strength and when it is at 90° to its original position, the field is zero and the beam undeflected. Turning the magnet still further produces a reversed field which moves the beam in the opposite direction. This becomes maximum when the original positions of the N and S poles are reversed. The total radial distance through which a given spot may be moved on the screen is about 2 cm, i.e., ±1 cm about its mean (zero static field) position.

Adjustment of static convergence may be carried out using either crosshatch or dot patterns. Most service generators give both facilities and often the dot pattern is used for static and the crosshatch for dynamic convergence adjustments.

92

The principle of static convergence using a dot-pattern is illustrated in Plate 4.[1]

At (a) it is assumed that the three beams are completely out of convergence and attention is focused upon one of the three groups of primary coloured dots which then appear at the centre of the screen. The object of the adjustment procedure is to make one white dot from each group of three primary coloured dots.

By moving the red and green static convergence magnets the red and green spots may be made to move radially until they converge to make a yellow dot. This is shown at (c). Moving the corresponding blue magnet then shifts the blue dot until it is horizontally level with the yellow dot. Adjustment of the lateral blue magnet now shifts the blue spot sideways until it registers with the yellow dot to give a white dot. It will be observed that with three beams at 120° to one another, it is possible to converge any two of them by radial movements but not the three. One of the beams has to have freedom of movement at right angles to its radial movement. The obvious choice is blue since the blue gun is always on the tube's vertical axis, and it is easy to adjust for horizontally level blue and yellow spots and then to shift the blue spot sideways.

Dynamic convergence

It is helpful to begin by revising some basic principles of magnetic deflection of a c.r.t. beam. Figure 6.3(a) represents a single-beam tube in which the beam is deflected vertically by a simple cylindrical shaped deflector coil mounted on the neck of the tube.

When the electrons enter the magnetic field which is set up within the tube neck as a result of a steady current in the deflector coil, their direction of motion is continuously changed by a force which is always at right angles to their instantaneous direction.

For simplicity, suppose that the deflector coil's field is of uniform strength from one end to the other and that the field terminates abruptly at the ends of the coil. The path of an electron when passing through the field then forms an arc of a circle. On leaving the field the electron travels forward to the screen along a straight line path. Projected backwards this straight line forms a tangent to the arc and meets the tube axis midway along the deflector coil. As far as the screen is concerned the electron beam (treated as a light beam) appears to emanate from this *deflection centre*. This is illustrated in Fig. 6.3(a). The angle $\phi°$ between the electron path and the axis is proportional to the field strength which in turn is proportional to the deflector coil current.

To make the spot scan the screen the current must vary in a suitable way. If, as a first approximation, the deflector coil current waveform is assumed to be a linear sawtooth as in Fig. 6.3(b), then the angle of deflection changes linearly with time. However, this does not cause the scanning spot to move over the screen at a uniform speed. This is because the screen of a television c.r.t. is virtually flat and the distance from the deflection centre to the screen grows greater as the beam is deflected further from the axis.

[1] Inserted between pages 102–103.

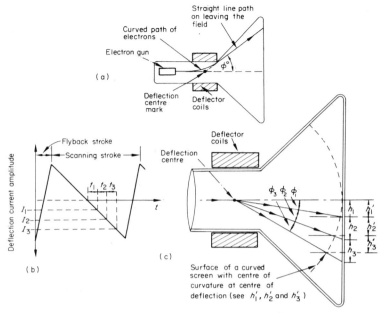

Fig. 6.3 *Magnetic deflection principles*

Showing the distortion which arises when the magnetic deflection field-strength varies linearly with time and the c.r.t. has a 'flat-faced' screen.

In Fig. 6.3(c) the field deflection in such a c.r.t. is first examined. The undeflected position of the spot is at the centre of the screen. This corresponds to the middle of the downward scanning stroke and at this point the current passes through zero. Three successive intervals of time, t_1, t_2, and t_3 are now considered. These give rise to equal increases ϕ_1, ϕ_2, and ϕ_3 in the angle of deflection. The corresponding vertical distances through which the spot moves are shown by h_1, h_2, and h_3. These are clearly not equal. The line is progressively 'stretched' with the rate of movement of the spot increasing as the angle increases.

The spot would only move through equal 'vertical' distances for equal angles of deflection if the screen were curved with the centre of curvature at the centre of deflection. This is illustrated in Fig. 6.3(c) by the arc lengths, h'_1, h'_2, and h'_3.

When the line and field timebases are considered together, the raster produced on a flat screen under the conditions specified, would show pincushion distortion. Such distortion may be minimized in a monochrome receiver by modifications to the basic design of the deflector coils, changing the shape of the scanning current to a non-linear sawtooth by S-correction of the basic sawtooth, and by the use of small peripheral permanent magnets mounted on the deflector coils.

In a shadow-mask tube the situation is further complicated because the three rasters produced differ in shape and each requires a different form of correction.

94

The uncorrected red, green, and blue rasters seen on the screen, have the shapes shown (in exaggerated form) in Plate 5.[1] These are what would be expected since, looked at from the front of the tube, the red gun (and hence the red deflection centre) lies *below* and to the *left* of the tube's axis; the green deflection centre is level with the red but to the *right* of the axis, whilst the blue deflection centre is *on* the vertical axis but above the tube centre. The furthest point from the red deflection centre is the top right-hand corner of the screen and the red raster shows its maximum stretching at this point. The green raster is clearly a mirror image of the red. The blue raster is symmetrical about the vertical axis and shows maximum stretching at the bottom corners where the distance from the blue deflection centre to the screen is greatest. It will be observed that the symmetrical pincushion shaped raster which is obtained in a single gun tube with its axial beam, is not produced by any of the three beams. This is because the guns are disposed around the axis and superimposed upon the normal pincushion distortion is an added trapezium distortion.

Since the raster distortions are a function of the non-uniform distances from the deflection centres to the screen over the scanning cycle, it is possible to arrive at an approximate idea of what corrective measures need to be taken, by concentrating upon these distances. As mentioned earlier, when these measures have been taken, the three rasters will be coincident, but still showing some common pincushion distortion (see Plate 5(b)). This is then corrected by other measures which are described in the next chapter.

In the simplified approach which follows, uniform deflection fields are assumed and the scanning current waveforms imagined to be of the linear sawtooth form discussed. It will be observed that to compensate for the increasing distance the beam has to travel to the screen as a scanning stroke progresses, the net deflection of the beam per unit time must be progressively reduced. But the deflector coil current cannot be changed to benefit one beam without changing the other two in an unwanted way. By pre-correcting the beams as they pass through their respective radial convergence fields, however, each may be adjusted by individually different amounts. It remains to assess the approximate form the continuously varying dynamic convergence currents in the field and line convergence coils must have and then to study circuitry capable of providing the required currents.

Before proceeding to do this, however, it is important to note the limitations of the radial convergence fields. *These fields can only move the beams radially.*

With the red and green beams, a radial movement may be resolved into two components; one horizontal and the other vertical. Both the line and field dynamic convergence currents, passing through their separate coils on the convergence yokes, cause radial movements. The net movement must result from the effective sum of these two magnetic fields.

The blue radial convergence field, however, has no horizontal component at all, since the field shifts the beam vertically up and down. For this reason it is as well to remember that any line frequency current fed to the line winding on the blue radial

[1] Inserted between pages 102–103.

convergence yoke can only modify the *vertical* position of the blue beam along a raster line. The horizontal position of the blue beam can only be changed by feeding a dynamic current to the coil wound on the blue-lateral convergence assembly.

It is easy to slip into the error of thinking that field and line convergence currents, like field and line deflection currents, only shift the beams vertically and horizontally respectively. This is quite untrue—a fact which soon becomes apparent when field and line convergence pre-set controls are adjusted.

The various parts of the convergence, purity, and main deflector coil assembly, which fits on the neck of a shadow-mask tube, may be identified in Plate 3. This shows a cut-away view of a typical unit.

Assessment of the shapes needed for the convergence current waveforms

Line convergence

An approximate idea of the required waveform shapes for dynamic line convergence currents is arrived at in Fig. 6.4. At (a) two successive raster lines are shown side by side and at (b) a linear sawtooth scanning current waveform is drawn.

At (c) the relative positions of the tube screen and the blue deflection centre are shown; again drawn twice side-by-side to allow successive cycles of corrective waveforms to be deduced. It is stressed that these diagrams are very much out of scale in order to emphasize the principles involved.

The blue deflection centre is on the vertical axis of the tube and the path length to the screen is shortest when the beam is directed at a point on this axis immediately in front of the blue deflection centre. If a graph is plotted of the path length from the blue deflection centre to the screen, the shape of the curve is roughly parabolic.

The object of the dynamic convergence current is to set up a magnetic field which —at each point along a raster line—will reduce the net deflection of the blue beam by an amount which compensates for the changes in path length. It follows that the current waveform must have a shape which is roughly the same as that showing the variation in path length.

Such a waveform is sketched at (d). Looking at the first of the two active raster lines the current has its greatest values at the beginning and end of the line (see points A and C) and its minimum value at the centre (see point B). On the next raster line it is obvious that the same line correction is needed. In a practical circuit, the current cannot of course switch off abruptly at the end of a line and on again at the start of the next. It will be observed that at the end of a line the waveform has its greatest positive-going rate of change but at the start of a line the rate-of-change is equal but negative-going. During the flyback period therefore, the waveform has the turnover hump shown on the diagram. In this period the rate-of-change of current reduces to zero and then builds up in the opposite direction. This simplified approach thus allows a picture to be built up of the approximate waveform which the blue line convergence current must assume. During the scanning stroke the waveform has the approximately parabolic shape shown at (d) by ABC and this is joined to the next similar parabola A′B′C′ by the flyback-stroke 'inverted parabola' CDA′.

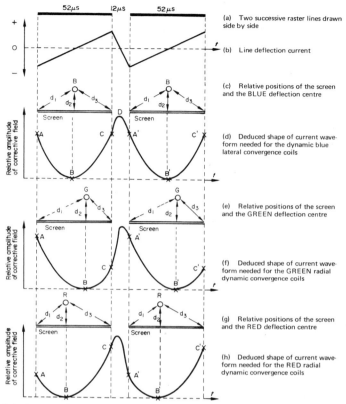

(a) Two successive raster lines drawn side by side

(b) Line deflection current

(c) Relative positions of the screen and the BLUE deflection centre

(d) Deduced shape of current wave-form needed for the dynamic blue lateral convergence coils

(e) Relative positions of the screen and the GREEN deflection centre

(f) Deduced shape of current wave-form needed for the GREEN radial dynamic convergence coils

(g) Relative positions of the screen and the RED deflection centre

(h) Deduced shape of current wave-form needed for the RED radial dynamic convergence coils

Fig. 6.4 *Simplified method of assessing the type of waveforms needed for the line dynamic convergence correction currents*

(*N.B.* The relative positions of the tube screen and the three deflection centres are very much out of scale, and the waveform characteristics are exaggerated, to establish the principle.)

It should be noted, however, that sideways corrections of the blue raster can only be obtained by feeding such a waveform to the dynamic lateral blue coil. The same waveform fed to the radial blue coil may be regarded as providing line modulation of the vertical convergence field. The effect of this is to give vertical correction along each raster line. In practice both of these corrective measures are taken.

In Fig. 6.4(e) the position of the green deflection centre relative to the screen is shown. When the distances to the screen are plotted the shape of the required correction current takes on the *tilted parabola* form shown at (f). During a raster line this current must be maximum when the spot is at the beginning of the line (see point A), minimum when the spot is directly in front of the green deflection centre (see B), and at some intermediate value when the spot is at the extreme right (see C). These current levels must repeat on the next line (see A', B', and C') and the flyback part of the waveform has the approximate shape shown between C and A'.

At (g) and (h) the corresponding waveform for the red line convergence current is deduced. As expected, it is a mirror image of the green waveform of (f).

Before going on to study how the waveforms such as (d), (f), and (h) may be obtained, the corresponding approximate shapes of the field convergence waveforms are deduced by a similar simplified approach.

Field convergence waveforms

Figure 6.5(a) shows two successive fields (viewed from the back of the screen) placed for explanatory purposes in sequence; one below the other. The relative positions of the three deflection centres are shown; again very much out of scale to make the results achieved more explicit.

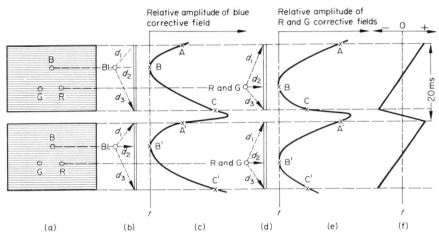

Fig. 6.5 *Simplified method of assessing the type of waveforms needed for the field dynamic convergence currents*

(a) Shows two successive fields (seen from the rear) drawn vertically beneath one another.
(b) Shows the relative positions of the blue deflection centre and the vertical centre line of the screen.
(c) Shows the deduced shape of the necessary blue correction current.
(d) Shows the relative positions of the red and green deflection centres and the screen.
(e) Shows the deduced shape of the necessary red and green correction currents.
(f) Shows the field deflection current waveform (assumed linear).
(*N.B.* The diagrams are drawn very much out of scale to emphasize the principles involved.)

The basic sawtooth field deflection current waveform is sketched at (f) and the two successive scanning strokes shown, coincide with the two fields at (a), whilst the flyback stroke is opposite the space between these fields.

Since the object here is to assess the approximate form of the required field dynamic deflection correction for the three beams, it is necessary only to study the distances from each deflection centre to all points along a vertical line drawn on the screen immediately in front of the given deflection centre.

At (b) the diagram shows a side view of the screen and the blue deflection centre.

A plot of the distances to the screen has the shape of the curve shown at (c), and this in turn gives an indication of the magnitude of the required dynamic field convergence current which must be passed through the blue radial convergence magnet. This current is minimum at B (i.e., when the spot is aimed directly in front of the deflection centre), has its maximum value at the end of a field scanning stroke (see C) and an intermediate value at the start of the scanning stroke (see A). Since the current has to change from level C at the end of a field to level A at the start of the next, the dynamic waveform must 'turn over' during flyback as indicated in the diagram.

As the red and green guns, and their corresponding deflection centres, are on the same horizontal level as one another they both (theoretically) need the same vertical correction currents. The shape of this waveform is deduced from (d), at (e). It will be observed that the waveform is once again of tilted parabola form, but with an opposite tilt to that of the blue gun. In practice, due to manufacturing tolerances in the tube itself together with slight differences in the deflection fields experienced by the red and green beams, provision is made for varying the dynamic fields to the two guns. This will be studied further when circuits are looked at.

Waveform components of a tilted parabola

The simplified method of assessing the approximate shape of the required dynamic line and field convergence waveforms has shown that the basic need is for an asymmetric parabolic waveform. The exception is the blue line waveform and the need here—because the blue deflection centre is opposite the vertical axis passing through the centre of the screen—is theoretically for a symmetrical parabola. In practice, again due to unavoidable discrepancies in tube manufacture and deflection fields, some tilt is often needed and provision for it is usually made in convergence circuitry.

If it is assumed that a parabolic waveform is available, it may be given the necessary tilt by the addition of a suitable sawtooth waveform of the same frequency. This is illustrated in Fig. 6.6. The basic line deflection scanning waveform is shown at (a) to allow the timing of the other waveforms to be seen in relation to the scanning and flyback strokes.

At (b) is a parabolic waveform which is symmetrical about the centre of the scanning stroke, i.e., the centre of the screen. This is basically suitable for the blue line convergence coils. At (c) and (d) are shown sawtooth waveforms having mutually opposite polarities.

If a sawtooth waveform at (c) is added to the parabolic waveform of (b), the tilted parabola shown at (e) is obtained. This is suitable for the red dynamic line convergence coils.

Adding the inverted sawtooth at (d) to the parabola at (b) gives a tilted parabola of the form shown at (f), which is suitable for the green dynamic line convergence circuit.

It is necessary to provide facilities for the adjustment of the component parts of each radial convergence waveform. If provision is made to adjust these independently,

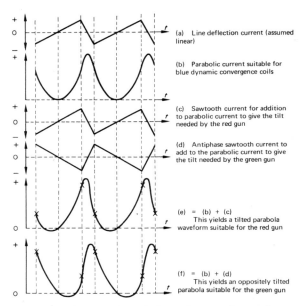

(a) Line deflection current (assumed linear)

(b) Parabolic current suitable for blue dynamic convergence coils

(c) Sawtooth current for addition to parabolic current to give the tilt needed by the red gun

(d) Antiphase sawtooth current to add to the parabolic current to give the tilt needed by the green gun

(e) = (b) + (c) This yields a tilted parabola waveform suitable for the red gun

(f) = (b) + (d) This yields an oppositely tilted parabola suitable for the green gun

Fig. 6.6 *Addition of parabolic and sawtooth waveforms*

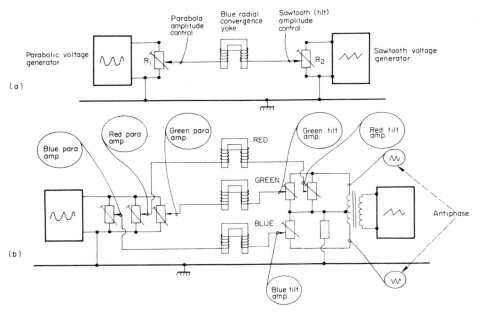

Fig. 6.7 *Basic dynamic convergence arrangements for field coils*

twelve controls are needed. There is a field and a line frequency waveform for each gun, i.e., six waveforms in all. Each waveform has a basic parabolic shape with a superimposed tilt from a sawtooth component. If the parabola and sawtooth amplitudes are to be made adjustable this makes $6 \times 2 = 12$ pre-set controls. In addition to these, a dynamic blue lateral control is desirable.

Figure 6.7 summarizes the basic form of a possible field convergence arrangement. At (a) the blue field convergence coil is shown connected to two generators (one parabolic and one sawtooth) which are effectively in series. The instantaneous voltage driving current through the coil is the sum of the two. With R_2 at zero, the current (assuming the coil is largely resistive at this low frequency) will be parabolic and of amplitude controlled by R_1. Increasing R_2 then introduces progressively more 'tilt'.

The red and green coils require similar provisions but a tilt of opposite sign. In Fig. 6.7(b) anti-phase sawtooth voltages are available to provide for the red and green field convergence coils as well as the blue.

Differential red-green controls

In practice convergence adjustments may be made easier by linking the red and green controls. Any adjustment to red and green beams shifts them radially. It is difficult to see exactly what adjustments are needed when the result of them produces diagonal movements of points being observed on the screen. However, it is subjectively easy to line things up vertically and horizontally. The technique of differential adjustment makes it possible to move the red and green beams together so that one of two things happens:

(a) Both move equally vertically but in opposite directions horizontally. On a cross-hatch pattern this means that vertical red and green lines may be brought together by a sideways movement. Meanwhile horizontal misconverged red and green lines are ignored (they do in fact move vertically by equal amounts).

(b) Both move equally horizontally but in opposite directions vertically. On a cross-hatch pattern red and green horizontal lines may be brought together whilst the convergence of vertical lines remains unaffected since red and green move sideways together.

Plate 6[1] illustrates one simple arrangement for achieving this. For simplicity only the parabolic input is shown equipped with a 'differential' control. With R_2 at the centre, equal parabolic currents pass through the red and green coils. At (b) a pair of central vertical (misconverged) red and green lines are shown. Intersecting them are a pair of horizontal lines. The arrows show the radial directions in which the currents in the convergence coils move the red and green beams. As R_1 is turned up the vertical lines move towards one another, but the horizontal lines move upwards by equal amounts. At (c) the vertical lines are converged to make a yellow line but the horizontals are higher up and still apart.

If R_2 is now adjusted off-centre ('downwards' in the diagram) the current through the green coil increases whilst that through the red coil decreases. This makes the

[1] Inserted between pages 102–103.

horizontal lines come together to form a yellow line because the green line moves upwards further whilst the red line 'backs' downwards as shown by the arrows at (c). Meanwhile the equal and opposite changes in current amplitudes cause the red and green vertical lines to move sideways together and they remain converged as a yellow line: see (d).

In Plate 6(e) a differential control is also provided in the sawtooth circuit. The two controls are labelled R/G tilt amplitude and R/G tilt differential. Again, the amplitude control brings vertical lines together and the differential control converges the horizontal lines.

It will be observed that the use of differential controls allows radial movements to be observed in terms of their vertical and horizontal components and for this reason service adjustments are made easier.

Differential controls are used in both the line and the field red and green convergence circuits. It is useful to remember that vertical crosshatch lines must be looked at when adjusting *amplitude* controls (whether they be parabola or tilt) and horizontal lines are observed when adjusting differential controls.

Adjustment procedures

Whilst the circuitry—the number of controls and their effects—and the approach to convergence generally differs considerably from receiver to receiver, it is instructive to consider a generalized crosshatch pattern adjustment technique based upon the deductions made so far. It is stressed, however, that a manufacturer's service manual is the best guide to obtaining the most satisfactory convergence in a given receiver.

Attention should be concentrated on the vertical axis passing downwards through the screen centre when adjusting field (or, as they are often called, vertical) convergence controls, and on the horizontal axis passing through the tube centre when adjusting line (or horizontal) convergence controls.

Plate 7[1] illustrates the misconvergence which may be obtained at the extremes of these two axes. It is assumed that static convergence has been adjusted to make the three beams converge accurately at the screen centre. The aim is to create white crosshatch lines down the central vertical axis and across the central horizontal axis. These axes are indicated by the dotted lines YY' and XX'. Colour triplets are shown at the ends of the red, green, and blue lines and the crosses mark the points at which the colour triplets must converge, under the action of the corrective dynamic convergence currents. Referring to the top triplet, the red and green beams have to be depressed and the blue beam raised to converge at the point marked x. To the right of the diagram is a sketch showing the approximate relative amplitudes of the currents needed to bring about the required convergence shifts, along the vertical axis. Similarly, below the diagram the approximate required horizontal current relative amplitudes are shown. In general the red and green beams have to move in opposite directions to the blue. However, all use waveforms derived from a common

[1] Inserted between pages 102–103.

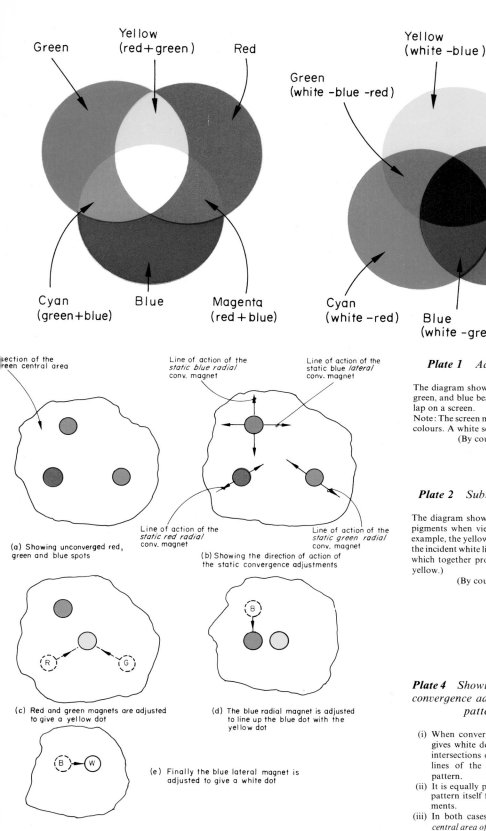

Green

Yellow (red+green)

Red

Cyan (green+blue)

Blue

Magenta (red + blue)

Yellow (white –blue)

Green (white –blue –red)

Red (white –blue –green)

Cyan (white –red)

Blue (white –green –red)

Magenta (white –green)

section of the green central area

(a) Showing unconverged red, green and blue spots

Line of action of the *static blue radial* conv. magnet

Line of action of the static blue *lateral* conv. magnet

Line of action of the *static red radial* conv. magnet

Line of action of the *static green radial* conv. magnet

(b) Showing the direction of action of the static convergence adjustments

(c) Red and green magnets are adjusted to give a yellow dot

(d) The blue radial magnet is adjusted to line up the blue dot with the yellow dot

(e) Finally the blue lateral magnet is adjusted to give a white dot

Plate 1 *Additive colour mixing*

The diagram shows the effect of projecting red, green, and blue beams of light so that they overlap on a screen.
Note: The screen must be capable of reflecting *all* colours. A white screen is suitable.

(By courtesy of British Broadcasting Corporation)

Plate 2 *Subtractive colour mixing*

The diagram shows the effect of mixing colour pigments when viewed under white light. (For example, the yellow pigment subtracts blue from the incident white light and reflects red and green, which together produce the visual sensation of yellow.)

(By courtesy of British Broadcasting Corporation)

Plate 4 *Showing the principle of static convergence adjustments, using a dot-pattern generator*

(i) When convergence is correct, this pattern gives white dots all over the screen, at the intersections of the vertical and horizontal lines of the corresponding 'cross-hatch' pattern.

(ii) It is equally possible to use the cross-hatch pattern itself for static convergence adjustments.

(iii) In both cases attention is focused on the *central area of the screen only*, for static convergence adjustments.

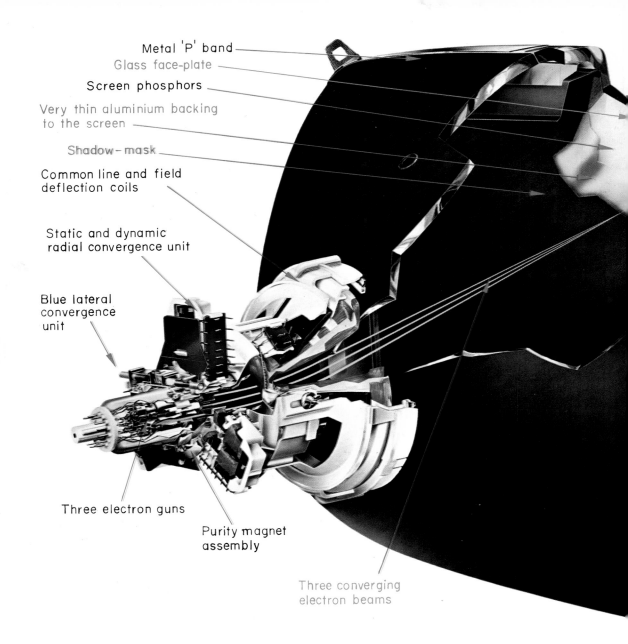

Metal 'P' band

Glass face-plate

Screen phosphors

Very thin aluminium backing
to the screen

Shadow-mask

Common line and field
deflection coils

Static and dynamic
radial convergence unit

Blue lateral
convergence
unit

Three electron guns

Purity magnet
assembly

Three converging
electron beams

Plate 3 *Showing the complete line and field deflection, static and dynamic radial convergence, purity, and static and dynamic blue lateral convergence assembly, on the neck of a shadowmask tube*

(Photograph reproduced by kind permission of Mullard Limited)

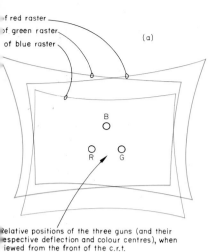

f red raster
of green raster
of blue raster

(a)

B

R   G

Relative positions of the three guns (and their
respective deflection and colour centres), when
viewed from the front of the c.r.t.

(b)

Ideal fully converged white raster,
with all distortion removed

Possible best practical convergence
before application of dynamic raster
shape correction

Plate 5   *Shadow-mask tube
convergence problems*

(a) Shows in exaggerated form the inherent red,
green, and blue raster distortions which arise
due to the non-axial positions of the three
guns and the flat screen.
(b) Shows the ideal raster shape (full line) and
(dotted) the form of 'pincushion' distortion
which may remain when practical convergence circuits have been adjusted. This residual distortion is removed by dynamic raster
correction techniques (chapter 7).

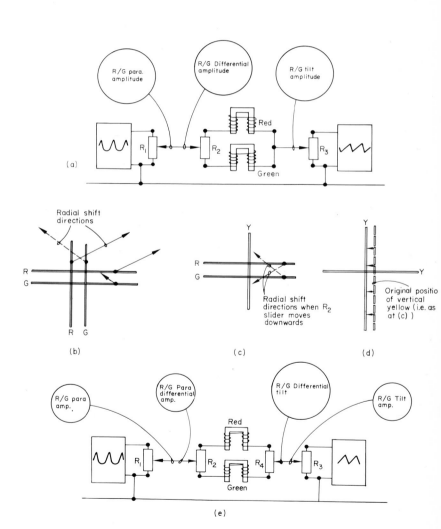

R/G para.
amplitude

R/G Differential
amplitude

R/G tilt
amplitude

R_1 R_2 Red   Green R_3

(a)

Radial shift
directions

R
G

R   G

(b)

Y
R
G

Radial shift
directions when R_2
slider moves
downwards

(c)

Y
Y

Original position
of vertical
yellow (i.e. as
at (c))

(d)

R/G para
amp.

R/G Para
differential
amp.

R/G Differential
tilt

R/G Tilt
amp.

R_1 R_2 Red   Green R_4 R_3

(e)

Plate 6   *Showing the principle of differential controls for the red and green
dynamic convergence coils*

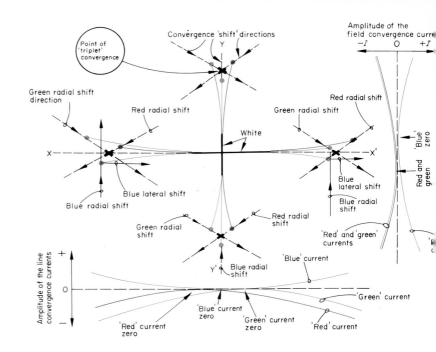

Plate 7 Dynamic convergence

(a) Convergence adjustments are carried out down the central vertical line and across the central horizontal line of the cross-hatch pattern.

(b) The diagram shows possible misconvergence along these lines.

(c) The lines do not in fact terminate in the 'dots' shown. These dots mark the points, on the red, green, and blue lines, which must move along the corrective path directions shown, to converge at the places marked by crosses. The lines are discontinued at the dots to avoid confusion.

(d) At the left and right sides, the blue dots can only be made to converge as a result of radial convergence correction (upwards), *and* lateral correction (to the right).

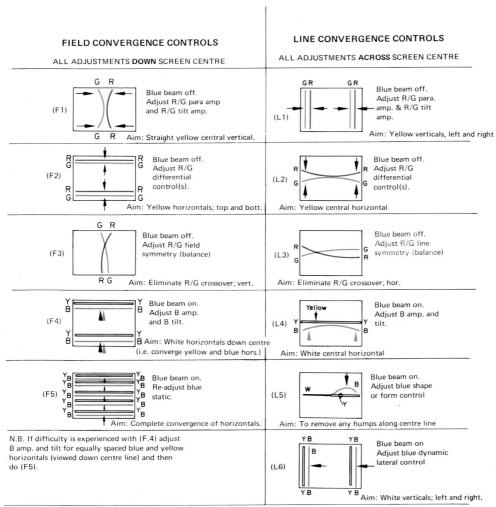

FIELD CONVERGENCE CONTROLS

ALL ADJUSTMENTS **DOWN** SCREEN CENTRE

(F1) Blue beam off. Adjust R/G para amp and R/G tilt amp.
Aim: Straight yellow central vertical.

(F2) Blue beam off. Adjust R/G differential control(s).
Aim: Yellow horizontals; top and bott.

(F3) Blue beam off. Adjust R/G field symmetry (balance)
Aim: Eliminate R/G crossover; vert.

(F4) Blue beam on. Adjust B amp. and B tilt.
B Aim: White horizontals down centre (i.e. converge yellow and blue hors.)

(F5) Blue beam on. Re-adjust blue static.
Aim: Complete convergence of horizontals.

N.B. If difficulty is experienced with (F.4) adjust B amp. and tilt for equally spaced blue and yellow horizontals (viewed down centre line) and then do (F5).

LINE CONVERGENCE CONTROLS

ALL ADJUSTMENTS **ACROSS** SCREEN CENTRE

(L1) Blue beam off. Adjust R/G para. amp. & R/G tilt amp.
Aim: Yellow verticals, left and right

(L2) Blue beam off. Adjust R/G differential control(s).
Aim: Yellow central horizontal

(L3) Blue beam off. Adjust R/G line symmetry (balance)
Aim: Eliminate R/G crossover; hor.

(L4) Blue beam on. Adjust B amp. and tilt.
Aim: White central horizontal

(L5) Blue beam on. Adjust blue shape or form control
Aim: To remove any humps along centre line

(L6) Blue beam on Adjust blue dynamic lateral control
Aim: White verticals; left and right.

Plate 8
Generalized dynamic convergence adjustment procedure

Plate 9   *Colour television test card F*

Plate 9 *Television test card F—which includes features to facilitate the testing of colour and black-and-white receivers*

a. As radiated on 625-line UHF services

b. As radiated on 405-line VHF services

source and the direction of shift is simply determined by the direction in which the currents are made to pass through the respective convergence coil windings.

It will be observed that the top and bottom triplets may be corrected by radial convergence correction only. However, the triplets to the right and left require the assistance of the lateral blue current.

Radial movements *only* of the red, green, and blue beams will produce a yellow and blue dot side by side. A dynamic lateral blue current is needed to shift the blue dots to the right to converge with the yellow dots. On a crosshatch, vertical yellow and blue lines at the sides of the raster are converged to form white lines by this adjustment.

Plate 8[1] shows a sequence of dynamic convergence adjustments. Vertical (or field) convergence adjustments are shown in the left-hand column and horizontal (or line) adjustments down the right-hand column.

The two sets of diagrams have been arranged in horizontal pairs for the added instruction this affords. For example, with the blue gun off, the R/G amplitude controls are adjusted at (F1) to bring together vertical red and green lines down the centre vertical axis. The corresponding *line* R/G amplitude controls bring together vertical lines on the extreme left and right as shown at (L1). (Notice that attention is directed at these lines where they cut the horizontal axis; and not in the screen corners.)

Similarly, at (F2) the R/G field differential controls converge horizontal lines where they cross the centre vertical axis. Meanwhile the R/G line differential controls at (L2) converge the two central horizontal lines along the horizontal axis.

As a general rule it is usual to go through all of one set of adjustments (say the field dynamic convergence) first and then to do the others in a similar sequence, e.g., adjustments (F1) to (F5) followed by (L1) to (L6). It should be noted that (F1) includes two controls; the amplitude controls for parabola and tilt. The same is true for (L1). In some receivers differential tilt, as well as differential parabola, controls may be fitted. If this is so, there are two adjustments at (F2) and/or at (L2). Referring to (F1), it may be that in a given receiver attention will be directed to the top of the red and green lines for the parabola amplitude control and to the bottom for the tilt amplitude. However, it is sufficient as a general rule to remember that these two controls are *together* responsible for bringing the central vertical red and green lines into convergence. Similarly the joint effects of the other pairs of controls embodied by (L1), (F2), and (L2) should be remembered.

Sometimes, as shown at (F3), the red and green lines cross one another and will not converge properly by adjustment of the dynamic radial controls. Similarly, the horizontal lines at (L3) sometimes cross. This indicates a lack of complete symmetry in the two halves of the field deflector coils in the case of (F3) and the line deflector coils in the case of (L3). Figure 6.8 shows how simple balancing controls fitted to the main field and line deflector coil circuits, allow the deflection fields to be balanced. The controls are adjusted, as indicated in Plate 8 at (F3) and (L3), to eliminate the crossover.

[1] Inserted between pages 102–103.

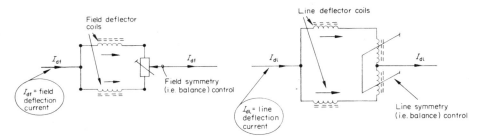

Fig. 6.8   *Field and line symmetry (or balance) controls*

The diagrams at (F4) and (L4) in Plate 8 draw attention once again to the fact that the blue dynamic convergence coil can only cause vertical movements of the blue beam. Hence all blue radial dynamic adjustments are made with reference to horizontal crosshatch lines. At (L4) the vertical movement at the ends of the raster lines is shown. This, as was established, is brought about by a line repetition parabola.

In some circuits, a blue hump is produced at one end of the central horizontal line. This is removed by a control which is often labelled as blue horizontal *shape*. This will be identified in circuitry studied in the next chapter. The effect arises from the method of derivation of the line convergence waveforms.

Finally, standing on its own because it is not a radial convergence adjustment, is (L6). This separate dynamic current to the blue lateral coil gives sideways shift to the vertical blue lines to the right and left of the screen to converge them with the adjacent vertical yellow lines.

It must be emphasized that all those adjustments normally carried out on monochrome receivers (such as height, width, focus, linearity, etc.), together with degaussing, purity, and static convergence, must be carried out before embarking upon dynamic convergence.

Some small readjustment of static convergence may be necessary during the dynamic convergence adjustments. This can be due to a d.c. component of dynamic convergence waveforms, causing a static shift of the beams. However, the effect is minimized by the inclusion of d.c. correction diodes in dynamic convergence circuitry.

104

7

Convergence and Raster-shape Correction Circuitry

Dynamic convergence waveforms are obtained from available waveforms already present in the receiver circuitry, which have the right frequency but the wrong shape. These are modified by waveshaping circuitry to produce the required waveforms.

It is useful before looking at practical dynamic convergence circuitry to summarize the main types of waveshaping circuits which may be met.

Waveshaping techniques

Differentiators and integrators

These circuits carry out the electrical equivalent of the mathematical operations of differentiating and integrating. They may be studied by writing an expression for the input waveform and predicting the output waveshape by carrying out the appropriate mathematical operation upon this expression. This yields another expression which describes the waveshape of the output signal. However, in this text their behaviour is stated in descriptive terms and those who wish to reinforce their understanding may do so by carrying out associated mathematical studies. It must be emphasized that the operation of most practical circuits only approximates to that of differentiation or integration and these terms should not be interpreted too rigorously.

The operation of an integrator is the reverse of that of a differentiator. The opposite roles which they play are implicit in the following simple descriptions of their behaviour:

DIFFERENTIATOR: the instantaneous *amplitude* of the output waveform is proportional to the *rate-of-change of amplitude* of the input waveform.

INTEGRATOR: the instantaneous *rate-of-change of amplitude* of the output waveform is proportional to the *amplitude* of the input waveform.

These verbal descriptions allow the approximate effect which the circuits have upon applied waveforms to be predicted by simple graphical considerations.

In television timebase circuits, waveforms of both sawtooth and pulse form are

105

readily available. Since parabolic, sawtooth, and pulse waveforms are found in convergence circuits, the action of differentiators and integrators is best demonstrated in terms of these waveforms.

Figure 7.1 shows a waveform, one cycle of which is really two parabolas in tandem. This type of repetitive waveform is of the approximate shape required for the parabolic component of a convergence coil current. It will be observed that the parabolas corresponding to two successive scanning strokes are connected by a shorter duration inverted parabola on the 'flyback stroke'.

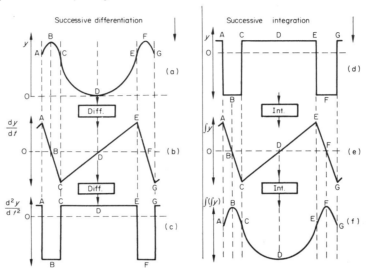

Fig. 7.1 *Examples of the effect of differentiating and integrating waveforms of the basic forms found in convergence circuits*

The result of differentiating the waveform (a), is shown at (b). At points B, D, and F, the rate-of-change of amplitude of (a) is zero and so the differentiator (by definition) yields zero output. Conversely the parabolic waveform has its greatest rate-of-change of amplitude (i.e., its steepest slope) at points A, C, E, and G. At A and E the slope is positive-going and the differentiator yields its maximum positive voltage amplitude at these points. Similarly, at C and G the slope is negative-going and the output at (b) has its maximum negative value. By taking various points on the parabola and scaling the amplitude of the differentiator's output in proportion to the slope at the chosen points, a sawtooth is obtained.

If the sawtooth waveform at (b) is now differentiated again the square-wave or pulse type waveform at (c) is obtained. Between A and C of (b), the sawtooth shows a constant negative-going rate of change of amplitude and the differentiator yields a negative voltage output of constant amplitude during this period. Between C and E the sawtooth at (b) is positive-going. The rate-of-change of amplitude is, however,

106

more gradual and the differentiator gives a constant positive voltage output of an amplitude which is less than the negative voltage produced by the steeper slope of the other sawtooth-leg between A and C.

In the second column of diagrams in Fig. 7.1, the process is reversed. The pulse type waveform at (d) is integrated once and this yields the sawtooth at (e). Integration of the sawtooth at (e) yields the parabola at (f). Again the waveforms may be built by considering the action at various chosen points. At (d), between A and C, the amplitude of the input to the integrator is a constant negative voltage. The integrator gives an output which shows a constant negative slope the rate-of-change of which is proportional to the amplitude of the applied negative voltage. (*N.B.* The sketches are arbitrarily drawn to show the principle and no scales are shown.) Between C and E the waveform at (d) shows a constant positive voltage and the integrator responds by giving an output showing a constant positive-going rate-of-change of amplitude. The slope between C and E is more gradual than that between A and C because, referring to (d), the voltage between C and E has a smaller amplitude than between A and C.

When the sawtooth voltage is integrated, points of zero voltage at (e) (i.e., B,

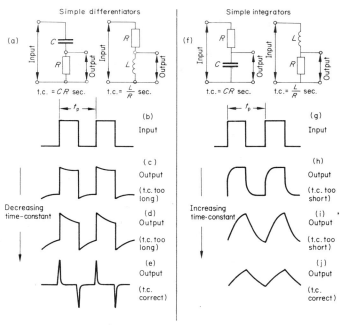

Fig. 7.2 *Showing the influence of time constants on the behaviour of simple differentiators and integrators*

Note:
(i) The circuits at (a) only truly differentiate the input signal (b), when their time constants are short compared with the periodic time (t_p) of the signal, see (e).
(ii) The circuits at (f) only truly integrate the input signal when their time constants are long compared with t_p, see (j).

107

D, F), yield points of zero slope on the output waveform at (f). At points A and E at (e), the input voltage has its maximum positive amplitude and the slope of the integrator's output at (f) shows a maximum positive-going rate-of-change at these points. Similarly at C and G the sawtooth at (e) shows its maximum negative amplitude and the slope of the waveform at (f) has its greatest negative-going rate-of-change at these points. If the parabola at (f) is integrated an S-shaped waveform results. This additional step is not shown on the diagram but it is mentioned because on occasions an S-shaped waveform is needed and it may be derived in this way.

The time constant of a differentiator must be short compared with the periodic time of the applied waveform if the result is to approximate to true differentiation. Conversely an integrator must have a time constant which is long compared with the waveform's periodic time. Figure 7.2 illustrates what may loosely be described as the varying degrees of partial differentiation and integration which result when the time constants do not meet these provisions.

Simple examples of differentiators and integrators are shown at (a) and (f) respectively.

Figure 7.3 shows a network which illustrates how these basic principles may be applied, to produce a tilted-parabola waveform from a pulse-type input signal. L_x and R_x form an integrator which operates upon the input signal to give a sawtooth voltage across R_x (see Fig. 7.1(d) and (e)). C_1 removes any unwanted d.c. component from the input source. Since C_1 must not change the waveform, the network $C_1 R_1$ must have a long time constant. The reactance of C_1 is made much less than the resistance of R_1 to minimize the attenuation between R_x and R_1.

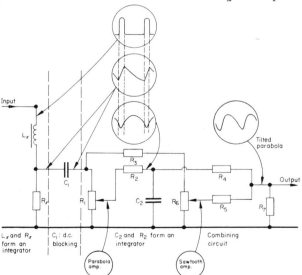

Fig. 7.3 *Example of a waveform shaping network which produces a tilted parabola output from a pulse input*

108

The sawtooth voltage from R_1 is applied to a second integrator C_2R_2 so that a parabolic output appears across C_2 (see Fig. 7.1(e) and (f)). The amplitude of this parabolic component is adjusted by R_1, which varies the amplitude of the sawtooth input to the integrator.

The sawtooth signal across R_1 is also applied via the isolating resistor R_3 to the potentiometer R_6. The parabola and sawtooth are combined across R_7 and the amount of tilt is controlled by R_6.

Both in the circuits of Fig. 7.2 and in Fig. 7.3, the inputs and outputs are all voltages. However, in a convergence circuit, it is the current waveform through the convergence coils which is important, since it is this which determines the nature of the corrective magnetic deflection of the beam. It is necessary when studying these circuits to remember that the inductance of the dynamic convergence coils may play a large part in determining the shape of the current waveform passed by them. This is particularly true for the line circuits because at the line frequency the coils are predominantly inductive. Even at the field frequency, however, the inductive reactance sometimes plays a significant part in the final shaping of the current waveform. A pure inductor acts as an integrator, passing a current which has a waveform equivalent to that of the integrated input voltage. It follows that the voltage waveform across a convergence coil, as perhaps monitored on an oscilloscope, is no guide to the shape of the current waveform or to the way in which the resulting dynamic corrective field varies.

Use of tuned circuits

In many circuits the dynamic convergence coils are connected across a low value resistor through which an approximately sawtooth current is passed. The integrating action of the coils makes the current which results from the applied sawtooth voltage, take-on a tilted parabola shape. The parabolic component may then be enhanced by adding other components to the circuit, connected in shunt with the coils.

Sometimes the coil is made to resonate at (or near) the scanning frequency by a shunt capacitor with which it forms a low-Q parallel tuned circuit (see C_1 in Fig. 7.4). The circulating current which flows in the tuned circuit, modifies the shape of the convergence current to make it approximate to the required tilted-parabola.

Another tuned circuit, resonating at the second harmonic of the scanning frequency, may be included in series with the first capacitor. The second-harmonic sine wave component in the circulating current through the coil, makes the final convergence current more nearly parabolic.

Without the second tuned circuit the tilted waveform may be suitable for red and green line-frequency dynamic convergence but with it present the more symmetrical parabola is suitable for the blue line frequency convergence current.

Another device sometimes used is to choose a capacitor which makes the convergence coil resonate at approximately two-thirds of the line frequency. The circulating current which this produces when a sawtooth voltage is applied, again takes on a form which is approximately what is needed for dynamic convergence.

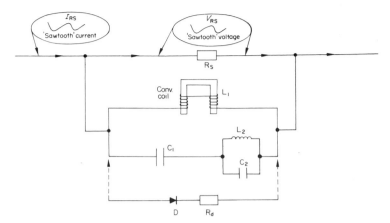

Fig. 7.4   *Use of tuned circuits in convergence waveform shaping circuitry*

In both these types of circuit the inductive reactance of the convergence coil plays an important part in determining the waveshape of the current which passes through it.

D.C. component

Altering the controls in dynamic convergence circuits changes the shape of the convergence current waveform and in turn alters the d.c. component of the waveform. This can cause a change in the accuracy of static convergence and may necessitate readjustment of the latter following dynamic adjustments. To obviate the need for this, d.c. correction diodes are often found in convergence circuits and these introduce a unidirectional current in the coils which helps to maintain the static convergence reasonably accurate for the normal range of dynamic adjustments made in a practical installation procedure. Such a diode is shown as a dotted-in addition on Fig. 7.4.

Field convergence circuits

Convergence derived from field output stage, anode and cathode waveforms

At the low field frequency of 50 Hz, a field output stage may be regarded approximately as a simple resistive loaded amplifier which is required to pass a sawtooth current through the load. In practice, to achieve the desired degree of raster linearity the input waveform is modified by negative feedback derived from the output load circuit. However, for simplicity, the input voltage and anode current waveforms may be considered to be roughly of sawtooth form. For dynamic convergence purposes, two field frequency waveforms are needed; a parabola and a sawtooth. The latter is readily obtainable by using a separate secondary on the output transformer. If this is centre tapped, sawtooth voltages of either polarity are available.

The valve works as a class A amplifier with a cathode resistor developing the

110

necessary bias to place the working point at a suitable position under the I_a/V_g characteristic. If this resistor is decoupled by a capacitor of value large enough to make the time constant long compared with the 20 ms periodic time of the working signal, then the sawtooth current gives rise to a parabolic voltage across the cathode network, i.e., the cathode circuit behaves as an integrator.

In the outline circuit of this type shown in Fig. 7.5 the convergence coils are connected between the parabolic voltage at the cathode and a sawtooth voltage developed across the separate output transformer secondary. With the slider of a tilt potentiometer at the centre, there is zero tilt to the associated parabola and moving it either side of centre tilts the parabola one way or the other; as required.

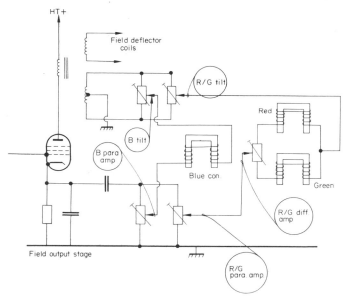

Fig. 7.5 *Outline circuit of a field dynamic convergence system using parabolic and sawtooth waveforms derived from the field output stage*

Blue needs an opposite direction of tilt from red and green and the one centre tapped winding serves both requirements. A differential control is shown fitted to the red and green coils.

This simplified account pre-supposes that the field convergence coils are largely resistive so that the current waveform is very much a facsimile of the waveform of the net applied voltage.

In some circuits, however, where the inductive reactance of the coils at 50 Hz is significant, the cathode voltage waveform may be more sawtooth than parabolic. This waveform when applied to the coils is then partially integrated, giving the current a more parabolic shape. At the same time the anode derived waveform may show a pronounced pulse during the flyback stroke. The partial integration of this pulse by the coils adds to the sawtooth nature of that part of the net coil current which derives from the anode component of the two applied signals.

The presence across the cathode circuit of the shunting convergence circuitry can change the working conditions of the amplifier and the linearity of the picture, particularly at the bottom, may be adversely affected.

As an alternative it is possible to derive the convergence waveforms by monitoring the current through the cathode capacitor. If the convergence circuitry placed in series with the capacitor is of low impedance there is negligible feedback across this circuitry and the amplifier performance is not degraded.

In a practical circuit, adjusted for normal raster linearity, it is found that the current through the capacitor is roughly of tilted parabola form. The tilt is of the same sign as that needed for the blue convergence coil but is normally rather too pronounced. By providing a sawtooth at the anode which imparts an opposite direction of tilt, all needs are met. The anode sawtooth waveform may be made to reduce the cathode current tilt so that the net result is suitable for the blue convergence coil. For the red and green coils the anode sawtooth amplitude may be made predominant so that the net waveform tilt is of opposite phasing in these coils. A centre tapped winding is therefore not needed for this circuit.

Figure 7.6 shows a complete practical circuit which uses the principles described. The two 50 Ω parabola amplitude controls are in parallel and only place a net resistance of 25 Ω in series with the 400 μF cathode decoupling capacitor. The red and green convergence coils are fed with the cathode derived parabola via a 50 Ω differential control. The sawtooth amplitude may be varied by a 50 Ω R/G tilt control.

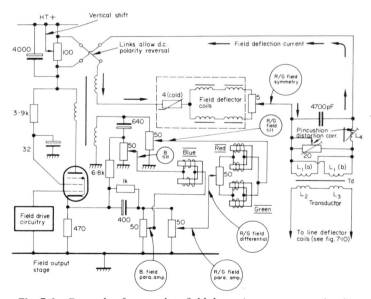

Fig. 7.6 *Example of a complete field dynamic convergence circuit*

112

As stated previously, the cathode parabola has the right phase of tilt for the blue convergence coil. The required net blue tilt is arrived at by feeding a sawtooth waveform from the transformer secondary via a 640 μF capacitor.

A small amount of d.c. correction is obtained from the cathode bias voltage by the 1 kΩ resistor connected to the parabola controls.

Other points of interest in this circuit are:

(a) The 5 Ω deflection-coil balancing or symmetry control, which is adjusted, as described earlier, to eliminate cross-over of red and green crosshatch lines.

(b) The output valve's total HT current produces a small steady voltage (about 3 V) across the 100 Ω resistor and 4000 μF capacitor network in the anode circuit. This provides a d.c. shift current for the deflector coils. The amplitude of shift is varied by the 100 Ω pre-set resistor and there is provision for reversing the direction of shift by changing the connections to this pre-set resistor.

(c) Each field convergence coil consists of two windings; one on each limb of the yoke. To minimize the impedance the two windings are connected in parallel.

(d) The field deflector coil current passes through a winding on the pin-cushion distortion correcting transductor Td. The principle of this is described later.

Convergence derived from the field deflection current

In these circuits the convergence waveforms are derived from the voltage developed across a resistor placed in series with the main deflector coils. The deflection current waveform is of a distorted sawtooth form which is already not too far removed from that needed for convergence purposes and this waveform appears across the resistor. The convergence circuitry is shunted across the resistor and since the main deflection current must not be modified by the convergence circuitry, the resistor has to behave as a source of constant voltage. For this to be so the resistor must have a low value compared with the shunt impedance presented by the convergence circuits.

The convergence coils are designed so that their impedance is such that they give some integration of the applied voltage and pass a current which is part parabolic and part sawtooth, i.e., of tilted parabola form.

This type of circuit is particularly useful in single ended push-pull transistor field output stages, since there is no transformer from which to develop the sawtooth voltages. In total the output circuit is less complicated than most valve output stages.

Figure 7.7 shows an example. The following points should be noted:

(a) The field deflector coil current passes around the loop ABCDE.

(b) To achieve symmetry the 5 Ω potentiometer R_1 allows the division of this current between the two halves of the field deflector coils to be balanced.

(c) Provision is made by the potentiometer $R_2R_3R_4$ for the adjustment of a d.c. component through the deflector coils to give vertical picture shift.

(d) The deflector coil current is passed via the 400 μF capacitor C_1 into the three-way network between B and C. The main convergence coil voltages are developed across R_5 (for red and green) and R_6 (for blue). C_1 blocks the d.c. component from the convergence coils.

(e) With the slider of the R/G tilt control R_8 set to zero and the slider of the R/G differential control R_9 at the centre, the red and green coils, which are in series, pass equal currents. R_5 acts as an amplitude control for them both.

(f) The network C_2, R_8 is connected across R_5. C_2 passes a current which is roughly of sawtooth shape and a voltage of this shape appears across\ R_8. When R_8 is turned up the net voltage applied to the red and green convergence coils equals the algebraic sum of the R_5 and R_8 voltages.

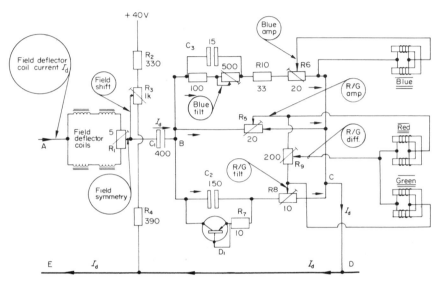

Fig. 7.7 *Field dynamic convergence circuit in which the required waveforms are derived from the field deflector coil current*

(g) The shape of the actual convergence current is then determined by the extent to which the net applied waveform is integrated by the coils.

(h) Differential adjustment of the red and green convergence currents is given by R_9. When the slider is moved, one coil takes more current and the other less.

(i) A tilt of opposite phase is needed by the blue convergence coil. C_3 and R_{10} give partial differentiation of the voltage across R_5. The net current through R_6 has a sawtooth component which tilts the waveform in the right direction for blue convergence.

(j) The diode D_1 introduces a d.c. component into the red and green convergence circuit. This reduces the change of static convergence which would result from adjustment of the dynamic controls. It may be regarded as exerting a clamping action on the red and green convergence waveform.

114

Line frequency convergence circuits

There are two main types of circuit arrangement; those in which the convergence waveforms are derived from line frequency pulses obtained from the line output transformer and those which derive the waveforms from the line deflector coil current.

Line pulse circuits

High amplitude flyback pulses are readily available from the line output transformer. As shown in Fig. 7.1(d) and (e), integration of such a waveform yields a sawtooth output and if this in turn is integrated a parabolic waveform is obtained.

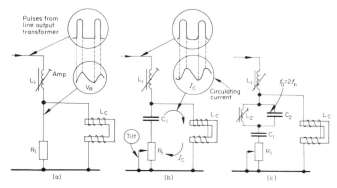

Fig. 7.8 *Basic circuits used in line dynamic convergence systems which are driven by flyback pulses from the line output stage*

In Fig. 7.8(a), if the inductive reactance of L_1 is much greater than the total circuit resistance, the circuit behaves as an integrator and the current passed by it is of sawtooth shape. The sawtooth voltage across R_1 is applied to the convergence coils L_c and a further integration takes place so that a parabolic current passes through L_c. A current must also flow directly through L_c from L_1. If the inductive reactance of L_1 is considerably greater than the impedance of L_c the current through L_c is similar in shape to the sawtooth current through R_1. The net current through L_c has parabolic and sawtooth components and is of tilted parabola form.

In Fig. 7.8(b) a capacitor is added in series with R_1. This may serve to modify the convergence coil current in a number of different ways. Sometimes it is chosen to have a low reactance compared with that of L_1, so that the current through it has the sawtooth form dictated by L_1. This yields a small parabolic voltage across C which has the effect of causing the sawtooth current through L_c to be partially cancelled.

This is because integration of a parabola yields an S-shaped waveform. The S-shaped component through L_c is roughly like an anti-phase sawtooth current which tends to cancel the direct sawtooth component, leaving a net convergence current having a less tilted shape.

The design may, however, be based upon the tuned-circuit waveshaping methods described earlier. Without C_1 and R_1 present at all, the current through L_c is of saw-tooth form. If C_1 is now chosen to resonate with L_c at a frequency near to the scanning frequency, a circulating current flows in the tuned circuit formed by L_c and C_1. The frequency of this current is locked to the scanning frequency but its 'shape' varies according to the natural frequency of resonance (f_0) of the tuned circuit. This shape is much influenced by the Q-factor of the circuit. Basically it may be described as a distorted sine-wave. The low-Q-factor causes the second-harmonic content to be high and it is this which provides the parabolic-type 'hump' in the waveform. Also present is a third-harmonic component which can cause an unwanted asymmetry. This component may be minimized by making f_0 approximately equal to two-thirds of the scanning frequency and C_1 is often chosen to make this so.

Assuming the circuit of Fig. 7.8(b) is of this type, R_1 may be used as a 'tilt' control. When R_1 is increased the Q-factor falls and the current through L_c assumes a more sawtooth-like shape since it is less affected by the properties of the tuned-circuit. The amplitude of the current is varied by changing the reactance of L_1.

In Fig. 7.8(c) the second-harmonic component is increased by the inclusion of the tuned circuit L_2C_2 which resonates at $2f_h$. This increases the parabolic content and steepens the rate-of-change of current at the start and end of each scanning stroke. The part of the current waveform which falls during the scanning stroke (i.e., between the applied pulses), becomes more symmetrical about its mid-point and this waveform is more suitable for the blue line convergence coil.

Figure 7.9 shows an example of a line pulse driven convergence circuit using the integrator and tuned circuit techniques discussed above. The blue circuit is the same

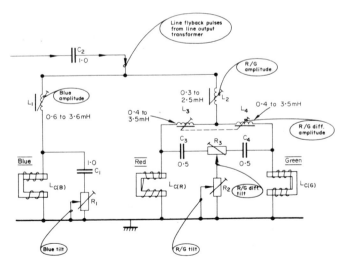

Fig. 7.9 *Example of a line dynamic convergence circuit in which the waveforms are derived from line flyback pulses*

116

as (b) in Fig. 7.8. The red and green circuits are matrixed and L_2 provides a common amplitude control. Differential amplitude control is achieved by the variable reactances L_3 and L_4. When $L_3 = L_4$, the sawtooth current developed by the integrating action of L_2, is shared equally between the red and green circuits. At any other setting of the R/G differential amplitude control, the reactances offered by L_3 and L_4 differ and more current passes through one arm than the other.

Both the red and green coils are tuned by $0.5 \mu F$ capacitors. With the differential tilt control slider at the centre the tilts introduced into each branch are equal; growing greater as R_2 is increased. Moving the slider of R_3 away from the centre introduces more resistance into one arm than the other. The circuit with the higher resistance has a lower Q-factor than the other and hence the tilt in this arm increases whilst that in the other arm decreases.

In receivers designed for dual-standards working, the dynamic line convergence circuitry must be duplicated because the action of the circuits is a function of the applied pulse frequency and any given values which create acceptable convergence on one standard, cannot produce the same result on another. In 625/405 dual standards receivers therefore, the line convergence coils are switched over from one set of components to another when the systems switch is operated. It is necessary to carry out a full convergence procedure on the two standards successively, when the receiver is installed.

Line deflection current circuits

These follow the pattern already described for field convergence circuits. Again the basic principle is to develop a voltage across a resistor through which the main deflector coil current passes. This yields a waveform which is already something like that needed for convergence.

Figure 7.10 shows such a circuit and since many of the principles have been described it is convenient to list the main features of the circuitry which should be noted:

(a) The main path of the line deflector coil current is marked by the letters ABCDEFGHIJKLMN.
(b) To achieve deflector coil symmetry the inductors L_a and L_b are used. By varying the position of the core the amount of inductive reactance in one arm may be reduced whilst the other is increased. At line frequency, with wide angle scanning, the use of a potentiometer as a balancing control (as found in the field circuit) would involve excessive losses.
(c) Provision is made for driving a d.c. component through the deflector coils to give lateral picture shift. For this purpose the smoothed cathode voltage from the line output valve is used. The polarity may be reversed by changing over fly-leads. Inductor L_d offers a high impedance at line frequency and prevents the line scanning current from passing through the cathode circuit instead of through the convergence network.

117

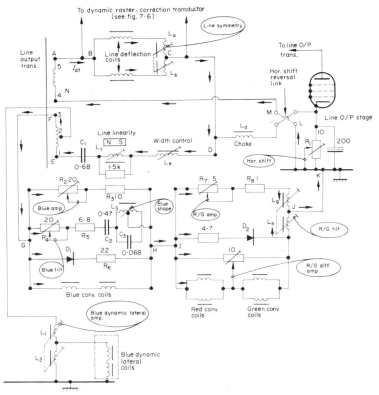

Fig. 7.10 *Example of a dynamic line convergence circuit in which the waveforms are derived from the line deflector coil current*

(d) In the deflector coil current path are linearity and width coils of conventional form, together with the S-correction capacitor C_1.

(e) For the blue convergence coil the resistors across which the deflection current produces the required drive waveform are R_2 and R_3. The corresponding resistors for the red and green coils are R_7 and R_8.

(f) The two blue convergence coils are connected in series to give an adequate field strength, but the two coils for each of the red and green convergence yokes are in parallel to lower the impedances in these circuits.

(g) Both the blue and the red-green branches of the circuit include d.c. static convergence correction diodes.

(h) Because of the axial position of the blue gun the blue convergence current has to be much more nearly truly parabolic than the red and green currents, which are markedly tilted. To achieve this and to give the required steepness at the start and end of raster lines, the tuning capacitor C_2 and the second harmonic tuned circuit L_3C_3 are provided.

118

(i) The centre tapped inductor L_gL_h gives control of the tilt of the red-green convergence waveform. By increasing the inductive reactance in the R_7R_8 arm and decreasing it in the convergence coil arm, the sawtooth component through the coils is increased.

(j) R-G amplitude and tilt controls together with the R-G differential adjustment provides all the control that is needed to establish satisfactory shapes and amplitudes for the red and green currents.

(k) The tuned circuit in the blue current shaping arm is often adjusted to flatten out humps at the end of the centre horizontal crosshatch line, as shown at (L5) in Plate 8.

(l) *Blue dynamic lateral correction* is also provided for in this circuit. Once again use is made of a line repetition flyback pulse. In this circuit it is of some 200 V amplitude. Inductor L_1 integrates this pulse to provide a sawtooth current. To give correction at the ends of the raster line this is the basic shape which the dynamic current needs to have. It is shaped by adjustment of the core of L_1L_2 which increases or decreases the rate-of-change of current at the start and end of each current waveform through the convergence coil.

Dynamic raster shape correction

When convergence correction has been made, there remains some pincushion distortion of the three converged rasters. It is possible to design deflector coils to reduce this distortion but the quality of focus at wide deflection angles must not be compromised. Coils are designed to give a satisfactory focus over the entire picture area and the remaining pincushion distortion may be removed, or much reduced, by external means. Figure 7.11(a) shows a sketch of a raster with much exaggerated pincushion distortion. The bowing inwards of the top and bottom is referred to as distortion along the N–S axis, and at the sides the distortion is along the E–W axis. The corrective measures aim to change the raster shape to that shown by the dotted line. This involves increasing the vertical deflection along the N–S axis and reducing the width at the top and bottom of the raster until it is the same as that along the E–W axis.

Correction is achieved by introducing some cross modulation between the two deflection fields. The device used for this purpose is a transductor and its action may be described by considering the two forms of correction in turn.

(a) *E–W correction*

Figure 7.11(b) shows, in a simplified way, what is done. The transductor acts as a shunt load connected across the line deflector coils and the extent to which this by-passes the deflector coil current is made proportional to the amplitude of the field scanning waveform. When the spot is at the centre of the screen (i.e., the field deflection is zero) the shunt load has its highest impedance and hardly influences the amplitude of the line deflection current which passes through the line deflector coils. As the field deflection current increases in amplitude, the shunt load impedance falls and an increasing proportion of the deflection current passes through the shunt load instead of through the deflector coils, so that the width is reduced.

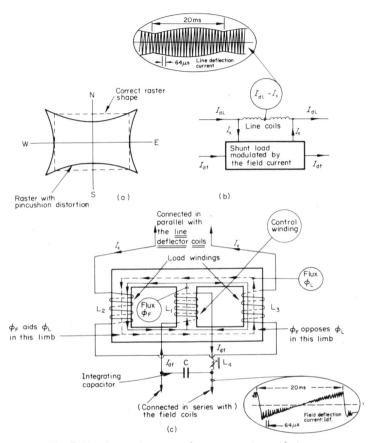

Fig. 7.11 *Dynamic raster-shape correction techniques*

(a) Shows the nature of the pincushion distortion which has to be corrected.
(b) Shows the principle of E–W correction by a shunt load having an impedance which grows less as the field current increases.
(c) Simplified diagram of a transductor.
(*N.B.* Fig. 7.6 shows a transductor connected in a field output stage and Fig. 7.10 shows the cross connection to the line output stage.)

Figure 7.11(c) shows a diagram of a transductor. L_1 is called the control winding and it is through L_1 that the field current is passed. L_2 and L_3 are the load windings and these two series windings are connected in shunt with the line deflector coils. The direction in which L_2 and L_3 are wound is such that the e.m.f.'s induced in L_1 as a result of the line frequency current in L_2 and L_3, are in anti-phase, i.e., there is

120

no transformer action from load to control windings. As will be seen later, this only holds good when the field current flowing in L_1 is small.

When the field current is zero, the only flux in the E-shaped Ferroxcube core is that due to a small line frequency current through L_2 and L_3 and this flux (shown as ϕ_L) is confined around the outer limb.

The core is unsaturated and the inductive reactance at the line frequency is high compared with that of the deflector coils so that the amplitude of the line current through L_2 and L_3 is small.

As the field current through L_1 builds up it sets up a flux (ϕ_F) down the centre limb and through the two outer limbs which bear L_2 and L_3. The field frequency flux is in the same direction as the line flux in one outer limb (the left one in the diagram) but opposing it in the other. As the field current increases the total flux in the left-hand limb causes an increasing degree of magnetic saturation and the total impedance presented by the load windings decreases. This causes the line frequency current to increase in amplitude which still further saturates the left-hand limb. The nature of the core is such that the change in the shunt load causes a parabolic modulation at field frequency of the amplitude of the line deflector coil current. The further the beam is deflected in the vertical direction away from the central E–W axis, the smaller becomes the line deflector coil current amplitude and this has the desired effect of decreasing the raster width at the top and the bottom so removing the concave shape of the sides of the picture.

(b) *N–S correction*

Since it is only one of the two outer limbs which saturates, it is evident that the two anti-phase e.m.f.'s induced in L_1 as a result of the line frequency current in L_2 and L_3, are no longer of equal amplitude once saturation begins. As the left-hand side of the core saturates the e.m.f. induced in L_1 by the current in L_2 gets less and less. The result of this is that successive line scanning strokes produce a net e.m.f. in L_1 and this e.m.f. increases the further the spot moves from the centre of the screen in the vertical direction. A capacitor is connected across L_1 for the purpose of integrating the line frequency pulses to produce a voltage which in turn drives a current through the deflector coils to aid the vertical deflection.

This on its own is inadequate to remove the top and bottom distortion. The inductor L_4 is included to adjust the phasing of the line frequency modulation of the field scanning waveform. It is sometimes made to resonate with the integrating capacitor to increase the total correction voltage across C.

The extent of the pincushion correction may be varied by a potentiometer across the control winding. In practice a fixed resistor is fitted to set the amplitude.

A complete diagram of a transductor circuit is included in the vertical convergence circuit shown in Fig. 7.6.

It will be noted that the control winding L_1 is in two sections. These are connected in such a way that there is no transformer action from L_1 to L_2 and L_3. In this way the only influence which the field current can have on the line deflection circuit is by the variable loading effect already described.

A negative temperature coefficient resistor in series with the field coils compensates for the increase with temperature of the resistance of the field coils and the amplitude of the deflection current is held nearly constant.

8

Chrominance Signals: General Principles of Quadrature Amplitude Modulation and Demodulation

Revision

Previously the two components of the chrominance signal which represent the two colour-difference signals, have been represented by phasors which are mutually at 90°. The resultant phasor formed by the combination of these two, represents the chrominance signal. Its phase depends upon the hue, and its magnitude upon the saturation and amplitude, of the originating colour. The chrominance phasor may have any angle between 0° and 360°, relative to the reference axis. By convention, in phasor diagrams, the reference axis lies along the horizontal, to the right of the origin (i.e., along the '+x' axis) and in colour television work the $+(B' - Y')$ chrominance component lies along this axis.

To prevent overmodulation of the vision carrier (see chapter 3), the chrominance signal has to be amplitude restricted. This is achieved by reducing the amplitudes of the colour-difference signals by the application of weighting factors. The weighted colour-difference signals are referred to as the U and V signals, where:

$$U = 0.493(B' - Y') \quad \text{and} \quad V = 0.877(R' - Y')$$

The reference axis in phasor diagrams then becomes the $+U$ axis.

It is now necessary to make a more detailed study of the nature of Q.A.M. chrominance signals. To dispel possible misunderstandings, the following points are stressed:

(a) Colour-difference signals are simply voltages which may be positive, negative or zero, at any given instant during a scanning line.

(b) In the transmitted vision signal, the two colour-difference signals have to be represented by radio frequency modulation components. At the receiver these modulation components then allow the two original colour-difference voltages to be recovered and amplified for presentation to the c.r.t. The 'missing' third colour-difference signal (i.e. $(G' - Y')$) is obtained by matrixing the other two.[1]

(c) Chrominance signal phasor diagrams show the *r.f. modulation components* corresponding to the two original colour-difference signals. They *do not* represent the colour-difference signals themselves. In colour television literature, the x and y axes of phasor diagrams are variously labelled $\pm(B' - Y')$ and $\pm(R' - Y')$; or, more correctly, $\pm U$ and $\pm V$. It is important to remember that these axes depict the relative amplitudes of the chrominance signal modulation components which bear the *information* shown by the labels.

(d) To further illustrate this point, suppose a given area of colour in a picture gives rise to colour-difference signal voltages of $(R' - Y') = 0.4$ V and $(B' - Y') = 0.2$ V. These voltages will remain steady whilst the camera scanning beams traverse the width of the colour area. It is clearly nonsense to draw a phasor diagram showing these two voltages on axes mutually at right-angles and then to construct a resultant! They are both simply steady voltages and phase angles have no meaning. However, if they are each made to amplitude-modulate separate carriers (i.e., the colour sub-carriers), then they each produce alternating r.f. signals whose amplitudes are proportional to the colour-difference voltages. [For reasons which are discussed later, the carrier components of these two a.m. signals are suppressed, so that the r.f. signals referred to each represents the sum of the remaining sideband components of one of the two a.m. signals.] If the two carriers are phased at 90° to one another then the two carrier-suppressed amplitude modulated r.f. signals *may* be represented by two phasors at 90°. In addition, if these two modulated signals are then added together, the two phasors may be combined to produce a resultant phasor which has a phase angle between the two (in this case 53° 26′), and a magnitude computed by finding the square root of the sum of the squares of the individual phasor amplitudes.

(e) Colour television phasor diagrams are therefore *r.f. diagrams*. They relate to the modulated chrominance signal and its two component parts. For convenience the axes are labelled as described and scaled between 0 and 1.0. By their use it is possible to portray how coloured information in the picture is represented in the vision signal.

Q.A.M. chrominance signals have interesting properties. Phasor diagrams alone do not allow these to be demonstrated adequately. This is because a phasor has a static 'frozen' appearance and it is easy to forget that it represents the peak amplitude of an alternating electrical signal which is varying in a cyclic manner at the sub-carrier frequency of 4.43361875 MHz. In this chapter the emphasis is directed at the

---

[1] The three colour-difference signals are related by the expression:
$$(G' - Y') = -0.51(R' - Y') - 0.186(B' - Y')$$
As is shown in chapter 16, this expression may be established by a simple derivation from the luminance equation,
$$Y' = 0.30R' + 0.59G' + 0.11B'$$

alternating nature of the chrominance signal. The insight which this gives into the way in which the colour-difference signal information is carried by the chrominance signal, then allows a clear understanding to be gained of the principles of receiver chrominance demodulation circuitry.

As an introduction to these studies it is helpful to summarize some of the salient features of Q.A.M. chrominance signals which have been mentioned either above, or in earlier chapters.

Summary of some of the salient features of Q.A.M. chrominance signals

(a) The chrominance signal is the combination of two separate modulated signals.

(b) One of these bears U information and the other V.

(c) Each of these two signals is a double-sideband amplitude-modulated radio-frequency signal with the carrier component suppressed.

(d) The carrier frequencies employed for the two signals are the same, but the phase angle of the V carrier leads by 90° on the U carrier in the NTSC system, and alternates on a line-by-line basis from $+90°$ to $-90°$ in the PAL system.

(e) The carrier frequency used in the PAL system is 4·43361875 MHz. This is referred to as the colour *sub-carrier* frequency (f_{sc}).

(f) When these two separate a.m. signals are added to form the chrominance signal, their individual characteristics are not lost since at any instant the amplitude and phase of the single chrominance signal made from them, is entirely determined by the amplitudes and phases of the two component parts.

(g) Each of the two components has two possible phase angles to take account of the fact that the colour-difference signals which modulate the two sub-carriers may be either positive or negative. The phase of the U sub-carrier when bearing positive $(B' - Y')$ information is taken as the reference phase angle of 0°. When $(B' - Y')$ is negative, the U sub-carrier is at 180°. Correspondingly, for positive or negative $(R' - Y')$ colour-difference voltages, the V sub-carrier component is at 90° and 270° respectively. (*N.B.* The phase reversal on alternate lines of the V component in the PAL system, is not considered for the moment.)

(h) Because of (g) it follows that the phasor sum of the two components may lie in any of the four quadrants, i.e., the chrominance signal phasor may have any phase angle from 0° to 360°.

(i) Since it represents the vector sum of two signals mutually at right angles (i.e., in quadrature), the chrominance signal is known as a Quadrature Amplitude Modulated (Q.A.M.) signal.

(j) Although the chrominance signal is itself an r.f. signal of a complex character, having a bandwidth of 2 MHz, centred upon 4·43 MHz, it is treated merely as additional video information which forms part of the composite video signal which finally modulates the vision carrier at the transmitter.

(k) The sub-carrier frequency of 4·43361875 MHz is so chosen that the chrominance signal fits into the upper frequency end of the video bandwidth. The various factors which determine the precise choice of frequency, were studied in chapter 2.

(l) On monochrome information the colour-difference signals are zero and the chrominance signal disappears.

Suppressed carrier a.m. signals

A knowledge of the properties of double-sideband suppressed-carrier a.m. signals is essential if NTSC and PAL chrominance signals are to be fully understood.

It is well known that when a carrier wave of frequency f_c Hz is amplitude modulated by a single sine-wave of frequency f_m Hz, the resulting signal has three frequency components; a carrier component of frequency f_c Hz, together with upper and lower 'side-frequency' components at $(f_c + f_m)$ Hz and $(f_c - f_m)$ Hz respectively. These two side-frequency components, produced by the process of amplitude modulation, are together known as the *modulation-product*.

Normal a.m. signals are much more complex but each single frequency component in the modulating information yields its own individual pair of side-frequencies. The groups of side-frequencies above and below the carrier are collectively known as the upper and lower sidebands respectively. The modulation-product is then the sum total of all the sideband components.

Since every modulating frequency component has its own representatives in both sidebands, it follows that the total information being handled by an a.m. system can be conveyed by transmitting either one, or both sidebands, without the carrier. To recover the information at the receiver, however, a carrier must be re-inserted. Then, both the upper and the lower sidebands, in combination with the carrier, yield the information. Thus:

$$(f_c + f_m) - f_c = f_m \quad \text{and} \quad f_c - (f_c - f_m) = f_m$$

The carrier must have precisely the correct frequency and, moreover, be exactly in phase with the original suppressed carrier, if the information in the sidebands is to be correctly retrieved.

Double sideband working *with* the carrier is widely used for broadcast purposes because the receiver is relatively simple. Single sideband working is widely used in carrier telephony work and in radio communications. Television vision signals use vestigial sideband working, i.e., have one complete sideband and one partially suppressed sideband.[1] It is in the chrominance signal of the NTSC and PAL colour television systems that suppressed carrier double sideband working has found one of its most useful applications.

There are three main reasons for this:

(a) The nature of double-sideband suppressed-carrier signals allows positive and negative colour-difference signals to be readily identified, as will be seen in this chapter.

---

[1] See pages 46–53 of *Television Receiver Theory*: Part 1, by G. H. Hutson, published by Arnolds of London.

(b) A further quality of these signals makes it possible to combine two of them in such a way that both are easily recovered at the receiver.

(c) It is necessary to minimize the interference produced by the chrominance signals both on monochrome receivers when they are working on colour transmissions and in the luminance channel of colour receivers themselves. Most of the power in a normal a.m. signal is in the carrier component and for normal depths of modulation only relatively little energy rests where it is really needed, i.e., in the information-bearing sidebands. The ratio of the sideband power to carrier power increases with the depth of modulation but even at maximum (i.e., at 100% modulation), two-thirds of the total power is in the carrier and only one-third is useful sideband power. Since so much energy is in the carrier component, suppressing it clearly eliminates much potential interference. In addition to this, the colour-difference signals which constitute the modulating information are zero when the picture detail is non-coloured (i.e., on greys, black, or white), so that at such times the sidebands also disappear leaving no chrominance signal components *at all* in the video signal.

The reconstitution of a sub-carrier having the correct frequency and phase is not unduly difficult because of the non-continuous nature of the transmitted chrominance signal. The time-sequential transmission of picture and synchronization information once per line makes it possible to send a reference burst of the original sub-carrier once per line during the back porch of the line blanking period. This facilitates the accurate locking of a sub-carrier reference oscillator at the receiver. This matter is dealt with fully in chapter 15.

Graphical representation of a.m. and suppressed carrier a.m. signals

When a carrier wave is modulated by a sinusoidal signal, the resulting a.m. wave takes on the characteristic appearance shown in Fig. 8.1(b). In this diagram the ratio of the carrier to the modulating frequency is made very low so that the actual waveform of the resultant a.m. signal (i.e., the waveform 'in the envelope') may be studied.

Note that:

(1) The waveform inside the envelope is the result of adding three sine-waves of frequencies f_c, $(f_c + f_m)$, and $(f_c - f_m)$.

(2) This waveform has a periodic time equal to that of the carrier. Its frequency is the same as the carrier because this is the average frequency of the three components.

(3) The 'envelope' of the a.m. signal has the same shape as the original modulating information. For this reason the latter is recovered by simple rectification.

(4) The 'upper' envelope is simply a line drawn to connect the positive peaks of the a.m. signal and has no significance other than this. Similarly, the bottom envelope traces out the varying amplitude of the negative peaks.

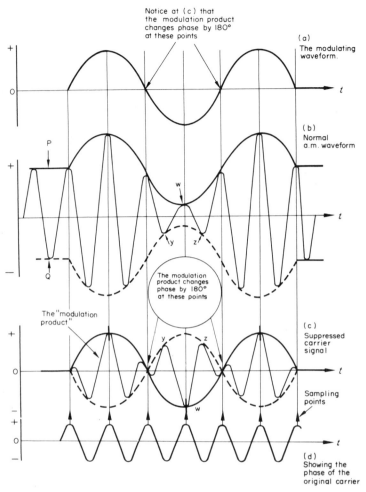

Fig. 8.1 *Showing the effect of suppressing the carrier in an amplitude modulated signal*

When the carrier component is suppressed, the signal takes on a completely different form, as shown at Fig. 8.1(c). Notice particularly that:

(5) The waveform now seen represents the graphical addition of two sine-waves; one the upper side frequency of $(f_c + f_m)$ Hz, and the other the lower side-frequency of $(f_c - f_m)$ Hz.

(6) The upper and lower envelopes are no longer sinusoidal. Humps appear at a frequency equal to the difference between the two components, i.e., at $(f_c + f_m) - (f_c - f_m) = 2f_m$ Hz. This is sometimes referred to as the *beat-frequency*. The original modulating frequency can no longer be recovered by rectification.

128

(7) The waveform inside the envelope still has a frequency equal to that of the suppressed carrier (i.e., f_c Hz) since it is the average of $(f_c + f_m)$ and $(f_c - f_m)$.

(8) The shape of the original modulating signal shown at (a), may still be discerned by reference to the upper and lower envelope humps in alternate sequence. Thus the waveshape of the upper envelope of (b) which is shown in full-line, can be seen in full-line at (c); the first half cycle being above—and the second below— the zero line. Similarly the dotted lower envelope shape of (b) may be seen at (c).

(9) The waveform at (c) may be predicted by imagining that the mean signal levels shown at P and Q in (b), are pushed downwards and upwards respectively to meet at the x axis. If the waveform in the envelope is imagined to be attached to it at the points of contact it will be 'pulled' to take up the form shown at (c). For example, the positive peak **w** is pulled below the x axis by the upper full-line envelope, whilst **y** and **z** are pulled above the x axis by the dotted envelope.[1]

(10) The waveform inside the humped envelope changes phase by 180° each time the original modulating signal passes through zero. (See (a) and (c) at the points marked.)

(11) If the waveform at (c) is 'looked at' or 'sampled' at times corresponding to the positive peaks of the original suppressed carrier (shown at (d)), the shape of the original modulating signal (a) is recovered.

The points (10) and (11) above are vitally important. Clearly, the higher the ratio of the carrier frequency to modulating frequency, the more accurately is the shape of the latter recovered. Figure 8.2 is included to demonstrate this. The dots on the envelope at (b) show the relative amplitudes of the voltages recovered by the 'once-per-carrier-cycle' sampling method. A curve joining these dots clearly reproduces the shape of the modulating information shown at (a).

To add further perspective to the subject, Fig. 8.3 shows the simple graphical addition of two sine waves of differing frequency. By inspection and logical deduction the following points are evident:

(a) The frequency of the resultant must be the mean of the two frequencies.

(b) Over a period of time maximum points must be reached when the two signals directly reinforce one another. Similarly, assuming they are of equal amplitude (which pairs of side frequencies in an a.m. signal **are**) the two must sometimes cancel out to give zero points.

(c) After each zero point the phase of the resultant must reverse.

(d) The maxima (i.e., hump peaks) and zero points must occur at the 'difference' (i.e., beat) frequency.

(e) Since there is 180° phase change after each hump, the resultant signal (i.e., the waveform inside the envelope) takes two humps to complete one cyclic change. This shows the presence of a component at half the hump frequency. In a sup-

---

[1] This rather 'non-scientific' device is useful to establish what a suppressed carrier signal 'looks like' when bearing a given modulation. The voltage waveform of the modulating signal is first drawn as the upper and lower envelopes of a normal a.m. signal. The 'unmodulated' carrier levels P and Q are then pushed to the x axis.

129

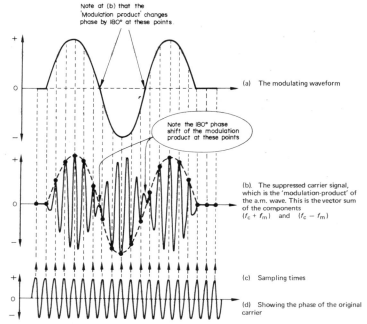

Note at (b) that the
'Modulation product' changes
phase by 180° at these points.

(a) The modulating waveform

Note the 180° phase
shift of the modulation
product at these points

(b). The suppressed carrier signal,
which is the 'modulation-product' of
the a.m. wave. This is the vector sum
of the components
$(f_c + f_m)$ and $(f_c - f_m)$

(c) Sampling times

(d) Showing the phase of the original
carrier

Fig. 8.2 *Showing a further example of a suppressed carrier amplitude modulated signal*

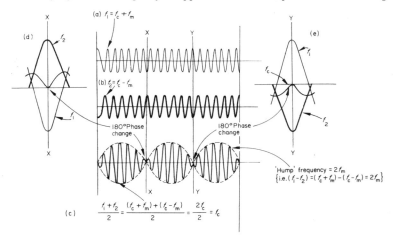

Fig. 8.3 *Graphical addition of two sine-waves of differing frequency*

pressed carrier a.m. signal this latter component is of course the modulating
frequency component of f_m Hz.

The 180° phase change of the resultant each time the modulating signal passes
through zero may also be demonstrated vectorially.

130

By analysis of a simple a.m. signal (at a time $t = 0$) the following facts may be established:

(i) The upper side-frequency (U.S.F.) component lags by 90° on the carrier.

(ii) The lower side-frequency (L.S.F.) leads by 90° on the carrier.

(iii) The maximum voltage amplitude (corresponding to 100% modulation) of each side-frequency is half the carrier amplitude.

In Fig. 8.4 carrier and side-frequency phasors are drawn at intervals over a period of time equivalent to one cycle of the modulating waveform.

By convention phasors rotate anti-clockwise. The carrier phasor therefore rotates at f_c Hz, the U.S.F. at $(f_c + f_m)$ Hz and the L.S.F. at $(f_c - f_m)$ Hz.

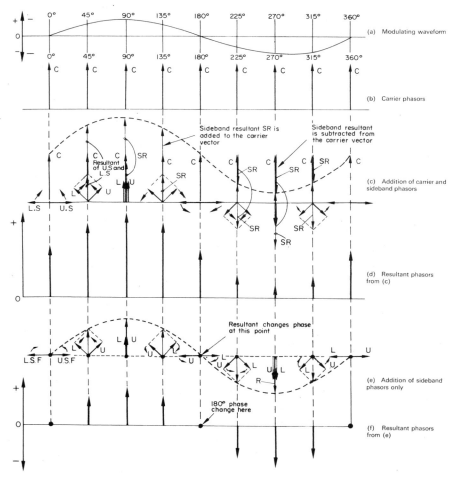

Fig. 8.4 *Showing the phasor diagram method of deducing the change of amplitude of a modulated wave over one cycle of the modulating signal*

131

If the carrier phasor is imagined 'frozen', then relative to this stationary phasor the U.S.F. phasor (being f_m Hz faster), will appear to rotate anti-clockwise at f_m Hz, whilst the L.S.F. phasor (being f_m Hz slower), will appear to rotate clockwise at f_m Hz.

The phasors at (c) are drawn at intervals of 45°. At each step the resultant of the two side frequency phasors is found and then this is added to the carrier phasor. Notice that:

(1) The resultant of the two side frequencies is always along the carrier phasor line; in phase with it and reinforcing it for one half cycle of f_m; in anti-phase and diminishing it for the other half-cycle.

(2) Because the sum of the two side-frequency components can never exceed the amplitude of the carrier, the resultant of the three components is always *in phase* with the carrier. (*N.B.* This can be seen again, by comparing (b) and (d) in Fig. 8.1)[1]

(3) The dotted line connecting the resultants shows the shape of the upper envelope of the a.m. signal.

At (e) the side-frequency phasors are again drawn but this time without the carrier phasor. This allows the corresponding double-sideband suppressed carrier signal to be studied over one modulating cycle.

In this case, the final resultant phasor clearly changes phase by 180° every time the modulating waveform at (a) passes through zero.

Notice that (b) shows a series of phasors each representing positive half cycle peaks of the carrier. By comparison with (b), the diagrams at (e) and (f) show clearly that the suppressed carrier signal waveform is in phase with the original carrier for the first half cycle of the modulating sine-wave and in anti-phase for the second. This again confirms the diagrams shown at (c) in Fig. 8.1 and (b) in Fig. 8.2.

It will be appreciated that inverting all the phasors at (c) produces the other half of the a.m. signal envelope.

Similarly inverting the phasors at (e) yields the other halves of the 'humped' diagrams shown in Fig. 8.1(c) and Fig. 8.2(b).

In all the diagrams so far studied, simple sinusoidal modulating waveforms have been assumed. This allows important principles to be established with a minimum of difficulty. More complex modulating waveforms produce a whole series of side frequencies in each sideband. Since these are in pairs, equally spaced either side of the carrier, the average frequency is still equal to the carrier frequency and a suppressed carrier double-sideband signal may therefore still be represented as a single resultant waveform at carrier frequency.

In all the work which follows, colour-difference modulating voltages are shown as 'square-waves'. The significance of this is that it is assumed that stripes of colours are being considered. For the width of a given stripe the luminance, hue, and saturation are all assumed to remain constant. The standard colour-bar signals discussed

---

[1] On 100% modulation the resultant has a maximum value of twice the carrier's amplitude and a minimum value of zero.

in chapter 3 are of this type but in the present chapter the amplitudes are arbitrarily chosen for convenience since a study of general principles does not necessarily require specific degrees of saturation and amplitude to be employed.

As a first example of this, Fig. 8.5 is included. At (a) an arbitrary colour-difference signal is shown, corresponding to a section along one scanning line which passes through a black stripe, two adjacent coloured stripes of different hue and a white stripe. On the black and white strips at W and Z the colour-difference signal is zero. At X the colour is such that the colour-difference signal has a constant positive value of $+0.2$, whilst at Y the colour gives rise to a negative colour-difference voltage of -0.4.

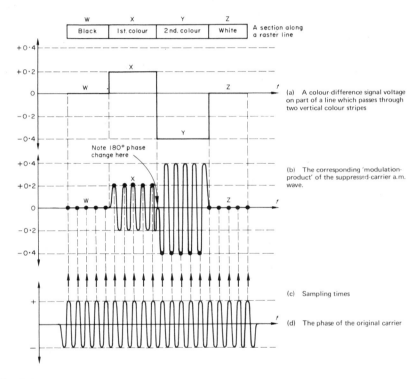

Fig. 8.5 *A suppressed carrier signal produced by an arbitrary colour-difference signal*

At (b) the corresponding suppressed-carrier double-sideband a.m. signal is sketched. This is referred to, as mentioned earlier, as the *modulation-product*. It constitutes the r.f. signal which is transmitted to represent the given original colour-difference signal. At W and Z, where the modulating signal is zero, there are no side-bands produced at all. Since the sub-carrier itself is suppressed, there is 'nothing left', i.e., the suppressed carrier signal is of zero amplitude.

133

At X the modulation product has an amplitude which is directly proportional to that of the colour-difference signal. This has again been scaled at $+0.2$ to indicate this direct relationship. It should be noted that the y axes in these (and in all the following diagrams of this chapter) are scaled merely to show relative amplitudes and polarities. The actual voltage levels corresponding to the originating colour-difference signal on the one hand and to the suppressed carrier signal's amplitude on the other, will of course be much different. It is the principle of direct proportionality between these two quantities, which is important to establish here.

Notice by comparison with the carrier at (d) that the modulation product during the stripe X (when the colour-difference voltage is positive), is *in-phase* with the original (but now suppressed) sub-carrier. This reiterates the point made earlier.

Conversely, at Y, when the polarity of the colour-difference signal is negative instead of positive, the modulation-product is in anti-phase with the original suppressed carrier. The phase change of 180° takes place at the transition from X to Y. Once again the amplitude of the modulation product is directly proportional to the corresponding colour-difference voltage and the y scale shows this as 0·4.

Finally the recovery of the correct colour-difference signal waveform from the modulation-product must be considered. Looking upwards from the positive peaks of the sub-carrier drawn at (d), these will be found to correspond in time to the black dots on the modulation-product at (b). If the modulation-product's amplitude is imagined as being sensed (or sampled) at the moments designated by the arrows at (c), i.e., once each positive peak of the sub-carrier, the shape arrived at by connecting the dots is that of the original colour-difference signal at (a).

The way in which the suppressed carrier signal takes account of the polarity of the modulating colour-difference signal, and an insight into the method of synchronous demodulation, is now apparent. It will be noticed that whereas the colour-difference signal clearly shows what polarity a given colour produces, the corresponding suppressed carrier signal for a given colour is a sine-wave with equal positive and negative half-cycles. On an oscilloscope it would not be possible to deduce the polarity of the colour-difference signal represented by the sine-wave. It is the peak amplitude of the sine-wave half-cycles which correspond in time to the original suppressed carrier's *positive* half cycles which actually designate the 'hidden' colour-difference signal's amplitude and polarity. The importance of re-introducing the sub-carrier at the receiver, with the correct frequency and phase will now be understood.

A very important point must now be noted. If the carrier drawn at (d) is imagined to be shifted sideways by a distance equivalent to one quarter of a cycle to represent a phase change of 90°, then the sampling-point arrows will correspond at (b) to moments when the modulation-product is passing through zero. This demonstrates that if the re-inserted carrier is 90° out of phase with the original carrier, a demodulator gives zero output. It is because of this fact that two separate modulation-products, stemming from two carriers of equal frequency but having relative phases at 90° to one another, may be added without losing their individual identities. From the

134

reference oscillator at the receiver, two sub-carrier outputs, mutually at 90° are obtained. These are fed to two demodulators. In the several diagrams which follow later in this chapter, it will be clearly demonstrated that from the combined chrominance signal each of the demodulators recovers its own particular colour-difference signal only, and ignores the other. This is because the injected sub-carrier to a given demodulator (say the $(R' - Y')$ circuit) has a phase appropriate to that demodulator only. It is 90° out of phase with the sub-carrier appropriate to the unwanted modulation-product (in this case the $(B' - Y')$ component) so that the latter yields no output at all. The converse is the case with the other demodulator.

Before exploring this point further, however, it is very instructive to consider a simple circuit capable of producing a double-sideband suppressed-carrier a.m. signal of the type discussed.

A simple outline circuit of a double push-pull balanced modulator is shown in Fig. 8.6. The colour-difference signal is fed to the control-grid of the phase splitter valve which passes on anti-phase signals to the control-grids of the balanced modulator pentodes V_1 and V_2. The a.c. coupled colour-difference signals are d.c. restored by keyed clamps which are operated during each line-blanking period by suitable line-repetition pulses.

The sub-carrier is simultaneously fed to the suppressor (g_3) grids of V_1 and V_2. Again the drives are in anti-phase; hence the expression 'double push-pull'.

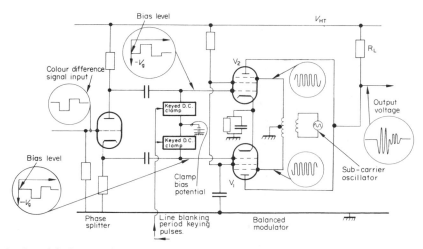

Fig. 8.6 *Simplified circuit diagram showing how a suppressed carrier double-sideband amplitude-modulated signal may be produced*

(*N.B.* The waveforms of Fig. 8.7 should be studied in conjunction with this circuit diagram.)
Note:
(i) The output from the balanced-modulator is referred to as the 'modulation-product' since it represents the sum total of the sidebands only. It is called a balanced modulator because the carrier component is cancelled out.
(ii) The NTSC chrominance signal is formed by adding the outputs from two such balanced-modulators. These receive sub-carriers of equal frequency but in phase quadrature (see Fig. 8.8).

135

The mode of operation is best studied by reference to the waveforms in various parts of the circuit when a simple colour-difference signal is being handled.

A series of waveforms are shown in Fig. 8.7 for a section of a raster line passing through four vertical stripes. The first and fourth are shown as grey and the second and third are two colours which are assumed to produce colour-difference voltages of different amplitude and opposite polarity. The corresponding colour-difference signal inputs to V_2 and V_1 are shown at (d) and (e) respectively.

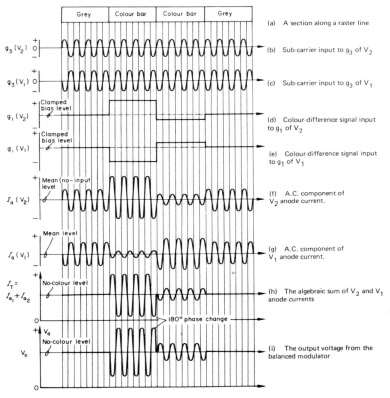

Fig. 8.7 *Waveforms applicable to the balanced-modulator shown in Fig. 8.6*

Each line-section should be studied in turn, by looking down the page at the waveforms which exist during that section.

Starting with the grey section on the left, the sine-waves at (b) and (c) show the antiphase sub-carrier inputs to the suppressor grids of V_2 and V_1. Since grey is present in the picture, the colour-difference signal input to the control-grids is zero. Assuming correctly balanced circuits, the a.c. components of the anode currents, shown at (f) and (g), are of equal amplitude but of opposite phase. Both are of course in phase with their respective suppressor grid sub-carrier voltage inputs. Since a

136

common anode load resistor is shared by the two valves, the sinusoidal anode currents at sub-carrier frequency, cancel out. The output voltage from the balanced modulator therefore rests at a 'no-colour' datum level determined by the circuit constants and the net bias to which the two valves are clamped.

During the next line-section a colour is present and the colour-difference signal is no longer zero. As seen at (d) and (e) the result is that V_2 control-grid receives a positive-going input whilst V_1 input is of equal amplitude but negative-going. The two anode current sine-waves shown at (f) and (g) are no longer equal. That of V_2 increases above the previous 'no-colour' amplitude and that of V_1 is correspondingly smaller.

The net a.c. current through the common anode load resistor, shown at (h), is the algebraic sum of the two unequal a.c. anode currents and since that of V_2 is the greater, the phase of the resultant sine-wave is the same as that of the V_2 current. The balanced modulator now delivers an output voltage of the form shown at (i).

On the third line-section, the hue is such that the colour-difference signal reverses its polarity. It is now the control-grid of V_1 which receives the positive-going input and V_2 grid has a corresponding negative-going input. The a.c. component of V_1 anode current now exceeds that of V_2 and the net output current through the anode load resistor now assumes the phase of V_1 anode current. At the transition from one colour-bar to the next therefore, the reversal in colour-difference signal polarity gives rise to a 180° phase shift in the output from the modulator. This is shown in the net output current waveform at (h) and the output voltage waveform at (i).

During the fourth line-section the picture detail is again 'grey' and the output voltage returns to the 'no-colour' level.

The balanced modulator is thus seen to give zero output when no colour is present in the transmitted picture and to respond to colour by delivering a sinusoidal output having an amplitude proportional to the amplitude of the colour-difference signal and a phase which switches through 180° when the colour-difference signal changes polarity.

Quadrature amplitude modulation

The chrominance signal is formed by combining the two suppressed carrier a.m. signals, corresponding to the two colour-difference signals. This is illustrated again in block diagram form in Fig. 8.8. Notice that the sub-carrier to the V balanced modulator is shown with a phase angle at $+90°$ to that fed to the U modulator. In the PAL system the V sub-carrier is switched $\pm90°$ line-by-line. When at $+90°$, the chrominance signal is identical to an NTSC signal but on the alternate lines, when the phase of the V sub-carrier is reversed, the signal is peculiar to the PAL system only. In this book, for convenience, the alternate lines are referred to as 'NTSC-lines' and 'PAL-lines'.

For the present, the chrominance signal will be considered with the V sub-carrier phased as for the 'NTSC-lines', at $+90°$ relative to the $+U$ reference axis. The added complication of the alternate 'PAL-lines' is discussed in the next chapter and this will be seen to be an easily understood modification, once the basic idea of Q.A.M. signals is clearly established.

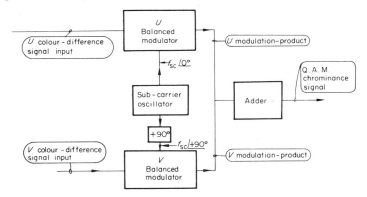

Fig. 8.8 *Showing in block diagram form how a quadrature amplitude modulated (i.e., Q.A.M.) chrominance signal may be produced by adding the outputs from two balanced modulators (e.g., of the form shown in Fig. 8.6)*

Figure 8.8 shows the outputs of the two balanced modulators being combined in an adding circuit. At its simplest this could be done by using two balanced modulators of the form shown in Fig. 8.6, connected to the same anode load resistor. The total current through the resistor would then be the algebraic sum of the two currents. When the diagrams of chrominance signals which follow in this chapter have been studied, the nature of the output voltage which results from this 'sum-current' will be seen. In practice, the two modulators may be followed by separate buffer amplifiers which share a common anode load resistor across which the Q.A.M. signal is then formed.

Practical Q.A.M. systems often employ two four-diode double-balanced ring modulators, working with transistor input and output circuitry. Complete circuits are not however included at this stage where the aim is to achieve a clear mental picture of the nature of Q.A.M. signals, rather than to make a detailed study of circuitry capable of producing such signals.

Q.A.M. chrominance signals

A series of four sets of diagrams now follows in which the two suppressed-carrier signals (referred to as modulation-products), are added to form the corresponding chrominance signal. The two sine-waves drawn to represent the two modulation-products, have amplitudes which are proportional to the weighted $(B' - Y')$ and $(R' - Y')$ colour-difference signals. Thus one is proportional to U, where $U = 0.493(B' - Y')$, and the other to V, where $V = 0.877(R' - Y')$. In common with normal practice, the phasors representing the modulation-products, are themselves labelled U and V. It will be observed that the symbols U and V are therefore used

138

both to describe the weighted colour-difference signals directly *and* to show the amplitude of the r.f. chrominance signal modulation-products which represent these colour-difference signals. This can be confusing and it is important to be clear about what it is that is being discussed at any given time. It is, however, the relative amplitudes of the two component modulation-products (as well as their polarities) which determines the character of a chrominance signal and since there is direct proportionality between the amplitudes of the modulation-products and the colour-difference signals they represent, it is perhaps reasonable to use the same symbols for both.

In the four sets of diagrams to be studied, four different arbitrarily chosen hues are considered. As established earlier, each modulation-product may have one of two possible phases, depending upon the polarity of the modulating colour-difference signal it represents. When $(B' - Y')$ is positive, the U modulation-product has a phase angle of $0°$ and this changes to $180°$ when $(B' - Y')$ is negative. On 'NTSC-lines' the phase angles for the V modulation-product are $+90°$ when $(R' - Y')$ is positive and $270°$ when $(R' - Y')$ is negative.

This gives four possible combinations of U and V phase angles. It is very instructive to look at an example of each of the four possibilities. This is done in the four diagrams; Figs. 8.9, 8.10, 8.11, and 8.12.

To allow attention to be concentrated upon the effect which the polarities of the U and V colour-difference signals have upon the phases of the two modulation-products—and in turn upon the phase of the chrominance signal itself—the amplitudes of the colour-difference signals are held constant for the four hues considered. The amplitudes of the U and V modulation-products (which are sine-waves when an unchanging colour is being scanned) are therefore constant in the four sets of diagrams and only their phases are changed. For convenience, these amplitudes have been chosen arbitrarily as 0.2 for U and 0.4 for V.

The first diagram, Fig. 8.9, deals with the case when both colour-difference signal voltages are positive, which would be true for a purple hue. For this diagram it follows that the amplitudes and signs of the colour-difference signals $(B' - Y')$ and $(R' - Y')$ are such that:

$$U = 0.493(B' - Y') = +0.2$$
$$V = 0.877(R' - Y') = +0.4$$

Since $(B' - Y')$ is positive, the U modulation-product at (b) is in phase with the system reference phase scale shown at (a). Similarly, since $(R' - Y')$ is positive, the V modulation-product at (c) has a phase which leads the reference phase by $90°$.

At (d) the chrominance signal is shown. This is arrived at graphically by the simple addition of the U and V components at (b) and (c). This resultant signal, being the sum of two sine-waves of equal frequency, is still sinusoidal. Its phase relative to the system reference has a leading angle. This shows up at (d) since the first positive sine-wave peak lies to the left of (hence occurs 'sooner than') the $90°$ point on the reference scale at (a).

139

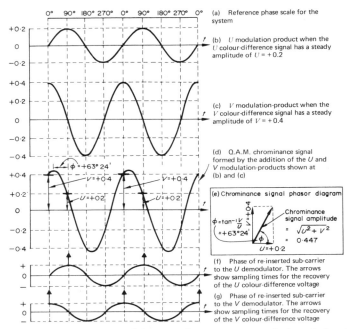

Fig. 8.9 *Formation of Q.A.M. chrominance signals (purple hue)*

The numerical values of both this leading phase angle, and the peak amplitude of the chrominance signal are both easily obtained from the phasor diagram shown at (e), from which it will be seen that $\phi = +63°\ 24'$ and the amplitude is 0·447.

Finally, the all important matter of the recovery from the chrominance signal of the individual U and V colour-difference signal voltages, must be considered.

At (f) a sine-wave is drawn representing the re-inserted sub-carrier component which must be fed to the U synchronous demodulator in the receiver. This must *always* have a phase lying along the $+U$ axis. It is most important to note that this has to be so, whatever the polarity of the U colour-difference signal, or, expressed in another way, it has to be so whether the U modulation-product is at 0° or 180°. Similarly, the re-inserted sub-carrier to the V demodulator, represented by a sine-wave at (g), must always have a phase angle of $+90°$ relative to the reference $+U$ axis, and this must be true whether the V modulation-product has a phase of $+90°$ or $+270°$. This point will be clearly seen when the next three diagrams are looked at. It is not so evident in this diagram because here both the U and V colour-difference signals have positive values and the corresponding U and V modulation-products have phases which are identical to the re-inserted sub-carriers at (f) and (g).

Looking upwards from the positive peaks of the re-inserted carrier at (f) to the chrominance signal at (d), it will be seen that at these points the latter has an amplitude of $+0·2$, i.e., has an amplitude equal to that of the U modulation-product shown at

140

(b). Examination of the diagrams shows that this must be so, since at these points the *V* signal is passing through zero and is therefore making no contribution to the amplitude of the Q.A.M. chrominance signal.

Similarly, sampling the chrominance signal at points corresponding to the positive peaks of the *V* re-inserted sub-carrier shown at (g), allows the *V* amplitude of 0·4 to be recovered, since here the *U* component at (b) is passing through zero and making no contribution to the chrominance signal's amplitude.

Sampling on each positive sub-carrier peak in this way, allows a succession of equal voltages to be read-off throughout the width of a uniform piece of colour information along a line (e.g., through a colour-bar). The demodulator output circuit includes a low-pass filter and this 'smooths' the successive output voltages (which are pulses at sub-carrier frequency), to give a steady voltage representing the original colour-difference voltage.

The principle of Q.A.M. signal demodulation is clearly demonstrated by the diagrams. A sub-carrier which is in phase with the original suppressed-carrier of one of the modulation-products, must automatically be 90° out of phase with the sub-carrier applicable to the other modulation-product. As already established and now demonstrated in a different way, a reintroduced carrier which is 90° out of phase with the original suppressed carrier produces no information from a suppressed carrier signal. Hence if the Q.A.M. chrominance signal is fed to two synchronous

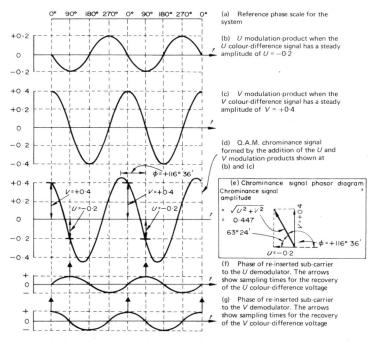

Fig. 8.10 *Formation of Q.A.M. chrominance signals (orange hue)*

141

demodulators receiving re-inserted sub-carriers mutually at 90°, each demodulator delivers only information from the modulation product for which the sub-carrier has the correct phase, and no information at all about the other modulation-product. For example the demodulator receiving inputs corresponding to (d) and (f) delivers *U* information but not *V* information, whilst the demodulator receiving (d) and (g) yields *V* information and not *U*.

It should be noted that in most synchronous demodulator circuits the re-inserted sub-carriers have relatively much greater amplitudes than the chrominance signals. The sub-carrier sketches at (f) and (g) are essentially there to indicate phases and not amplitudes.

The diagrams in Fig. 8.10 correspond to an orange hue which gives rise to a negative value for the *U* colour-difference signal (i.e., −0·2) and a positive value (+0·4) for the *V* signal. The phase angles of the *U* and *V* modulation-products are therefore +180° and +90° respectively.

Adding these gives the chrominance signal shown at (d). The phasor diagram at (e) shows that the chrominance phasor is now in the second quadrant with a phase angle of +116° 36′ (i.e., 180° − 63° 24′) relative to the reference axis and an amplitude which is again 0·447. The leading phase angle is also evident from (d). This is seen

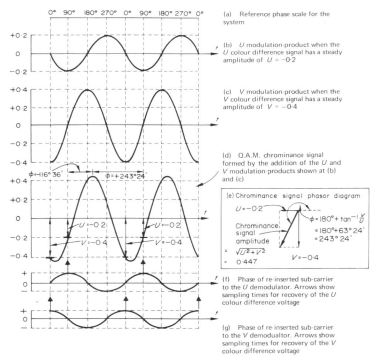

Fig. 8.11 *Formation of Q.A.M. chrominance signals (green hue)*

by looking at the positive peaks of (d) and comparing these with the 90° points on the reference scale at (a).

Once again the re-inserted sub-carriers are shown at (f) and (g). These, as explained above, have the same phases as in Fig. 8.9. Examination of the chrominance signal at (d), at the sampling points indicated for the U and V signals, shows that the correct values of -0.2 and $+0.4$ are recovered.

The green hue represented in Fig. 8.11 gives rise to negative voltages for both the $(B' - Y')$ and the $(R' - Y')$ colour-difference signals, i.e., $U = -0.2$ and $V = -0.4$. These in turn cause the U and V modulation-products to have phases relative to the reference axis of 180° and 270° respectively.

The chrominance signal is shown at (d) and the appropriate phasor diagram is at (e). The chrominance signal phasor is now in the third quadrant, with a phase angle which is at $+243° 24'$ relative to the $+U$ axis. This phase angle may again be seen by comparing (d) with the reference scale at (a). A useful method of deducing the phase angle from the sine-wave sketches is to look at the first positive half cycle of the chrominance signal and measure the angular displacement between this point and the first 90° point to the right of it on the reference scale at (a). All angles are best thought of as leading angles and then no confusion arises. By convention phasor diagrams are measured in an anti-clockwise direction for positive angles.

The fourth case is shown in Fig. 8.12 where a bluish-green hue gives rise to

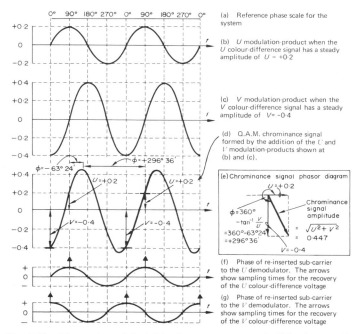

Fig. 8.12   Formation of Q.A.M. chrominance signals (bluish-green hue)

143

positive $(B' - Y')$ and negative $(R' - Y')$ voltages. These in turn cause the U and V modulation-products to have phase angles of $0°$ and $270°$ respectively.

The phasor diagram now shows the chrominance signal phasor to be in the fourth quadrant at an angle of $296° \ 36'$.

The U and V re-inserted sub-carrier phases are shown at (f) and (g). Sampling the chrominance signal at (d) at the points indicated by the arrows on (f) and (g), shows once again that the correct relative amplitudes and polarities of the original colour-difference signals are recovered.

It now remains to extend the concept of Q.A.M. chrominance signals to include the added complication of the PAL modification to the basic NTSC system.

9

Chrominance Signals: Principles of PAL Quadrature Modulation and PAL-S Demodulation

PAL Q.A.M. chrominance signals

In the PAL system the phase of the V modulation-product is inverted line by line. One line is of the form already discussed in Figs. 8.9 to 8.12 but on alternate lines the V signal is switched in phase by 180° (i.e., from $+90°$ to $+270°$ when $(R' - Y')$ is positive and from $+270°$ to $+90°$ when $(R' - Y')$ is negative).

In studying the effects of this it is advisable to start off by establishing the form of the chrominance signal on the NTSC-line and then to look at the effect of inverting the V component on the alternate PAL-line. This is done in Fig. 9.1 where the same colour signal is considered as in Fig. 8.9. Here the purple hue causes both the $(B' - Y')$ and the $(R' - Y')$ colour-difference signals to be positive. The corresponding U and V modulation-products shown in full-line at (b) and (c), have phases of 0° and $+90°$, with amplitudes of 0·2 and 0·4 respectively. The full-line waveform at (d) shows the corresponding chrominance signal for the NTSC-line.

The dotted sine-wave at (c) then shows the inverted V modulation-product on the alternate PAL-line. When this is added to the U signal at (b), the chrominance signal changes to the form shown by the dotted waveform at (d).

At (e) the corresponding phasor diagram for the chrominance signal is sketched. On the NTSC-line the phase angle ϕ is $+63° 24'$, changing to $-63° 24'$ on PAL-lines. These phase angles are also shown at (d).

In general, to deduce chrominance signal phase angles, the NTSC-line phasor angle should first be expressed as a positive angle relative to the $+U$ reference axis, and then the PAL-line phasor angle is simply the negative of the NTSC-line angle. The effect of inverting the V component on PAL-lines is to switch the chrominance phasor to the other side of the x axis (e.g., from the first to the fourth quadrants; the second to the third, the third to the second, and the fourth to the first).

It must be noted that this is not the same thing as switching the NTSC-line phasor by 180°. For example, in Fig. 9.1(e) switching the NTSC-line phasor through 180° gives an angle of $(63° 24' + 180°) = +243° 24'$. Expressed as a negative angle this is $(360° - 243° 24') = 116° 36'$, which is quite different from the true PAL-line phasor angle of $-63° 24'$. The reason for this is not hard to see. An NTSC-line phasor is the vector sum of the U and V components and inverting *it* is equivalent to inverting *both* the U and the V components, whereas on true PAL-lines it is only the V component which is inverted.

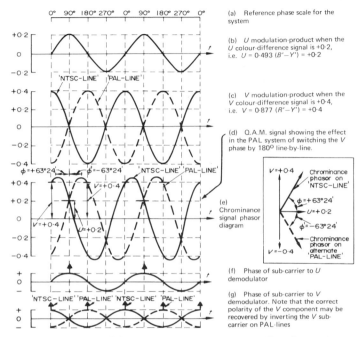

Fig. 9.1 *Formation of the Q.A.M. chrominance signal in the PAL system*

The converse is also obviously true; inverting a PAL-line phasor does not produce an NTSC-line phasor. In some PAL demodulating arrangements, recovery of the V component involves switching the PAL-line phasor through 180° and it is necessary to realize that this involves the inversion of both the U and the V components. This point is taken up again later in the chapter.

Chrominance signal demodulation in simple PAL receivers

In a Simple-PAL (usually known as a PAL-S) receiver, the chrominance signal is fed from the chrominance band-pass amplifier directly to the U and V synchronous demodulators which then extract the amplitudes of the U and V modulation-products from the Q.A.M. signal.

In a Delay-line (i.e., PAL-D) receiver there is an additional circuit between the chrominance amplifier and the demodulators. This has the function of separating the individual U and V r.f. modulation-products from the Q.A.M. chrominance signal and then these two r.f. signals go forward alone to their respective demodulators. The relative performance of these two systems is discussed later, but in this chapter only the PAL-S arrangement is considered.

Referring still to Fig. 9.1, it will be seen that inverting the V modulation-product does not change the position of its zero points. It follows that recovery of the U component is accomplished by sampling on the positive peaks of the re-inserted U sub-carrier in the same way as before, since at these points the V modulation-product makes no contribution to the chrominance signal's amplitude on either 'NTSC-lines' or 'PAL-lines'.

Recovery of the V component is a different matter. On NTSC-lines the situation is unchanged and the re-inserted sub-carrier to the V demodulator must have a phase of $+90°$ relative to the reference axis. On PAL-lines, however, a study of the chrominance signal at (d) shows that the correct value for the V component (which in this example is $+0.4$), is only obtained if the sampling points are shifted by $180°$. This is quite logical since the inversion of the transmitted V modulation product on PAL-lines creates the same effect on *this one component* as a phase shift of $180°$. To compensate for this the re-inserted sub-carrier may be switched by $180°$ on PAL-lines.

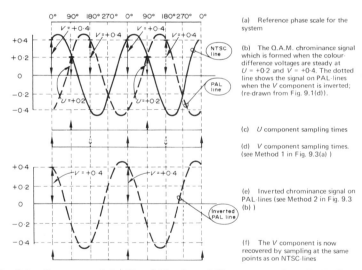

Fig. 9.2 *Recovery of the U and V colour-difference signals in PAL-S receivers*

Note:
(i) The U component may be recovered by sampling the chrominance signal at the points shown at (c), on both 'NTSC-lines' and 'PAL-lines'.
(ii) The V component may be recovered by two methods:
    Method 1 The sampling points may be switched by $180°$ on PAL-lines as shown at (d) (see also the block diagram in Fig. 9.3(a)).
    Method 2 The chrominance signal may be inverted on 'PAL-lines' as shown at (e), in which case the re-inserted sub-carrier has the same phase on both 'NTSC-lines' and 'PAL-lines', i.e., the sampling points are the same on both lines, as shown at (f) (see also the block diagram in Fig. 9.3(b)).

147

When this is done, the alternate NTSC- and PAL-lines both yield the same output voltage. The U component makes no contribution to the output since, as shown at (b), it is passing through zero at the sampling points marked by the arrows at (g).

Line-by-line phase switching (by $\pm 90°$ relative to the reference axis), of the re-inserted sub-carrier to the V demodulator, is not the only way of recovering the V component from a PAL-type signal. An alternative method is to leave the phase of the re-inserted sub-carrier to the V demodulator constant at $+90°$ and then to invert the chrominance signal itself on the alternate PAL-lines.

The effect of this is illustrated in Fig. 9.2 in which at (b) the chrominance signal discussed in Fig. 9.1 is re-drawn. At (e) the dotted PAL-line from (b) is shown inverted. It will be observed that the V component may be recovered by sampling this line with the same phase of re-inserted sub-carrier as is necessary to recover V from the alternate NTSC-lines shown in full-line at (b), i.e., with a sub-carrier having a phase of $+90°$ relative to the reference axis.

To sum up, the Q.A.M. chrominance signal shown at (b) is fed direct to the U demodulator which also receives a re-inserted sub-carrier with a phase of $0°$. As seen by looking upwards from the U sampling points shown at (c), the U information is then read off from both NTSC-lines and PAL-lines.

Meanwhile the V component may be recovered either by shifting the phase of the re-inserted sub-carrier to the V demodulator by $180°$ on PAL-lines (which means that this sub-carrier has a line-by-line phase alternation, relative to the $+U$ reference axis, of $\pm 90°$), or by leaving the sub-carrier phase constant at $+90°$ and inverting the chrominance signal on PAL-lines.

These two methods of demodulation are both known as 'Simple PAL'. The circuit arrangements are shown in block diagram form in Fig. 9.3.

Phase errors and their effect with NTSC signals

If, due to phase shift either in the transmission path or in the receiver itself, the relative phases of the chrominance signal and the reference sub-carrier burst are not the same on arrival at the receiver chrominance signal demodulators as they were at the transmitter, a normal NTSC-type Q.A.M. system renders an incorrect hue. This is illustrated in Fig. 9.4. The waveform at (b) is a repeat of Fig. 8.9(d), which represents a Q.A.M. chrominance signal resulting from the addition of U and V modulation-products of $+0.2$ and $+0.4$ respectively. At (d) and (e) in Fig. 9.4 the U and V re-inserted sub-carriers are shown. These allow the recovery of the correct U and V amplitudes if the signal arrives free from phase error.

At (c) the same chrominance signal is re-drawn, shifted in phase by approximately $+20°$ so that it is now at $+83° 24'$, instead of $+63° 24'$, relative to the system reference axis. This simulates the arrival at the detector of the chrominance signal and the sub-carrier burst with a relative phase error of $+20°$. For convenience the re-inserted sub-carriers are shown with precisely the correct phases relative to the original suppressed carriers and the phase error is 'lumped' against the chrominance

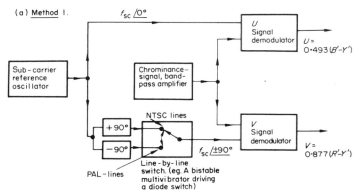

Fig. 9.3(a) *'Simple-PAL' chrominance signal demodulator arrangement, using a ±90° switched sub-carrier reference oscillator input to the V demodulator*

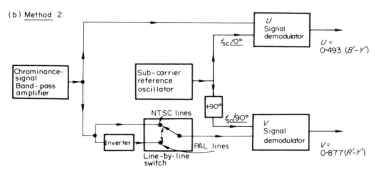

Fig. 9.3(b) *'Simple-PAL' chrominance signal demodulator arrangement in which the chrominance signal input to the V demodulator is inverted on alternate lines and the reference oscillator input is therefore held constant at +90°*

signal which in this example is shifted 20° to the left of its correct position. Note that a movement to the left on the diagram indicates that the chrominance signal has *advanced* in phase relative to the reference axis and the phase shift is described as being positive (i.e., +20° in this example).

Sampling this signal at the U and V points shown, now yields incorrect values for the U and V amplitudes. At the moments of sampling in no case is the extracted information representative of one original suppressed carrier modulation-product only. This is because the sampling points no longer correspond to places where one of the two original modulation-products passes through zero. Reference back to Fig. 8.9 will confirm this. Instead of $U = 0.2$ and $V = 0.4$ the recovered values are approximately $U = +0.05$ and $V = +0.45$. The phasor diagrams at (f) and (g) in Fig. 9.4 shows the result of this. The chrominance phasor has moved 'towards red' and 'away from blue' so that the reproduced hue is not correct.

149

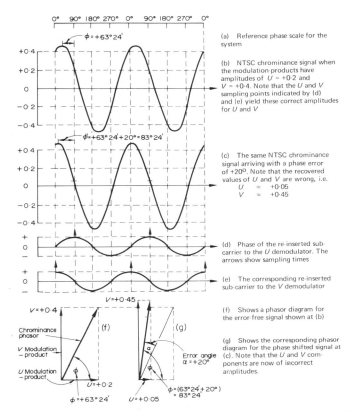

Fig. 9.4   Showing the effect of phase distortion on an NTSC signal

The chrominance signal at (b) is assumed to arrive as shown at (c), with a phase error of $+20°$ relative to the $+(B' - Y')$ reference axis. The original near-magenta hue of (b) is reproduced at the receiver as a hue with too high a red content.

Differential phase errors and their effect with PAL signals

In Fig. 9.5 the corresponding signal for the PAL system is studied. At (b) the original 'error-free' signal is shown, but at (c) both the NTSC- and the PAL-lines are re-drawn bearing the same $+20°$ phase error as was postulated for the NTSC signal of Fig. 9.4.

Notice now, however, that whereas on the NTSC-line the recovered V signal is greater than it should be and the U smaller, the reverse is true on the PAL-line. In a PAL-S-type receiver the effect of this will be that on a given transmitted hue any pair of time-sequential scanning lines on the raster, will show complementary errors. In this example the NTSC-line will be too red and the PAL-line too blue. The eye averages these out optically and the viewer appears to see the correct hue.

In this diagram it is assumed that demodulation of the V component is achieved by switching the phase of the re-inserted sub-carrier by 180° on PAL-lines. This corresponds to Method 1 of Fig. 9.3(a).

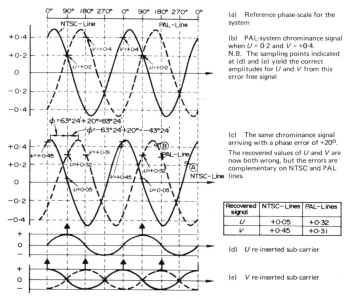

Fig. 9.5 *Showing the effect of phase distortion on a PAL signal*

The alternative method of inverting the chrominance signal on PAL-lines and leaving the phase of the re-inserted sub-carrier constant at $+90°$ (i.e., Method 2 of Fig. 9.3(b)) is shown for the same chrominance signal in Fig. 9.6. At (b) the PAL-line is shown inverted (see B′); as can be verified by comparison with (c) in Fig. 9.5 (see B). The same values as before are recovered for V, i.e., $V = +0.45$ on NTSC-lines and $V = +0.31$ on PAL-lines. These, with the corresponding U amplitudes of $+0.05$ and $+0.32$, yield the complementary 'too red' and 'too blue' hues which the eye averages to produce the impression of the near-magenta hue, originally transmitted.

It is this ability to negate the effect upon the reproduced hue of phase distortion, that constitutes the advantage of the PAL system over the original NTSC system.

Phasor diagrams

Also shown on Fig. 9.6 are a series of phasor diagrams which help to give perspective to these studies. At (d) and (e) are shown the original error-free chrominance phasors for the NTSC- and PAL-lines. The U components derived from these two phasors are clearly identical.

If the V component were recovered from (e) however, it would not be correct. Its amplitude would be right but obviously (since the transmitted V component is inverted) the polarity would be negative instead of positive.

151

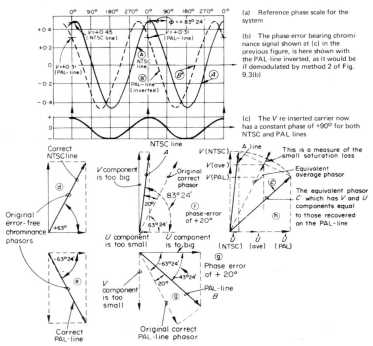

Fig. 9.6 *Showing the effect of phase distortion on a PAL signal*

At (b) the PAL-line shown as B in Fig. 9.5(c) is inverted (to form B′) for application to the *V*-demodulator in a PAL-S receiver using Method 2 of Fig. 9.3(b).

Phasor diagrams

(d) and (e) Show the NTSC-line and PAL-line phasors of the error-free signal shown at (b) in Fig. 9.5.

(f) and (g) Show the corresponding phasors when a phase distortion of +20° is present.

(h) Shows the NTSC-line phasor (A), together with an imaginary NTSC-type phasor C compounded of the *U* and *V* components which would yield the same hue in an NTSC receiver as the PAL-line phasor B does in a PAL-S receiver.

As pointed out earlier, the effect of inverting the PAL-line phasor (using Method 2 of Fig. 9.3(b)) *does not* produce a phasor which lies along the NTSC-line phasor. Looking at Fig. 9.6(e) and (d) it is clear that inverting the PAL phasor, which implies shifting the sine-wave by 180°, places the phasor in the second quadrant. However, the *V* component of this inverted phasor *is* equal to the *V* component of the NTSC-line phasor, since both components lie along the +*V* axis. In a similar way, if the re-inserted sub-carrier is phase shifted by 180° in order to sample a *non-inverted* PAL-line (using Method 1 of Fig. 9.3(a)), this is equivalent to moving 180° along the *V* sine-wave, i.e., equivalent to looking at the *V* component produced by the PAL-line phasor when this phasor has moved round by 180° to rest in the second quadrant.

The phasors at (f) and (g) show the corresponding NTSC- and PAL-lines for the +20° phase error condition. It is easy to be misled by combined phasor diagrams which are intended to show the net effect of the reception in a PAL receiver of a pair of successive lines such as (f) and (g), which yield complementary hue errors.

Such a combination is illustrated at (h) but it must be noted that inverting the PAL-line phasor B from (g) does not produce the phasor marked C in (h). Inverting the phasor at (g) places B in the second quadrant. The V component of this, as recovered by the demodulator, is then $+0.31$. Simultaneously U is being recovered; *not* from the inverted PAL-line, but from the phasor as it stands at (g). Hence from these two demodulators the recovered components are $U = +0.32$ and $V = +0.31$.[1] The significance of the phasor C drawn at (h) is now apparent. This is the *equivalent* chrominance phasor which (when treated to normal NTSC-line demodulation) would yield the same U and V amplitudes—and thus create the same hue—as the PAL-line at (g) yields in the PAL-S receiver.

Since the two successive equivalent NTSC-lines are now portrayed on one phasor diagram, it is meaningful to draw a third 'average' phasor between the two. This will be seen to lie at the same angle (in this example $+63° 24'$) as the original transmitted chrominance NTSC-line phasor. This now indicates, in diagram form, the concept of having two hue errors on successive lines, which, because they are represented by phasors equally spaced on opposite sides of the true phasor direction, give rise to hues which seen together create the optical illusion of the correct hue. The average phasor can be seen to be shorter in length than the original error-free phasor and this implies a small loss of saturation. In all the preceding examples the chrominance signal has been assumed to suffer only phase distortion, so that the chrominance phasors drawn have the same length, i.e., their tips lie on a circle having the origin as the centre. The *average phasor's* tip lies on a chord drawn between the two phasors of which it forms the average, and the distance between the chord and the arc is a measure of the loss of saturation. Clearly, the larger the phase error the greater the loss of saturation.

To further clarify the significance of chrominance phasor diagrams and to summarize the demodulation process in a PAL-S receiver, the same phase-distorted chrominance signal is represented again in Fig. 9.7. The phasors for the NTSC- and PAL-lines are here shown side by side to simulate the time-sequential arrival of these two chrominance signals at the receiver.

The NTSC-line at (a) is passed to both demodulators and these deliver the colour-difference signal output voltages which are defined in amplitude by the V and U rectangular co-ordinates into which the phasor at (a) may be resolved. For the given signal both the U and V colour-difference signal outputs from the demodulators are positive. These are shown at (c) and it is important to remember that these are simply voltages which, in this particular example, differ only in amplitude. As was stressed earlier, phase has no meaning after demodulation. It is simply voltage levels which are being discussed. These may be either positive or negative at any given time, and thus may differ in amplitude and/or polarity. Before demodulation their representative components (i.e., the modulation-products), in the r.f. chrominance signals are

[1] It happens that in this example the U and V components on the PAL-line are virtually equal. This is because the chrominance phasor is at $-43° 24'$, i.e., very nearly $-45°$. There is no other significance in this near equality of amplitudes.

sinusoidal functions for which 'phasor' diagrams *are* valid and meaningful. The demodulation process extracts the relative amplitudes and polarities of the original *weighted* colour-difference signal voltages from the r.f. sine-waves portrayed by the phasors.

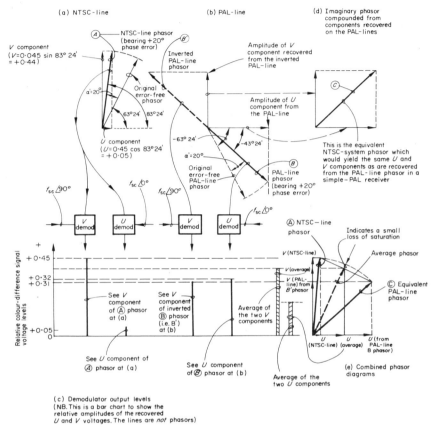

Fig. 9.7 *Phasor diagrams further illustrating the demodulation in a Simple-PAL receiver of the phase distorted chrominance signal shown in Figs. 9.5 and 9.6*

At (b) the PAL-line phasor is drawn. This is passed, with its phase unchanged, to the *U* demodulator which extracts the appropriate amplitude of the *U* component. The latter, as shown at (b), still lies along the $+U$ axis. This must be so since the formation of the transmitted PAL-line did not involve any change in the *U* component, i.e., only the *V* component is inverted, *not* the *U*.

Also shown at (b), is the PAL-line phasor swung through 180° (i.e., inverted) and it is this phasor (B′) which represents the chrominance signal fed to the *V* demodulator on the PAL-line. (The demodulation method here considered is that

154

shown as Method 2 in Fig. 9.3(b).) From this inverted phasor the V demodulator then extracts a positive colour-difference signal voltage of amplitude defined by the V vectorial component of B' shown at (b). The recovered U and V amplitudes are again portrayed at (c). It is possible to see from these successive pairs of U and V voltage levels, how the averages for the pair of lines may be computed.

The *imaginary* phasor C, shown at (d), is compounded of the U component from the PAL-line phasor B, and the V component from the inverted PAL-line phasor B'. This phasor C, though having no electrical counterpart in the incoming signal, does, however, show what NTSC chrominance phasor would produce (in an NTSC receiver) the same hue as is produced by the PAL-line in a PAL-S receiver. By placing this alongside the phasor A in the combined diagram at (e), the average equivalent phasor already discussed is then determined. This phasor has U and V components of amplitudes equal to the U and V averages for the two successive lines.

Finally it must be stressed that there is no electrical justification for drawing this 'average phasor' when describing the PAL-S demodulation process. Its significance, as stated, is merely to show the imaginary NTSC-type chrominance phasor which *alone* would produce the same visual sensation as is produced by the two hues seen on the screen which result from the two existing successive chrominance phasors. These two occur in time sequence but the adding process is due to the eye's action in giving a single response to two adjacent but different pieces of colour information and not due to the electrical summation of the two phasors.

This last point leads directly to the concept of designing a receiver in which the two successive chrominance signal lines *are* added electrically. Instead of two successive raster lines being of different—though complementary—hues, both will now be of the original correct hue.

There are distinct advantages in this electronic averaging of pairs of lines bearing complementary hue errors. The PAL-S receiver is satisfactory for small phase errors but beyond a certain order of error (i.e., about $\pm 5°$ or so) the eye is not completely deceived and visible evidence of error conditions becomes apparent to the viewer. It is aggravated because on the two successive interlaced rasters of one complete picture, lines of a given hue error are adjacent to one another in pairs.

Though one pair of space-sequential lines is complementary in hue to the next pair, the eye is not uniformly sensitive over the visible spectrum and a difference in relative intensity is noticed. In severe cases a pattern of horizontal bars, sometimes known as Hanover bars, or referred to as Venetian blinds, is seen.

In Delay-line (PAL-D) receivers, the electronic averaging of time-sequential lines eliminates this effect. Before dealing with their performance under error conditions, however, it is first necessary to understand how the system works when the incoming signal is normal and the next chapter opens with a study of the basic principles of PAL-D decoders.

10

Chrominance Signals: Basic Principles of PAL-D Demodulation

For the purpose of introducing the principle of PAL-D (i.e., Delay-line PAL) type receivers it is advisable to specify a given polarity for both the U and V colour-difference signals and then to follow the passage of the corresponding chrominance signal and its component modulation-products through the system. It is necessary to stress the need to watch polarities carefully because the line-by-line inversion of the V modulation-product in the PAL system causes this component to bear the opposite sign on PAL-lines to that designated by the polarity of the original $(R' - Y')$ voltage.

For convenience, the same arbitrary hue is used as in Fig. 9.1 where $U = 0.2$ and $V + 0.4$. To begin with, however, the amplitudes will be left out and the colour-difference signals merely recorded as each bearing a positive sign. On the NTSC-line the V modulation-product is at $+90°$ to the $+U$ axis but on the alternate PAL-line the V phase is switched to $-90°$. The corresponding phasor diagram is shown at (e) in Fig. 9.1. To describe the phasor diagram in symbols, 'j-notation' is convenient. The NTSC-line is then written as $(U + jV)$ and the PAL-line $(U - jV)$.[1] Note that these expressions are true only for hues which place the NTSC chrominance phasor in the first quadrant. To make the point clear Table 10.1 lists the symbolic description of chrominance phasors in the four quadrants.

By these expressions the chrominance phasor is described in terms of its two component modulation-product phasors and when specific values are given for U and V the amplitude and phase of the resultant chrominance phasor is then easily computed.[2]

Using this simple notation now allows the PAL-D receiver principle to be studied with a minimum of difficulty.

---

[1] The prefix '$+j$' written against a vector quantity indicates that the vector is at $+90°$ to the '$+x$' axis. Similarly the prefix $-j$ indicates that the vector is at $-90°$ to the $+x$ axis.

[2] Note that if, as is often done, the terms $+jV$ and $-jV$ are used to describe 'NTSC' and 'PAL' lines respectively, it is easy to become confused. For example, on greens the $+jV$ (NTSC) line produces a V phasor of $(-jV)$ and on the alternate $-jV$ (PAL) line the phasor is $(+jV)$. The descriptions 'NTSC-line' and 'PAL-line' avoid this confusion of meaning.

156

Table 10.1 Table showing symbolic expressions and corresponding quadrant positions of chrominance phasors on 'NTSC' and 'PAL' lines

Hue	'NTSC' line		'PAL' line	
	Chrominance phasor symbolic description	Quadrant in which phasor lies	Chrominance phasor symbolic description	Quadrant in which phasor lies
Purples	$U + jV$	1st	$U - jV$	4th
Red, orange, yellow	$-U + jV$	2nd	$-U - jV$	3rd
Greens	$-U - jV$	3rd	$-U + jV$	2nd
Cyan, blue	$U - jV$	4th	$U + jV$	1st

Fig. 10.1(a) shows the basic way in which the system works. Between the chrominance amplifier and the demodulator circuits, a delay-line and associated adding and subtracting circuits are interposed. The delay-line is designed to introduce a delay of one line period to the chrominance signal. (*N.B.* The actual delay is very slightly different from the line period of 64 μs for a reason which is explained when the delay-line itself is studied.)

The chrominance amplifier feeds the incoming chrominance signal three ways; to the adder, the subtractor, and the delay-line. The delay-line in turn feeds its output to both the adder and subtractor. The adder and subtractor circuits therefore receive

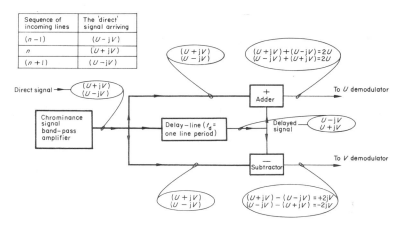

Fig. 10.1(a) *Showing the separation of the individual U and V modulation-products from a PAL chrominance signal, by the addition and subtraction of direct and delayed signal lines*

(i) When 'n' is the direct line: Adder output   = $+2U$
                                       Subtractor output = $+2jV$
(ii) When '$(n + 1)$' is the direct line: Adder output   = $+2U$
                                       Subtractor output = $-2jV$
It is assumed here that the delayed signal is subtracted from the direct signal. If the reverse were true (which is equally admissible) the subtractor would yield $\mp 2jV$ instead of $\pm 2jV$.

157

two signals simultaneously. These may be referred to at any given time as the *direct-line* and the *delayed-line*.

For the chosen hue, if the *present* incoming line is an NTSC-line, the signal entering the delay-line and also reaching the adder and subtractor, is $(U + jV)$. But the previous line must then have been the PAL-line $(U - jV)$ and this signal is simultaneously issuing from the delay-line.

The diagram should now be studied and the result of adding the two signals on the one hand, and subtracting them on the other, carefully noted. The upper of the pair of expressions in each balloon should be looked at when the 'NTSC-line' [i.e., in this example $(U + jV)$], is the direct-line.

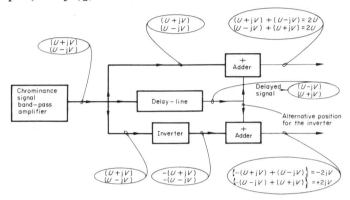

Fig. 10.1(b) *Showing a practical arrangement in which the subtractor is replaced by an adder preceded by an inverter*

(i) On line 'n':   Adder output = $+2U$; Subtractor output = $-2jV$
(ii) On line '$(n + 1)$':   Adder output = $+2U$; Subtractor output = $+2jV$

As an alternative arrangement the V component may be obtained by adding an inverted delayed signal to the direct signal. This would yield $\pm 2jV$ instead of $\mp 2jV$, and is therefore the practical equivalent of Fig. 10.1(a).

The result is very interesting. The addition of two picture lines (radiated in sequence but presented to the 'adder' simultaneously) yields a signal consisting of U information only; equal in amplitude to twice the amplitude of the chrominance signal's U modulation-product.

Conversely, the subtraction of the two lines produces a signal consisting only of V information, with an amplitude of twice that of the V modulation-product.

The next point to look at is the action on alternate lines. For the hue being discussed, the PAL-line chrominance signal is represented by $(U - jV)$. When this is the *direct-line* the delay-line must be delivering the previous 'NTSC-line' signal (i.e., $U + jV$). The lower of the two expressions in each balloon should now be studied. The adder still delivers the same output of $+2U$ but the *subtractor* now produces $-2V$.

This ingenious yet simple modification to the receiver thus recovers from the r.f. chrominance signal its two quadrature component parts. The output from the circuit consists of the two independent double-sideband suppressed-carrier r.f. signals, i.e., the *U* modulation-product and the line-by-line phase-inverted *V* modulation-product.

These two individual r.f. signals now go forward to their respective demodulators. As already made clear, each of these must also receive a re-inserted sub-carrier of correct phase to allow recovery of the colour-difference signal waveform.

It is evident that since it is no longer a Q.A.M. r.f. signal which is being handled, there is no longer an inescapable need for a synchronous demodulator capable of dealing with the Q.A.M.-type signal. In theory, the simple addition of a sub-carrier (which must *still* be of accurate frequency and phase), to its appropriate modulation-product and then the application of the now complete a.m. signal to a straightforward amplitude detector, would yield the colour-difference waveform.

In practice this method of demodulation is not favoured, partly because of the difficulty of maintaining an accurate constant 'no-colour' zero-voltage level, above and below which, the sometimes positive, and sometimes negative, colour-difference signal voltage, then varies.

This problem does not arise with the synchronous type detector circuits suitable for NTSC and PAL-S receivers because this no-colour zero-output is automatically established. These same synchronous demodulator circuits are therefore also used in PAL-D receivers, but this is no disadvantage since they are in any event uncomplicated and reliable circuits.

Instead of subtracting the delayed-line from the direct-line (or vice versa) to obtain the *V* component, the latter may equally well be extracted by adding an inverted direct-line to the delayed-line. This is illustrated in Fig. 10.1(b), where the same chrominance signal as before is considered. The simple equations showing the action on two successive incoming picture lines should be verified. The alternative to the latter method is to add an inverted delayed-line to the direct-line.

This study has appeared to show four distinctly different ways of obtaining the *V* modulation-product.

This is because 'subtraction' was first discussed as a separate single step; replaced in the last two methods by an 'inversion' of one signal before 'adding' it to the other. However, subtracting one sine-wave from another clearly necessarily involves the inversion of one of them. This corresponds to the practical application of the simple algebraic subtraction rule: 'change the sign in the bottom line and add'. It will be evident that the distinction is simply one of description of the operation which is carried out; either by using the one word 'subtractor' to embrace the complete circuit in which an inverter and adder may be discerned as parts, or by describing the action as being accomplished by two 'tandem' circuits which carry out the successive operations of inversion and addition. When studying practical examples of PAL-D decoder circuits it is necessary to have these considerations in mind.

To add perspective to the action of the arrangements shown in Fig. 10.1(a) and (b) the corresponding waveforms are depicted in Fig. 10.2.

At (b) the two successive chrominance signal waveforms are drawn for the NTSC- and PAL-lines. For convenience of identification these are labelled *A* and *B* respectively. If one of these (say A) is assumed to be issuing from the delay-line as the other arrives 'live' it is possible to add and subtract them to show the outputs produced by the adder and subtractor of Fig. 10.1(a). This is done at (f) where curve E is the result of adding A to B, and at (d) where curve C is the result of subtracting B from A.

One line later the position is reversed and it is B which issues from the delay-line and A is the incoming direct-line. Then B added to A gives E (as before), but subtracting A from B now yields D (as distinct from C).

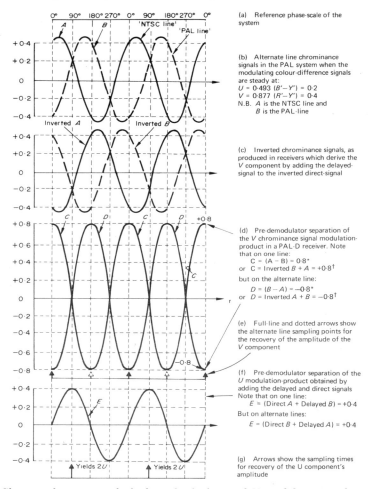

(a) Reference phase-scale of the system

(b) Alternate line chrominance signals in the PAL system when the modulating colour-difference signals are steady at:
$U = 0.493\ (B'-Y') = 0.2$
$V = 0.877\ (R'-Y') = 0.4$
N.B. A is the NTSC line and B is the PAL-line

(c) Inverted chrominance signals, as produced in receivers which derive the V component by adding the delayed-signal to the inverted direct-signal

(d) Pre-demodulator separation of the V chrominance signal modulation-product in a PAL-D receiver. Note that on one line:
$C = (A - B) = 0.8$*
or $C = $ Inverted $B + A = +0.8$†
but on the alternate line:
$D = (B - A) = -0.8$*
or $D = $ Inverted $A + B = -0.8$†

(e) Full-line and dotted arrows show the alternate line sampling points for the recovery of the amplitude of the V component

(f) Pre-demodulator separation of the U modulation-product obtained by adding the delayed and direct signals Note that on one line:
$E = ($Direct $A + $ Delayed $B) = +0.4$
But on alternate lines:
$E = ($Direct $B + $ Delayed $A) = +0.4$

(g) Arrows show the sampling times for recovery of the U component's amplitude

Fig. 10.2 *Showing the way in which the individual U and V modulation-products which are present in the chrominance signal are separated in a PAL-D receiver*

* Using the method shown in Fig. 10.1(a).
† Using the method shown in Fig. 10.1(b).

To show the corresponding action of the Fig. 10.1(b) arrangement, where an inverter and adder replace the subtractor to yield the V component, the A and B waveforms of (b) in Fig. 10.2 are shown inverted at (c).

The V component is then derived on one line by adding the inverted B waveform from (c) to A at (b) and on the next line by adding the inverted A from (c) to B from (b). These successive operations yield the waveforms shown at (d) as C and D respectively.

A study of the resulting 'output' waveforms at (f) and (d) confirms that:

(a) Adding a delayed-line to a direct-line produces an output of $2U$ (see (f)). This is obviously the logical outcome of adding two successive lines of chrominance information in the PAL system, since the V components on the two lines are in anti-phase and cancel out.

(b) Subtracting a delayed-line from a direct-line (or vice versa), or adding an inverted direct-line to a delayed-line (or vice versa) produces an output of $+2V$ on one line and $-2V$ on the next (see (d)). This again is logical since the U components on two successive lines are in-phase so that subtracting a PAL-line from an NTSC-line (or vice versa) must cause the cancellation of the U component.

Finally in Fig. 10.2 the question of recovery of the colour-difference signal amplitudes from the separated modulation-products which represent them, is considered. This clearly involves reading off the amplitudes of the r.f. waveforms shown at (d) and (f).

Once again, the concept of line-by-line sampling, at moments corresponding to the positive peaks of the two original suppressed carriers, is instructive. At (g) arrows are positioned below the 90° points of the reference phase-scale shown at the top of the page at (a). These correspond to the positive peaks of the $(B' - Y')$ sub-carrier and looking above these arrows at the E waveform shows that the 'read-off' amplitude is $+0.4$, i.e., is $+2U$, as expected. It should be noted that the waveform E is the *only* output from the adder of Fig. 10.1(a) (or the corresponding adder in Fig. 10.1(b)) so that shifting the sampling point to simulate a phase error in the re-inserted sub-carrier merely results in a lower amplitude of the $(B' - Y')$ voltage.

Similarly, at (e), arrows are positioned at points corresponding to the positive peaks of the original $(R' - Y')$ sub-carrier.

As established earlier when discussing the PAL-S arrangement, there are two ways of taking account of the line-by-line phase reversal of the original $(R' - Y')$ sub-carrier. One of these involves a line-by-line switching of the sampling point by 180°. The alternative is to leave the re-inserted sub-carrier constant in phase (i.e., at $+90°$ relative to the $+U$ axis) and to invert the chrominance signal modulation-product by a line-by-line switch.

The circuit arrangements for these two methods are shown in block diagram form in Fig. 10.3(a) and (b). These should be compared with the PAL-S block diagrams of Fig. 9.3(a) and (b). This will spot-light the essential difference between the two systems. In the PAL-S receiver it is the full Q.A.M. chrominance signal which goes forward to the synchronous demodulators, together with the appropriate re-inserted sub-carriers. In the PAL-D receiver the chrominance signal is 'taken apart' before

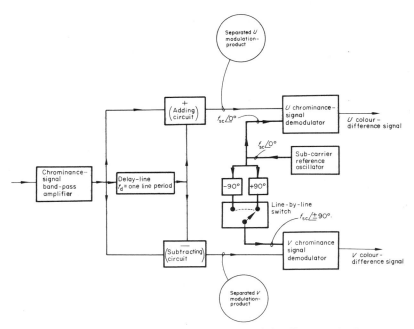

Fig. 10.3(a) *Chrominance signal demodulation in* delay-line *type PAL receivers: Method 1*

Here the reference oscillator input to the *V* Demodulator is switched by ±90° line-by-line.
Note: In this arrangement and the one opposite, the Subtractor may be replaced by an Adder preceded by an Inverter.
(This is shown in Fig. 10.1(b).)

reaching the demodulators and these each then receive only one of the two modulation-products; again with the appropriately phased re-inserted sub-carriers.

It will be observed that both systems finally yield the required colour-difference voltages. The PAL-D receiver differs in that it yields signals of twice the amplitude but of course this factor alone merely alters the relative amounts of gain needed between the demodulators and the c.r.t. in the two systems.

Another difference in the systems lies in their apparent maximum vertical resolution for colour-detail. With no phase error present, the PAL-S system is theoretically capable of describing as many different pieces of colour information down a vertical column as there are horizontal raster lines crossing the column. In the PAL-D system, where pairs of lines are of the same hue, the vertical resolution of colour-detail is reduced to one half that of the PAL-S value.

However, the eye is unable to discern colour-detail as fine as single raster lines and indeed, if it could, the chrominance bandwidth would need to be as wide as the monochrome bandwidth to transmit comparable colour-detail along horizontal lines. The available vertical resolution of colour-detail in the PAL-D system is therefore perfectly adequate to deal with the bandwidth restricted chrominance signal and this point of comparison does not represent a disadvantage of the PAL-D system.

162

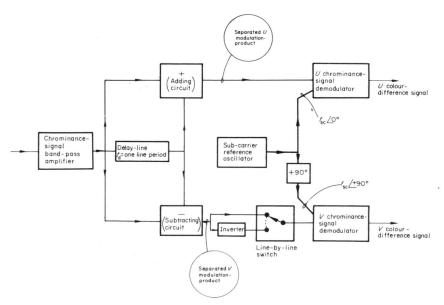

Fig. 10.3(b) *Chrominance signal demodulation in* delay-line *type PAL receivers: Method 2*

In this arrangement the reference oscillator input to the *V* Demodulator is held constant in phase, but the *V* component of the Chrominance Signal is inverted on alternate lines.

Except in so far as it is degraded by such influences as the Y-channel sub-carrier notch filter, the luminance resolution in both receivers is equal to that of normal monochrome receivers.[1]

As indicated earlier, however, it is in their relative performance under phase error conditions where the systems differ. The limitations of the PAL-S system have already been outlined. It is now necessary to examine the corresponding performance of the PAL-D receiver.

Phase-error correction in PAL-D receivers

As a basis for study, and to facilitate the easy comparison of the action of PAL-D and PAL-S receivers under phase-distortion conditions, the same signal as is shown in Figs. 9.5, 9.6, and 9.7 is considered.

The phasor diagrams in Fig. 10.4 allow the PAL-D receiver action to be studied. At (a) and (b) the original error-free NTSC- and PAL-lines are drawn. The signal represents a purple hue where the original colour-difference voltages are both positive and have relative amplitudes such that $U = +0.2$ and $V = +0.4$.

As established in the previous section, feeding the direct and delayed signals to

[1] For a full discussion of vertical and horizontal resolution in television receivers, see *Television Receiver Theory*, Vol. 1, by G. H. Hutson, published by Arnolds of London.

the adder yields an output r.f. signal in phase with the U component and equal in amplitude to the sum of the U components of two successive lines. Since no phase-distortion is present at (a) and (b), the adder therefore delivers a signal of amplitude $2 \times 0.2 = +0.4$ (i.e., $2U$).

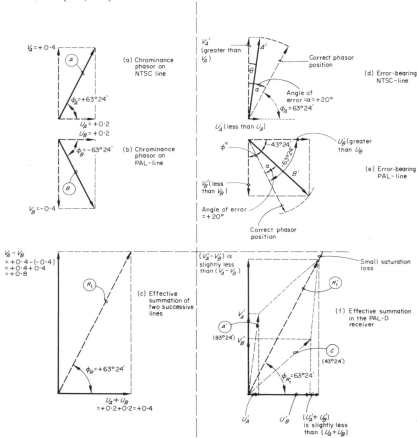

Fig. 10.4 *Showing the automatic phase-error cancelling action of a PAL delay-line receiver*

Similarly, the subtractor delivers an output equal in magnitude to the algebraic difference of the V components present on two successive lines. With no phase error present, this yields $+0.4 - (-0.4) = +0.8$.

At (c) the two separated r.f. modulation-products are shown as two phasors, one of amplitude $+0.8$ lying along the $+V$ axis and the other of amplitude $+0.4$ along the $+U$ axis.

It will be noticed that these phasors are drawn in full-line, whilst the equivalent (but non-existent) single chrominance signal phasor which would bear these two

164

quadrature components in an NTSC signal, is shown dotted as R_t. Conversely, at (a) and (b), the quadrature components are shown dotted and their resultant is in full-line. This is to emphasize the fact that before the delay-line process the U and V components have no separate existence and it is the combined chrominance signal which is being portrayed, but afterwards the Q.A.M. chrominance signal ceases to exist and the two quadrature components go forward as individual r.f. signals.

As will be appreciated from the work in the previous section, one line later the subtractor will yield $(V_B - V_A) = \{-0.4 - (+0.4)\} = -0.8$. To portray this the phasor diagram at (c) would have to be drawn with the V component pointing downwards. The equivalent NTSC phasor would then be dotted in at $-63° 24'$.

At (d) and (e) the same signal is shown bearing a phase distortion of $+20°$. These phasors were described in Figs. 9.6 and 9.7.

The adder now yields the sum of the two unequal U components U_A' and U_B' shown at (d) and (e). Similarly the subtractor yields the difference between the two unequal V components V_A' and V_B' and since the latter is a negative quantity this results in an output of $\{V_A' - (-V_B')\} = (V_A' + V_B')$.

The net U and V components are both smaller than they would be if no phase distortion were present. However, they still bear the same ratio to one another and hence—despite the chrominance signal phase error—the outputs from the U and V synchronous demodulators are still in the correct ratio and the reproduced hue is correct. The only effect of the phase error is a small loss of saturation due to the diminished amplitudes.

It is possible to demonstrate the validity of these conclusions in two ways; by scale drawing or by simple trigonometry.

At (f) in Fig. 10.4 the net outputs from the adder and subtractor are drawn as full-line phasors because they each represent the amplitudes of sine-waves which *actually exist* in a PAL-D receiver. The diagram is drawn to scale and the resultant R_t' is seen to have the same phase angle as the resultant R_t of the undistorted signal at (c). The length of R_t' is, however, slightly less than R_t and this demonstrates the small loss of saturation.

The unequal parts of the net U and V phasors may be identified as the rectangular co-ordinates of A' and C, where A' is the NTSC-line phasor from (d), and C the equivalent NTSC-type phasor which would yield the same U and V components as are recovered from the PAL-line in the PAL receiver.

The significance of the A' and C phasors was discussed in connection with Figs. 9.6 and 9.7. It was shown that in the PAL-S system, A' represents the line the information from which activates the c.r.t. on NTSC-lines and C is the corresponding equivalent phasor on the PAL-lines. Since these two phasors are representative of the actual reproduced hues on two successive lines they do have some individual meaning in the PAL-S receiver even though C has no electrical existence. However, in the PAL-D receiver, the c.r.t. is never activated by information from single lines but always from the effective sum of one NTSC- and one PAL-line. For this reason, the resultant phasor R'_t now truly represents the single equivalent NTSC-type chrominance phasor which would give rise to the hue *actually reproduced on the screen*.

In the PAL-D system, the averaging is done electrically and the light emitted from the c.r.t. is of the true original hue. This is evident from (f) because A' and C are at $83° 24'$ and $43° 24'$ respectively and hence the effective resultant R'_t has the same angle (i.e., $63° 24'$) as the error-free resultant R_t shown at (c). The eye is no longer called upon to integrate different hues since the ratio of the $(R' - Y')$ to $(B' - Y')$ information implicit in (f) is the same as that at (c) and hence the correct hue is reproduced.

Whereas with PAL-S, as soon as phase errors exceed a certain minimum level, the eye is aware of a deterioration in the picture, large phase errors in the PAL-D system pass unnoticed by the viewer. This is because there is no incorrect rendering of original hues and for any phase-errors which could normally be expected in the received signal, the viewer would be unaware of the slight loss of saturation. Even with a $30°$ phase error the apparent desaturation is only of the order of 13.5%.

Finally it is important to remember that the receiver circuitry itself may well introduce phase distortion. The PAL-D receiver reduces the effects of this as well. One result of the superiority of PAL-D over PAL-S receivers in cancelling the effects of phase errors, is that the shape of the vision receiver response curve needs to be more stringently controlled in a PAL-S than in a PAL-D receiver.

Simple trigonometry is now used to verify the conclusions arrived at above. The amplitudes of U'_A, V'_A, U'_B, and V'_B are first deduced and the net U and V inputs to the synchronous demodulators then found.

From (d)

$$U'_A = A' \sin \theta = A' \sin (90° - 83° 24') = A' \sin 6° 36'$$
$$V'_A = A' \cos \theta = A' \cos (90° - 83° 24') = A' \cos 6° 36'$$

From (e)

$$U'_B = B' \sin \phi = B' \sin (90° - 43° 24') = B' \sin 46° 36'$$
$$V'_B = B' \cos \phi = B' \cos (90° - 43° 24') = B' \cos 46° 36'$$

Since phase distortion only is being considered, the chrominance signal's amplitude remains constant and $A = A' = B = B'$. But from (a),

$$A = \frac{V_A}{\sin \phi_A} = \frac{0.4}{\sin 63° 24'} = \mathbf{0.4474}$$

Hence:

$$U'_A = 0.4474 \sin 6° 36' = 0.0514$$
$$V'_A = 0.4474 \cos 6° 36' = 0.4444$$
$$U'_B = 0.4474 \sin 46° 36' = 0.3251$$
$$V'_B = 0.4474 \cos 46° 36' = 0.3074$$

The net U and V signals are $(U'_A + U'_B) = 0.3765$ and $(V'_A + V'_B) = 0.7518$. These are the lengths of the phasors shown at (f).

166

The phase angle of the equivalent chrominance signal which would yield these two components is:

$$\phi'_R = \tan^{-1} \frac{0.7518}{0.3765} = \mathbf{63° \; 24'}$$

This demonstrates once again that the PAL-D system yields a correct hue even though a quite substantial phase distortion is present.

The loss of saturation may be assessed by comparing the amplitudes of R_t and R'_t from (c) and (f) respectively. Thus:

$$R_t = \frac{(U_A + U_B)}{\cos \phi_R} = \frac{0.4}{\cos 63° \; 24'} = 0.8935$$

$$R'_t = \frac{(U'_A + U'_B)}{\cos \phi_{R_t}} = \frac{0.3765}{\cos 63° \; 24'} = 0.8410$$

$$\text{Apparent reduction in saturation} = \frac{R_t - R'_t}{R_t} \times 100 = \frac{0.0525}{0.8935} \times 100 = 5.9\%$$

The reason why the hue remains correct despite the presence of phase distortion is that the relative proportions of the recovered $(B' - Y')$ and $(R' - Y')$ colour-difference signals are unaffected. Both are reduced in amplitude by the same proportional amounts. This was demonstrated above, both by scale drawing and by calculation. The net U and V components derived at the adder and subtractor were shown to correspond to the information which would be carried by an equivalent NTSC-type phasor R'_t having a phase angle of $63° \; 24'$, i.e., exactly the same phase angle as for the original undistorted signal.

It is instructive to refer back to Fig. 10.2 for further confirmation of this point. The same numerical results would be obtained if the V and U components at (d) and (f) were imagined to be shifted to the left by $20°$ to simulate the $+20°$ phase distortion assumed in the above discussion. Since the sampling points remain as at (e) and (g), the result of this phase shift is that the signals are sampled at points which are $20°$ down the sine-wave slopes from their peak levels of 0·8 and 0·4 respectively. This once again yields outputs which are in the ratio of 2:1 and the same purple hue as before is produced but at a somewhat lower saturation level.

The above reference to *apparent* loss of saturation is a reminder that the ultimate visual effect of the phase error depends upon a comparison of the *light outputs* from the receiver c.r.t. under the two conditions discussed.

The actual displayed degrees of saturation when R_t and R'_t are the effective equivalent amplitudes of the chrominance signal under normal and phase-error conditions respectively, may only be arrived at by computing the net G', R', and B' inputs to the tube and then raising these to a power appropriate to the tube's *gamma* (e.g., 2·8). This then allows the *relative light outputs* to be compared. In the particular example discussed, a comparison of the amounts of green light displayed indicates the relative levels of saturation, since an entirely saturated purple would contain no green light at all.

Calculations of the actual estimated visual effects of the saturation loss which accompanies phase errors in the PAL-D system, show that these are negligible for the levels of phase distortion likely to be encountered in practice.

Chrominance-lock receivers

In Fig. 10.2 it may be seen by inspection that the effect of a chrominance signal phase error of $+20°$ is to shift by $+20°$ the phases of the V and U components retrieved by the PAL-D process and that this could be shown on the diagram by moving the sine-waves at (d) and (f) to the left by $20°$.

It is important to note that a shift in phase of the chrominance signal makes no difference to the action of the PAL-D process in separating the U and V components. The chrominance signal sine-wave still consists of the sum of two quadrature components. Adding and subtracting direct and delayed lines must still lead to the separation of these quadrature signals, since the direct and delayed lines are both phase-shifted by the same amount.

The loss of saturation results because the sampling points remain where they were; locked in phase by the action of the incoming back-porch sub-carrier burst. This keeps the locally generated sub-carrier (from which the sub-carrier inputs to the U and V demodulators are derived) in step with the transmitted signal.

It is evident that if the sampling points moved to the left by $20°$, in step with the chrominance signal distortion, then the correct amplitudes of $(R' - Y')$ and $(B' - Y')$ would once again be recovered. Not only would the reproduced hue remain correct (as before), but in addition the saturation loss would no longer be present.

This is illustrated in the phasor diagrams of Fig. 10.5. The NTSC-lines and PAL-lines of the phase distorted signal shown at (d) and (e) in Fig. 10.4 are reproduced at (a) and (b) of Fig. 10.5. However, the U and V axes are shown rotated by $+20°$, which is the amount of the phase shift suffered by the chrominance signal phasors A' and B'.

Demodulation along these phase-shifted U and V axes once again yields the full net U and V output amplitudes of $+0.4$ and $+0.8$ respectively, i.e., the same outputs are obtained as from the undistorted signal in Fig. 10.4 at (a) and (b).

In practical terms this could be achieved by advancing by $20°$ the receiver reference sub-carrier inputs to the U and V synchronous demodulators. The fact that in terms of 'absolute time' the receiver sub-carriers are now out-of-step with those at the distant transmission source, is of no consequence whatsoever because the correct relative phases of the chrominance signal and the sub-carriers have been established at the receiver.

This result may be achieved at the receiver by employing the principle of 'chrominance-lock'. By this technique the reference oscillator is brought under the control of a synchronizing signal derived from the chrominance signal itself. The

168

back-porch burst is then used simply to set the initial sub-carrier phase at the start of each raster line and also to overcome a possible 180° phase ambiguity which could otherwise arise because of the nature of the synchronizing signal derived from the chrominance signal. Along the raster line, if the chrominance signal should show phase distortion, the synchronizing signal derived from it, imparts the same phase shift to the generated sub-carrier and the effect of the distortion is cancelled.

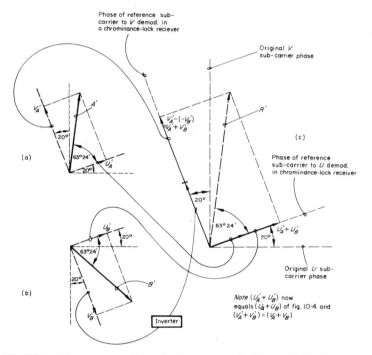

Fig. 10.5 *Showing the effect of 'chrominance lock' in a PAL-D receiver*

By shifting the phases of the reference sub-carrier inputs to the synchronous demodulators by an amount which equals the phase error of the chrominance signal, the full amplitudes of the $(B' - Y')$ and $(R' - Y')$ colour-difference signals may be recovered. This removes the saturation loss suffered by normal PAL-D receivers under the same phase error conditions. (*N.B.* Both systems produce the correct hue.)

The most common phase errors are due to differential (or 'amplitude-dependent') phase distortion. Here the amount of phase distortion changes with variations in the chrominance signal's amplitude, and/or its mean level (i.e., the luminance level about which the chrominance signal alternates). Arbitrary changes in picture detail then cause phase errors. In chrominance-lock receivers the sub-carrier phase keeps step with these arbitrary phase changes and cancels their effect.

It is important to note again, however, that such phase errors only cause slightly wrong saturation levels in PAL-D receivers, but *not* hue errors. Because this is so, the more complex and costly chrominance-lock reference oscillator system has not

169

(at the time of writing) found favour in domestic receivers but is more applicable to studio equipment.

One way in which chrominance-lock may be achieved is illustrated in Fig. 10.6. It is made possible by the properties of the PAL-D system. Samples of the U and V signals separated by the PAL-D process, are fed to frequency doublers the outputs from which are combined in an adder. This produces a signal of twice the sub-carrier frequency which is then used to lock the reference oscillator *at* the sub-carrier frequency. This principle, of locking an oscillator to a sub-multiple of a synchronizing frequency, is widely used in 'count-down' circuits and also in oscilloscopes where an X-timebase may be locked at a lower frequency than that of the waveform under examination, in order to display more than one cycle of it.

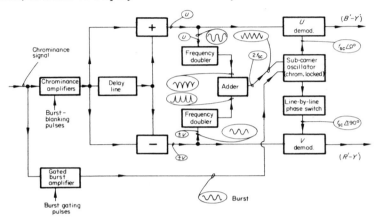

Fig. 10.6   *Showing the basic principle of chrominance-lock systems*

It is evident that any synchronizing signal derived from the U and V components of the chrominance signal, must be such that it is unaffected either by the 180° phase reversals which these components make when the colour-difference signals they represent change polarity, or by the additional line-by-line 180° phase switching of the V component. This is the reason for the frequency doubling process.

Figure 10.7 illustrates the point. A simple way of frequency-doubling the U and V signals is to apply them to full-wave rectifiers. The U component at (a) produces at the *cathodes* of the full-wave rectifier the positive-going waveform shown at (c). Clearly, if the sine-wave at (a) is inverted (following a colour-difference signal polarity change), the shape of the waveform at (c) is unaffected.

Similarly, the V component at (b) produces at the *anodes* of the full-wave rectifier diodes, the negative-going waveform at (d) and this is again unaffected by the inversion of the V sine-wave at (b). The dotted sine-wave at (b) is a reminder that this component of the PAL signal is phase alternated line-by-line but—as stated—this makes no difference to the shape of the output signal at (d).

170

When the waveforms at (c) and (d) are compared, it will be seen that their positive and negative peaks coincide in time so that they may be said to be 'in-phase'. Note that if the diodes in the rectifier at (b) were reversed and connected as are those at (a), the humps of (d) would interleave with those of (c), showing a 180° phase relationship. This is logical since doubling the frequency of two signals which are at 90° must yield two signals at 180°. By reversing the diodes in the second full-wave rectifier relative to those in the first rectifier the two waveforms are brought into phase. This is more clearly perceived if the humped waveforms produced by rectification are imagined to be replaced by sine-waves.

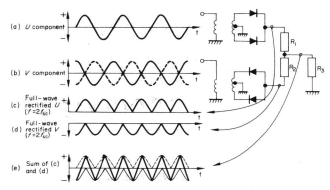

Fig. 10.7   *Showing how a chrominance-lock synchronizing signal of twice the sub-carrier frequency may be produced by using full-wave rectifiers to frequency-double the U and V signals*

The synchronizing signal of frequency $2f_{sc}$, which results when the waveforms of (c) and (d) are added, is shown at (e). Any phase distortion causes both the U and V sine-waves at (a) and (b), to move sideways on the time axis by equal amounts, and the synchronizing signal at (e) moves by precisely the same extent. The reference oscillator is in this way made to maintain a constant phase relationship to the U and V components, so that the desaturation which accompanies phase shift in the normal PAL-D receiver, is removed.

It is necessary for the oscillator to continue to run at the correct frequency in the absence of colour. The burst signal is applied to the oscillator at the start of each line to set its frequency and phase. The phase established is then that of the transmission source sub-carrier. During the active picture line the oscillator is a slave of the chrominance signal. It follows that if no colour is present along a line, the Q-factor of the oscillatory circuit must be such that it can run at the sub-carrier frequency for at least one line period following synchronization by the burst. At the same time, when colour *is* present, the Q-factor must be low enough to permit the frequency to be pulled by the chrominance signal if the latter's phase changes due to distortion during a line period. A compromise is needed, and Q-factors of between 10 and 20 have given adequate performance.

171

Finally, a synchronizing signal of frequency $2f_{sc}$ carries with it the possibility of a 180° phase ambiguity, since during one sub-carrier cycle period, there are two points on the synchronizing signal of the same level. The use of the burst at the beginning of the line overcomes this ambiguity provided the oscillator stability is such that no appreciable phase shift occurs in a line period, e.g., if the first part of a raster line is monochrome and the latter part is in colour, the oscillator must not have drifted to the point where the application of the chrominance-derived synchronizing signal, will lock-in the oscillator with the 180° error mentioned.

Chrominance signal waveforms on a colour-bar signal

In this and the previous two chapters, attention has been focused on the nature of chrominance signals.

To further consolidate this concept before moving on to study actual demodulation circuitry, the standard 95% saturated, 100% amplitude colour-bar signal is studied in Fig. 10.8.

At (a) and (c) the U and V suppressed-carrier amplitude-modulated signals, referred to in the text as modulation-products, are shown, whilst (e) shows the corresponding Q.A.M. signal, formed by the addition of the two components at (a) and (c).

On an oscilloscope displaying (e), the individual sine-waves in each of the bars cannot of course be seen; nor can the 180° phase inversions which take place when the colour-difference voltages change polarity, be identified.

At (a) and (c), however, the shape of the original colour-difference voltage waveforms is superimposed in heavy line on the r.f. waveform. Attention is particularly directed at the red and blue bars.

The V component, being representative of the $(R' - Y')$ colour-difference signal, is positive on the red bar and negative on the blue. The dotted envelope outline at (a) shows the polarity reversals of the V component on the alternate PAL-lines.

Conversely, the U component, representing the $(B' - Y')$ colour-difference signal, is negative on the red bar and positive on the blue.

At (b) and (d) the sine-waves within the red and blue bars of (a) and (c) are expanded out to show their polarities. These sine-waves, at sub-carrier frequency, should be related to the reference phase scale at the top of the page in the same way as was done in the many previous diagrams.

Since the V component has its phase inverted on each line, two sine-waves are shown for each colour-bar at (b); the NTSC-line and PAL-line sine-waves being shown in full and dotted lines respectively.

There is no such inversion of the U component and hence single sine-waves only appear at (d) to represent the U signal on the red and blue bars.

At (f), the corresponding chrominance signal sine-waves for the two bars are shown. It will be noticed that the full-line NTSC sine-wave is much closer in phase to the dotted PAL-line on the blue bar than on the red.

172

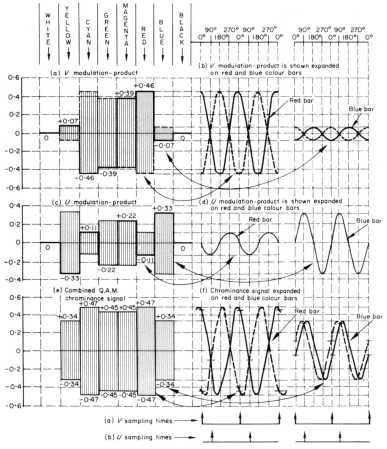

Fig. 10.8 *Showing the U and V modulation-products and the combined chrominance signal waveforms for a 95% saturated, 100% amplitude colour-bar signal*

(NTSC-lines are shown in full-line; PAL-lines are dotted)

On the red bar, the $(R' - Y')$ colour-difference voltage is much larger than the $(B' - Y')$. Hence the V component has a much greater amplitude than the U. It follows that the chrominance signal, which is the sum of the two, is very much influenced by the line-by-line phase inversion of the V component and shows a pronounced phase change on PAL-lines. (The phase change would be 180° if the U component were reduced to zero.)

On the blue bar, the U signal predominates and the phase inversion of the small V component shows up on PAL-lines as only a slight phase shift of the chrominance signal.

173

Finally the following points of revision are worth noting:

(a) In a PAL-S receiver the Q.A.M. chrominance signal at (e) is fed to both demodulators. The amplitudes of the individual U and V modulation-products are then obtained by sampling using sub-carriers of appropriate phase.

(b) In a PAL-D receiver the chrominance signal at (e) is passed to the delay-line and simultaneously to the adder and subtractor circuits. The latter produce from the direct and delayed signals, outputs corresponding to the original modulation-products shown at (c) and (a), but of twice the amplitude.

(c) In the PAL-D receiver the V and U demodulators then only receive their appropriate modulation-products and sub-carriers. Each is thus isolated from the influence of the other component.

11

Synchronous Demodulators

The most widely used synchronous demodulators employ either two or four semi-conductor diodes. Also used are various thermionic valve circuits. In this chapter a variety of practical circuits is studied. If the nature of the chrominance signal with its two constituent modulation-products (i.e., the U and V signals) is kept well in mind, the action of the demodulators is easy to understand.

Almost all PAL receivers now in use employ the PAL-D principle, so that each of the two synchronous demodulators only receives one of the two modulation-products (i.e., either U or V) together with the necessary correctly phased sub-carrier from the receiver's reference oscillator. However, the majority of the synchronous demodulators in use in PAL-D receivers, would work perfectly well in PAL-S receivers where each demodulator receives the full chrominance signal instead of one only of its two components.

Most circuits may be understood by considering them as sampling devices. In previous chapters, in order to arrive at a clear understanding of the way in which colour-difference signal information may be extracted from either the chrominance signal (i.e., PAL-S), or from the already separated U and V signals (i.e., PAL-D), it was convenient to imagine the signals to be sampled for an instant of time only. In practical circuits, however, the sampling is not instantaneous but extends over a finite part of one half-cycle of the signal being demodulated. This does not alter the fact that the voltage output is truly proportional to the amplitude of the appropriate colour-difference signal which the demodulator is designed to extract.

This is illustrated in Fig. 11.1. The chrominance signal at (c) is the sum of the U and V components shown at (a) and (b). If, to obtain the U information in a PAL-S receiver, the chrominance signal is sampled—not at the instant t_s (when V is exactly zero)—but for the period t_1 to t_2, the output is still independent of V information. This is because, as seen at (b), V passes through zero in the middle of the sampling period (t_{sp}) being (in this example) negative before and positive after the centre time t_s. The net V output from the U demodulator is therefore zero.

The interval t_1 to t_2 is often referred to as the angle of flow of the demodulator. This is because the diodes (or sometimes valve(s)) are conductive only for this portion of one cycle of the applied sine-wave from the reference oscillator. The angle of flow varies widely from circuit to circuit and may be as little as $30°$ or (at maximum) $180°$.

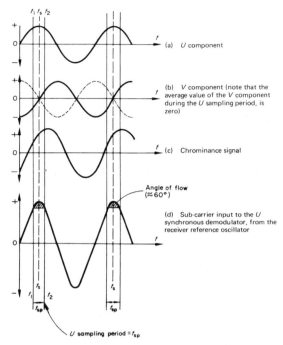

(a) *U* component

(b) *V* component (note that the average value of the *V* component during the *U* sampling period, is zero)

(c) Chrominance signal

Angle of flow (≈60°)

(d) Sub-carrier input to the *U* synchronous demodulator, from the receiver reference oscillator

U sampling period = t_{sp}

Fig. 11.1 *Synchronous demodulator 'sampling' periods*

It will be appreciated that in adjusting synchronous demodulators it is important to time the applied reference sub-carrier so that the centre of the angle of flow coincides with the peak value of the modulation-product which is being demodulated. In a PAL-S receiver, failure to do this will result in cross-talk between the two components. In a PAL-D receiver, the output from the given demodulator, will be less than the maximum available colour-difference signal amplitude. If the phases of the sub-carriers to *both* demodulators are equally in error, then the two colour-difference signals will still be in the original relative amplitude ratio, so that the hue will be correct but a loss of saturation will be experienced. If, on the other hand, the timing of the sub-carriers is such that the errors are different (or one sub-carrier phase is correct and the other is in error) then the hue will be incorrect, because the ratio of the colour-difference signal amplitudes will be wrong. The setting of the phases of the sub-carriers to the two synchronous demodulators, forms an important part of the alignment of a receiver.

Two-diode circuits

(i) *Fig. 11.2(a)*

The action of this circuit may be summarized by saying that the resistance between points W and X is reduced from a very high to a low value once per reference sub-carrier cycle, so allowing the chrominance signal's amplitude to be sensed by the colour-difference signal transistor amplifier.

The chrominance signal (or, more usually, one individual modulation-product previously separated by the delay-line process), is fed to the junction of the cathode of D_1 and the anode of D_2. Except when switched on by the re-inserted sub-carrier, these diodes are cut-off by the charges on C_1 and C_2. The sub-carrier, correctly phased to initiate this switching action at the right time for sampling the applied chrominance signal, is applied from the secondary of the r.f. transformer T_1, to the anode of D_1 and the cathode of D_2. Since opposite ends of the secondary are in anti-phase relative to the grounded centre-tap, the diodes are switched on simultaneously, during the sub-carrier half-cycle which makes D_1 anode positive and D_2 cathode negative.

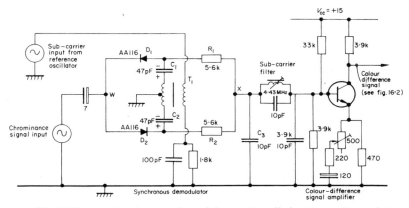

Fig. 11.2(a) *Synchronous demodulator. Two-diode circuit: Example 1*

Note: A second circuit, identical to this one except for the phase of the reference sub-carrier, is used to recover the other colour-difference signal. (Associated diagram Fig. 16.2.)

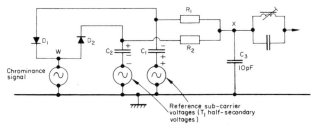

Fig. 11.2(b) *Simplified representation of Fig. 11.2(a)*

Capacitors C_1 and C_2 are in series with resistors R_1 and R_2 so that the total capacitance C_t in this loop is $(47/2)$ pF and the total resistance R_t is (2×5.6) kΩ. The approximate time-constant, ignoring the T_1 secondary, is $C_t R_t$ seconds = $(47/2 \times 10^{-12} \times 2 \times 5.6 \times 10^3 \times 10^6)$μs = 0.26 μs. The periodic time of the sub-

177

carrier is approximately $0.23\ \mu s$ ($f_{sc} \approx 4.4\ MHz$), hence the charges on C_1 and C_2 hold the diodes cut-off for a part of each sub-carrier cycle.

The simplified diagram at (b) allows the operation of the circuit to be studied more easily. Looking towards the diodes from point X, the voltages across C_1 and C_2, relative to 'earth', are equal and opposite when the chrominance signal input is zero (i.e., when 'grey' information is present in the picture). The input to the colour-difference signal amplifier (i.e., the voltage across C_3), is therefore also zero.

When colour is present, point W will be either positive or negative to earth at the moment when the diodes switch on. When positive, the net input to D_2 (which is the amount by which the algebraic sum of the chrominance signal at point W and the reference sub-carrier across half of T_1 secondary, exceeds the voltage on C_2) is greater than the net input to D_1. This is because the positive input at point W is presented to the *anode* of D_2 and the *cathode* of D_1, so aiding the conduction of D_2 but opposing that of D_1. C_2 now receives a greater charge than C_1 and the algebraic sum of the C_1 and C_2 voltages is no longer zero. The net input at point X to the colour-difference amplifier is therefore positive. If the chrominance signal remains the same for a short period (e.g., during a colour-bar), the positive input to the colour-difference amplifier persists. When the chrominance signal is negative at the moments of diode conduction, D_1 conducts more than D_2 and the net input at point X is then negative.

Since the amplitude of the input to the amplifier is clearly proportional to the amplitude of the chrominance signal present at point W, the waveform of the original colour-difference signal is fully recovered at point X, both in terms of polarity and of amplitude.

For satisfactory operation it is necessary to make the amplitude of the re-inserted sub-carrier from the reference oscillator greater than the chrominance signal, so that the diodes are switched by the former and not by the latter.

The output circuit of a synchronous demodulator includes a filter to remove the sub-carrier component. In this particular circuit, a parallel tuned circuit is placed in series with the signal path, for this purpose. The tuned circuit is made to resonate at f_{sc} and hence offers a high series impedance to this unwanted sub-carrier component.

A second synchronous demodulator, identical to Fig. 11.2 except for the phase of the reference sub-carrier, is used for the recovery of the other colour-difference signal.

(ii) *Fig. 11.3*

This circuit is very similar in its mode of operation. Once again the reference sub-carrier is coupled into the centre-tapped secondary of an r.f. transformer (T_1) and the series-connected diodes switch on simultaneously as before. Instead of being returned to 'earth', a fast time-constant circuit, $C_2 R_2$, is placed in series with the centre-tap connection. With $R_2 = 390\ \Omega$ and $C_2 = 68\ pF$, the time constant is approximately $0.026\ \mu s$, or about one-tenth of the periodic time of the chrominance

178

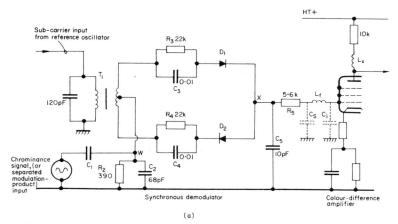

Fig. 11.3(a) *Synchronous demodulator. Two-diode circuit: Example 2*

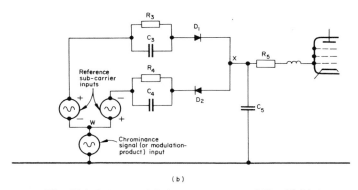

Fig. 11.3(b) *Simplified representation of Fig. 11.3(a)*

signal. The voltage across R_2C_2 is thus able to follow the chrominance signal which is applied to the network via C_1.

The networks C_3R_3 and C_4R_4, which have relatively long time constants of 220 µs, hold the diodes cut-off for a substantial part of each applied sub-carrier cycle. When the diodes are switched on the chrominance signal voltage amplitude at point W is effectively transmitted over to C_5 at point X. When the chrominance signal is zero (on greys), the circuit is balanced and there is no voltage output. When it is positive D_1 conducts more than D_2 and C_5 becomes positively charged. Similarly, when the original colour-difference signal is negative, the chrominance signal is on a negative half-cycle when the diodes are switched-on. This makes D_2 conduct more than D_1 and C_5 develops a negative voltage. The colour-difference signal is therefore recovered across C_5 and applied to the amplifier. The diagram in Fig. 11.3(b) shows the action of the circuit in a simplified way.

179

The r.f. sub-carrier is filtered by the action of R_5 and L_f, together with stray shunt capacitance and the input capacitance to the colour-difference amplifier.

(iii) *Fig. 11.4*

When compared with Figs. 11.2 and 11.3 this circuit will be seen to differ in the way in which the chrominance signal is applied. In effect the diodes exercise a clamping action on the potential across the chrominance coupling capacitor C_3. Once per sub-carrier cycle, the diodes are switched on for the brief period during which the peak reference sub-carrier input exceeds the automatic bias voltage across the two networks $C_1 R_1$ and $C_2 R_2$. When this happens the coupling capacitor charges up through the diode circuit to a potential determined by the amplitude and polarity of the chrominance signal at the moment of conduction. If terminal D of the chromi-nance amplifier is positive at the moment of conduction of the diodes, the right-hand plate of C_3 is left negatively charged when the diodes cut off. This in turn gives rise to an input of negative polarity to the colour-difference amplifier. Similarly, if D is negative the right-hand plate of C_3 is left positively charged and the input to the colour-difference amplifier is a positive voltage.

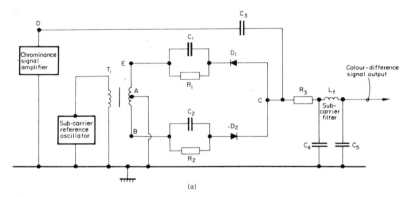

Fig. 11.4(a)   *Synchronous demodulator. Two-diode circuit: Example 3*

As a further aid to an understanding of this circuit, a simplified diagram Fig. 11.4(b) is again included. Here the circuit is redrawn to emphasize that there are essentially two loops in the synchronous demodulator; with one diode, two input signals and an 'auto-bias' CR network, in each loop. The input signals in each loop are shown as before as 'generators' and these represent one-half of the T_1 secondary reference sub-carrier voltage and the chrominance signal voltage. The circuit connections may be identified by the letters in Fig. 11.4(a).

Assuming the positive polarity chrominance signal discussed (i.e., positive at the moment the diodes are conductive), the sub-carrier and chrominance voltages are in the same sense as far as D_1 is concerned but opposing one another in the D_2 loop. The D_1 current charges the top plate of C_3 negatively whilst that of D_2 charges it

180

positively. In this example the D_1 current is greater because the net input to D_1 is greater than that to D_2. There is therefore a net output across C_3 which is of negative polarity.

Note that the 'angle of flow' of the diode currents is determined by the time constants of the 'auto-bias' networks. The reference sub-carrier is of greater amplitude than the chrominance signal so that *it* is responsible for switching the diodes on. Once they are on, however, it is the chrominance signal which determines which one of the two diodes conducts more than the other.

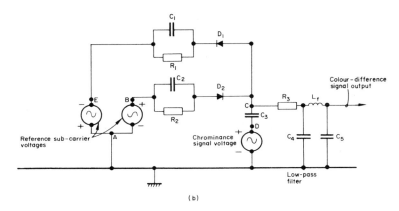

(b)

Fig. 11.4(b)   *Simplified diagram of Fig. 11.4(a)*

Finally, the fact that an input of positive polarity from the chrominance amplifier gives rise to a colour-difference signal of negative polarity, is of no consequence. The important point is that the output from the demodulator changes sign when the input changes sign. At any given point in the transmitter/receiver chain, what started off as a positive polarity signal may be either positive or negative, since clearly the polarity changes sign through every normal amplifier stage.

(iv) *Fig. 11.5*

The mode of operation of this circuit is different from the three previous two-diode arrangements. Here the diodes are connected 'back-to-back' and not in series as before.

When the chrominance signal is zero the only input is from the reference sub-carrier. This is applied in the same phase to both diode anodes from the secondary of r.f. transformer T_1, via the centre tap of the secondary of r.f. transformer T_2. Since the circuit is balanced the two output voltages developed across the time constant circuits $C_1 R_1$ and $C_2 R_2$ are equal and opposite. The net output between points A and B is therefore zero.

181

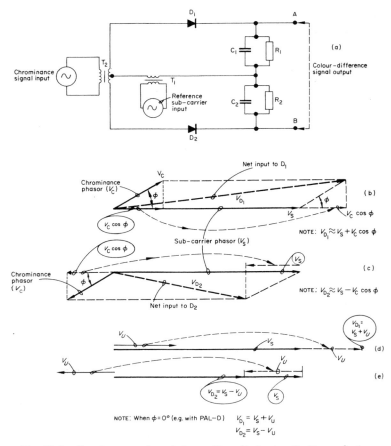

Fig. 11.5 *Synchronous demodulator. Two-diode circuit: Example 4*

The chrominance signal is fed to the two diodes in a push-pull manner from the secondary of T_2. It is evident that since opposite ends of this winding are in antiphase relative to the common centre-tap connection, one of the two diodes must be driven more positive by the chrominance signal and the other less positive. It is assumed that the reference sub-carrier is substantially greater in amplitude than the chrominance signal. If this is so both diodes are continuously conductive for that part of the reference-sub-carrier's positive half-cycle which causes the input to be greater than the auto-bias voltages developed across the cathode time-constant circuits. Under these conditions the chrominance signal merely influences the circuit's degree of balance. At times when the original colour-difference signal makes the phase of the chrominance signal such that the D_1 end of T_2 secondary is positive to the centre-tap and the D_2 end is negative, D_1 conducts more than D_2 and a positive output voltage is developed between terminals A and B. Similarly, when the colour-difference

182

signal reverses in polarity, the chrominance signal inverts its phase and now D_2 conducts more than D_1 giving a negative output voltage across AB.

The phasor diagrams beneath the circuit illustrate how the net inputs to the two diodes may be determined. Assuming the demodulator is intended to extract the $(B' - Y')$ component from a full chrominance signal (PAL-S system), the phase of the injected sub-carrier is properly shown lying along the $+(B' - Y')$ axis.

The chrominance phasor V_c will be at some angle $\phi°$ to this axis. The input to D_1 is the resultant of the parallelogram shown. If the reference carrier is much greater in amplitude than the chrominance phasor V_c, the resultant V_{D_1} is approximately equal to $(V_s + V_c \cos \phi)$; where V_s is the amplitude of the re-inserted sub-carrier.

In a similar way the net input to the other diode is reduced by the presence of the chrominance signal and becomes $(V_s - V_c \cos \phi)$.

Since the outputs from the two diodes are in opposition to one another, the net output must be proportional to the difference between the net inputs.

Hence

$$V_o \approx \{(V_s + V_c \cos \phi) - (V_s - V_c \cos \phi)\} \tag{1}$$

i.e.,
$$V_o \approx 2V_c \cos \phi. \tag{2}$$

The *cosine component* of a Q.A.M. chrominance signal is the U or $(B' - Y')$ component, so that this demodulator recovers the required $(B' - Y')$ colour-difference signal.

In a second demodulator of the same kind, the sub-carrier would be injected at $90°$ to the $+(B' - Y')$ axis. In this event the net inputs to the two diodes would be $(V_s + V_c \sin \phi)$ and $(V_s - V_c \sin \phi)$ and the output would be:

$$V_o \approx (V_s + V_c \sin \phi) - (V_s - V_c \sin \phi) \tag{3}$$

i.e.,
$$V_o \approx 2V_c \sin \phi. \tag{4}$$

This 'sin' component of the chrominance signal is the V signal yielding $(R' - Y')$ information.

In this chapter the line-by-line switching systems discussed in the last two chapters, and summarized in the PAL-S and PAL-D block diagrams of Figs. 9.3(a) and (b) and Figs. 10.3(a) and (b) respectively, are not considered. Complete circuitry will be studied in a subsequent chapter.

However, it is worth noting that if PAL-D is considered, then the modulation-product fed to the circuit in Fig. 11.5 would produce a phasor V_u lying along the V_s axis shown in the phasor diagrams. This, would then create inputs of $(V_s + V_u)$ and $(V_s - V_u)$ to the two diodes; with a corresponding output of $2V_u$.

The effect is the same as if the $(R' - Y')$ component in the V_c phasor shown at (b) and (c) were reduced to zero. This would make the angle $\phi = 0°$ in the expression shown at (1) above. The result is shown in phasor form at (d) and (e).

Four-diode ('diode-bridge') circuits

Fig. 11.6

A suitably phased input from the reference sub-carrier oscillator is applied between the terminals PQ of the diode bridge. On the half-cycle which makes P positive to Q the four diodes become highly conductive and of low resistance. When this happens, point X is effectively connected to point W, and the modulation-product voltage at W appears across the capacitor C_1. The time constant of the C_1R_1 circuit is of the order 0·23 μs which again is comparable to the periodic time of the sub-carrier. This output circuit is able to respond quickly to changes in chrominance signal amplitude and polarity but the inclusion of the filter L_fC_f removes the unwanted sub-carrier component. The resistors R_2 and R_3 limit the peak diode currents.

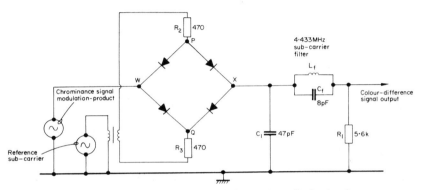

Fig. 11.6 *Synchronous demodulator. Four-diode circuit*

It should be noted that this particular circuit is used in PAL-D type receivers where only one modulation-product is presented at point W. The object is therefore simply to sense the amplitude and polarity of this single signal. Unlike the other circuits discussed, the diodes are here fully conductive for one complete half-cycle of the applied reference sub-carrier. However, provided the phasing is correct, the demodulator deals with only one half-cycle of the modulation-product present at point W. The output at point X therefore always has an amplitude which is proportional to the original colour-difference signal's amplitude and a polarity which changes sign as the modulation-product inverts its phase following a change of colour-difference signal polarity.

In the diode circuits so far described, only one of the required pair of synchronous demodulators has been shown in the diagrams. The second one of each pair is identical to the first except for the phase of the reference sub-carrier.

In the valve circuits which follow, the pairs of synchronous demodulators are conveniently drawn side by side.

184

Triode circuits

In essence these circuits are gated amplifiers. The simplified diagrams in Fig. 11.7(a) and (b), show their mode of operation.

Looking first at Fig. 11.7(a), which is suitable for NTSC or PAL-S working, the chrominance signal is applied to the control grids of both triodes and suitably phased inputs from the receiver's reference sub-carrier oscillator are applied to the cathodes. The sub-carrier input to the cathode of each valve has a high amplitude. Included in the common cathode circuit is a bias network $C_k R_k$ and the circuit is so arranged that the bias developed across this network holds the valves cut-off except during the peaks of the negative-going sub-carrier half-cycles.

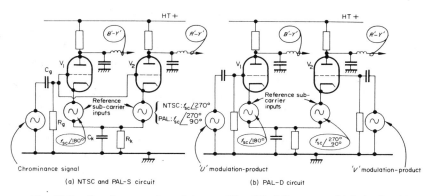

Fig. 11.7 *Synchronous demodulators. Simplified diagrams of triode circuits*

If V_1 is the $(B' - Y')$ demodulator, it is necessary that its anode current shall vary in sympathy with the amplitude and polarity of the $(B' - Y')$ r.f. modulation-product of the applied chrominance signal. For this to be so the valve must be conductive at moments corresponding to the positive peaks of the original suppressed $(B' - Y')$ transmitter sub-carrier. Since it is the negative half-cycle of the sub-carrier applied to the cathode which drives the valve into conduction, it follows that the phase of this sub-carrier must be at $180°$ relative to that at the transmitter.

The amplitude of the anode current during this period of conduction varies with the amplitude of the chrominance signal present at the grid. On greys the grid input is zero and the anode current will assume a 'no-colour' level entirely determined by the constant amplitude of the sub-carrier applied to the cathode. When colour is present the chrominance signal may be showing either a positive or a negative-going half-cycle at the grid when the valve is 'gated' and the anode current will then be respectively greater than, or less than, the no-colour level. The anode voltage varies inversely as the anode current, so that a positive-going chrominance signal half-cycle at the grid produces an output which is negative-going relative to the no-colour level. One stage of amplification following the detector then inverts this signal to yield a

185

positive polarity colour-difference signal corresponding to the positive-going chrominance signal, which in turn corresponds to the positive-polarity of the original colour-difference signal.

V_2 demodulates the $(R' - Y')$ component in the same manner. To extract this component the valve has to be gated by a cathode sub-carrier having a phase which is 90° advanced on that applied to V_1. When referred to the transmitter's reference axis this represents a phase of +270°.

To adapt this circuit as a PAL-S demodulator the sub-carrier to the cathode may be inverted by a line-by-line switch to have an angle on NTSC-lines of +270° and on PAL-lines of +90°.

Alternatively, the sub-carrier phase may be held constant at +270° and the chrominance signal to the grid of V_2 must then be inverted on PAL-lines.

In a PAL-D receiver (see Fig. 11.7(b)), V_1 receives the U and V_2 the V modulation-products. Again, the line-by-line inversion of the V component may be countered by synchronous switching either of the sub-carrier's phase or of the V component's phase. As in the previous demodulators, the output circuits include sub-carrier filters in the colour-difference signal paths.

Figure 11.8 shows an example of this type of detector as used in a PAL-D receiver. The modulation-products are fed to the triodes by transistor amplifiers which in turn receive their inputs from the delay-line circuitry. Included in the path from the delay-line to the V modulation-product amplifier is a line-by-line inverter.[1] The diagram indicates this by showing the input to Tr$_7$ as V (rather than $\pm V$) and the corresponding sub-carrier input then has a constant phase of +270°. The sub-carriers are obtained

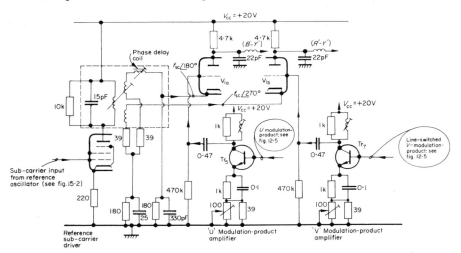

Fig. 11.8 *Synchronous demodulators. Example of triode circuits in a PAL-D receiver*

(Associated diagrams: Figs. 12.5, 13.2, 14.3, 15.2, 17.5)

[1] This is described under Fig. 12.5 and under Fig. 13.2.

from secondaries coupled to the tuned primary in the anode of the reference sub-carrier driver stage. The phase angle of the sub-carrier to the U demodulator is delayed by 90° relative to the V sub-carrier by the inclusion of an inductor shown in the diagram as a 'phase-delay coil'. The amplitudes of the modulation-products are individually adjusted by pre-set potentiometers in the emitter circuits. These give a small range of control of gain by variation of negative feedback.

Pentode circuits

These and similar circuits (e.g., heptode) involve the application of the chrominance and sub-carrier signals to two successive grids modulating the electron current to the anode. In effect they work as 'mixers' in the same way as in a superhet frequency changer. Unlike the latter, however, the chrominance signal demodulator receives two input signals of the same frequency. One of these, the sub-carrier, is a simple continuous sine-wave of constant amplitude, but the other, which is constantly varying in amplitude and phase, represents the sum total of the upper and lower sideband components of a double-sideband suppressed carrier signal.

As with normal mixers, the output signal is a function of the product of the two individual signals. This is logical since the anode current is influenced first by the voltage on the control grid and then by that on the next signal grid. The result of this 'multiplicative' mixing is that sum and difference frequencies are produced. The difference frequency in mixers yields the i.f. together with the sidebands which now exist as sidebands centred on the i.f. instead of the signal frequency. In the output from the synchronous demodulator, the difference frequency (i.e., the i.f.), is zero and the sidebands (or modulation components) are produced directly. This is best thought out by imagining the original transmitter sub-carrier to be modulated by a simple sine-wave of low frequency. This yields two side frequencies only from the

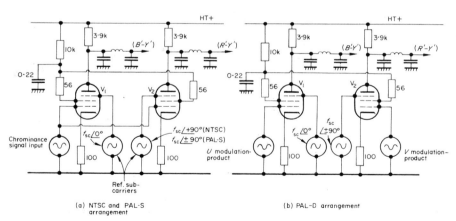

Fig. 11.9 *Synchronous demodulators. Simplified diagrams of pentode circuits*

187

balanced modulator. These are positioned one above and one below the sub-carrier frequency. Mixing such a chrominance signal modulation-product at the receiver, with a reconstituted sub-carrier produces the original low modulating frequency from both the sidebands (i.e., $(f_c + f_m) - f_c = f_m$ and $f_c - (f_c - f_m) = f_m$).

The simplified diagrams of Fig. 11.9 illustrate the arrangement of this type of demodulator. The phases of the re-inserted sub-carriers must be the same as those suppressed at the transmitter. For $(B' - Y')$ this is $0°$; whilst for $(R' - Y')$ on NTSC it is $+90°$ and for PAL-S $\pm 90°$, switched line-by-line.

As established in chapter 9 re-insertion of a sub-carrier with a phase error of $90°$ with respect to the original suppressed carrier, causes cancellation of the sidebands. For this reason V_1 yields no output of $(R' - Y')$ information and V_2 similarly yields no $(B' - Y')$ information.

In the PAL-D circuit at (b) the suppressors now receive individual modulation-products from the delay-line circuitry. The required sub-carrier phases are the same as before. For PAL working the chrominance signal in the PAL-S circuit at (a) or the V component in the PAL-D circuit at (b), may be line-by-line switched instead of the sub-carrier in which case the latter is held constant with the NTSC phase of $+90°$.

Brief notes on further demodulation techniques

(a) *High-level demodulators*

All of the circuits so far described are followed by colour-difference amplifiers which amplify the output from the demodulators to a level suitable for application to the c.r.t. An associated matrixed amplifier develops the missing $(G' - Y')$ signal.

Also possible, are demodulators which work on a high amplitude chrominance signal and deliver their output direct to the c.r.t. These are again essentially gated amplifiers and follow closely the principles discussed.

(b) *Pre-delay-line re-insertion of the sub-carrier*

Circuits have been developed in which the reference sub-carrier is re-inserted into the chrominance signal path in front of the delay-line. When this is done the two signals recovered from the delay-line circuitry are now no longer suppressed-carrier signals but complete double-sideband a.m. signals. These may then go forward to normal rectifying type detectors. One disadvantage of the method is that when the chrominance signal bears a phase error, cross-talk takes place between the U and V signals; in addition to the loss of saturation discussed in chapter 10.

(c) *Demodulation along the X and Z axes*

Equiband chrominance signals need not necessarily be demodulated along the $(B' - Y')$ and $(R' - Y')$ axes. These do of course have the advantage of direct recovery of two of the required three colour-difference signals and the third $(G' - Y')$, is recovered by matrixing these two.

However, it is possible to demodulate using sub-carrier reference phases which differ from the quadrature phases of the $(B' - Y')$ and $(R' - Y')$ components. If this is done it is self-evident by a consideration of the effect of sampling a chrominance signal at other than the quadrature points, that the information recovered will contain both $(B' - Y')$ and $(R' - Y')$ information. The matrixing then needs to be designed to recover all three colour-difference signals from this information. Whilst at first sight this seems an added complication, NTSC receivers in the U.S.A. make wide use of this system. The reason for this is that by a particular choice of axes the colour-difference amplifier matrix circuit may be made attractively simple and stable. The axes used are 260·5° for X and 197·5° for Z (see Fig. 11.10).

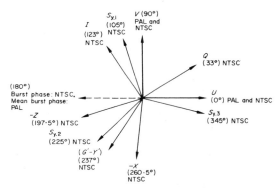

Fig. 11.10 *Examples of demodulation axes used for quadrature modulated chrominance signals*
(a) Axes used for PAL are: U and V.
(b) Axes used for NTSC are: (i) I and Q, or (ii) U and V, or (iii) $-Z$ and $-X$, or (iv) S_{y_1}, S_{y_2}, and S_{y_3}.
(*N.B.* To demodulate along given axes, the re-inserted sub-carriers must have the phases shown for those axes.)

Although technically possible to adapt this system to the PAL signal, the added complications necessary to take account of the switched V component make the method unattractive since the disadvantages outweigh the advantages.

XZ demodulation is mentioned in this chapter because it is often referred to in literature dealing with the NTSC quadrature modulation system. It is a device aimed at economical circuitry rather than optimum performance.

(d) *Symmetrical demodulators*

It is possible to obtain the $(G' - Y')$ component in a separate demodulator rather than by matrixing $(B' - Y')$ and $(R' - Y')$. It is shown in chapter 16 that:

$$(G' - Y') = -0·51(R' - Y') - 0·186(B' - Y')$$

Since the amplitudes of the U and V components of the chrominance signal are related to $(B' - Y')$ and $(R' - Y')$ by the expressions $(B' - Y') = U/0·493$ and

189

$(R' - Y') = V/0.877$, it follows that:

$$(G' - Y') = -\left(\frac{0.51}{0.877}\right)V - \left(\frac{0.186}{0.493}\right)U$$

therefore
$$(G' - Y') = -0.5816V - 0.3743U$$

These proportions of U and V are obtainable on an axis at an angle of $\theta = \tan^{-1}(-0.5816/-0.3743) = 180° + \tan^{-1}(+0.5816/+0.3743) = 180° + 57° = 237°$.

This demonstrates in another way that although it is the $(R' - Y')$ and $(B' - Y')$ colour-difference signals which modulate the chrominance signal, it is nonetheless true that since $(G' - Y')$ bears a fixed numerical relationship to the other two colour-difference signals it is automatically transmitted with them.

In the U.S.A., NTSC receivers have been developed which employ three synchronous demodulators. It is evident from the above that demodulating along an axis of 237° (i.e., employing a sub-carrier having a phase suitable for sampling the chrominance signal at 237°), would yield $(G' - Y')$ information directly, just as $(B' - Y')$ and $(R' - Y')$ information is obtained on axes of 0° and 90° respectively. For convenience the various axes are shown in Fig. 11.10.

The three so-called symmetrical demodulators do not, however, demodulate exactly along these axes. Three axes are chosen which lie at 120° to one another; hence the description symmetrical. These axes are so chosen that each of them lies near to one of the 'colour-difference' axes. The maximum separation between the chosen axes and the adjacent U, V, and $(G' - Y')$ axes is 15°. The angles chosen are 105° (i.e., 15° from $(R' - Y')$), 225° (i.e., 12° from $(G' - Y')$), and 345° (i.e., 15° from $(B' - Y')$). These three axes for symmetrical demodulation are shown as S_{y_1}, S_{y_2}, and S_{y_3} in Fig. 11.10, where for convenience of reference the various demodulation axes are portrayed.

The symmetrical axes demodulators yield information which is only slightly different in amplitude from the true colour-difference signals. The correct values are then obtained by simple resistor matrixing.

Because of the symmetry of the system, changes of working conditions (e.g., supply voltage variations), affect the three colour-difference signals equally, so that the reproduced hue (assuming perfect symmetry) remains constant, and only luminance changes result. A further advantage of the circuit symmetry is that inter-demodulator cross-talk is minimized.

As with the XZ system, the method is not simple with the PAL signal because of the complication of the switched V axis.

(e) *I' and Q' demodulators*

As stated earlier, in the original NTSC system the unequal bandwidths of the two quadrature modulation-products I and Q, together with the asymmetrical nature of the I signal, was designed to tailor the colour television signal closely to the characteristics of the eye whilst meeting all the other dictates of overall quality and compatibility. The recovery of all of this 'colour' information requires demodulation along the I and Q axes. Both of these recovered signals contain $(R' - Y')$ and $(B' - Y')$ information so that a more complex matrixing operation is needed to retrieve the three colour-difference signals. Despite the availability of this extra information, many NTSC receivers treat the chrominance signal as though it consists of two equiband modulation-products. (See, for example, XZ demodulators above.) This involves a bandwidth restriction to filter off the then discarded higher frequency elements of the I signal. The added simplicity of the receiver is preferred at the cost of a small reduction in colour resolution.

The NTSC system I and Q axes, which are at 123° and 33° respectively, are discussed in Appendix A at the end of the book and are also shown in Fig. 11.10.

The I and Q axes are not applicable to the PAL system where equiband transmission is used.

12

PAL-D Decoder Techniques: Chrominance Signal Delay-lines and Associated Circuitry

In this chapter the nature of chrominance signal delay-lines is studied, together with their associated input and output circuitry.

Calculation of the required delay

The object of the delay-line is to delay the chrominance signal by almost exactly one line period of 64 µs. To permit the addition and subtraction of *direct* and *delayed* signal lines, the delay-line must introduce a delay which is equivalent to the duration of an exact number of half-cycles of the chrominance signal.

This requirement would not be met if the line introduced a delay of *exactly* 64 µs. At a frequency of 4·43361875 MHz the number of cycles which take place in 64 µs is:

$$4 \cdot 43361875 \times 10^6 \times 10^{-6} \times 64 = 283 \cdot 7485998 \text{ cycles}$$

i.e., approximately 283·75 cycles.

A delay-line which introduces a delay equal to the duration of 283·5 sub-carrier cycles is therefore suitable. This is equal to a time delay of:

$$t_d = (\text{periodic time of one sub-carrier cycle} \times 283 \cdot 5)\mu s$$

$$= \left(\frac{10^6}{4 \cdot 43361875 \times 10^6} \times 283 \cdot 5 \right) \mu s = \mathbf{63 \cdot 943 \ \mu s}$$

It is interesting to note that the effect of making the line an odd multiple of one half-cycle long is to produce a delayed signal which is 180° out of phase with the direct signal. To be strictly accurate this fact ought to be considered when determining how to achieve separation of the *U* and *V* components by the addition and subtraction of the chrominance signal from the direct and delayed lines.

For example, referring back to Fig. 10.2, when the NTSC-line is the 'direct' signal, the PAL-line simultaneously emerging from the delay-line has a relative phase, not of the original PAL-line shown at (b), but shifted in phase by 180° and therefore equivalent to the inverted PAL-line signal shown at (c). The direct addition of these two lines yields the V modulation-product. To produce the U component, the emerging *inverted delayed signal* must be phase shifted by 180° and then added to the direct signal.

To this extent therefore the inverter mentioned in chapter 10 may be considered to be an integral part of a $283\frac{1}{2}$ cycle delay-line but as it operates on the signal in advance of the point where the delayed signal is taken off, an 'external' inverter is now needed in the delayed-signal path to the U demodulator. Alternatively to compensate for the effective 180° phase shift by the delay-line, the direct-signal may be inverted *before* application to it. The delayed-signal from the delay-line may then be combined with a non-inverted direct-signal in an adder to produce the U component and in a subtractor to produce a V component.

To have made this point in the previous chapter when introducing the PAL-D principle would only have caused confusion and the question of the effective 180° phase shift by the delay-line was ignored. In any event since reversal of the output connections of the delay-line counteracts the 180° phase shift, it is usually unnecessary to complicate the reasoning by taking this 180° into account.

A further point of academic interest is that the delay-line never in fact 'contains' $283\frac{1}{2}$ chrominance signal cycles at any one time. This is because the chrominance signal is interrupted for 12 µs once per line by the line blanking period so that the maximum continuous sequence of sub-carrier cycles lasts only 52 µs and this represents approximately 230·5 cycles. This makes no difference to the phase considerations discussed above since the transmitter sub-carrier does not of course 'switch on-and-off' at the beginning and end of each active line period; it is merely blanked out of the radiated video signal to accommodate the line pulse information and sub-carrier burst. The burst itself is prevented from entering the delay-line by a chrominance amplifier burst-blanking circuit situated ahead of the delay-line.

Finally it is evident that the use of a delay-time which is not exactly equal to the length of one video-signal line must mean that there is a small departure from absolute registration of colour-detail in the combination of any two successive lines. However, since it is a fractional part of one cycle of the 4·43 MHz chrominance signal which is being considered, this small error does not cause any visible degradation of the colour information in the reproduced picture. This information has a maximum bandwidth of 1 MHz which indicates that the registration error along a line is smaller than the smallest visible colour detail.

Delay-line temperature tolerance

It is necessary that the delay-time of 63·943 µs shall remain substantially constant for all normal changes of temperature met in a receiver. In practice the delay is held within limits of $\pm 0·003$ µs (i.e., ± 3 nano-seconds) at 25°C with a maximum drift of ± 4 nano-seconds over the range $+25°$C to $+50°$C. Expressed as a manufacturing tolerance, 3 ns represents an accuracy of;

$$\pm\left(\frac{0{\cdot}003}{64} \times 100\right)\% = \pm 0{\cdot}047\%$$

A maximum error at 25°C of 3 ns, implies a maximum inherent phase error of 5° for the signal emerging from the delay-line.

The chrominance delay-line is made of a specially selected glass and the property which the glass must possess to meet this temperature stability requirement is mentioned in the next section where the structure of the delay-line is discussed.

Principle of the ultrasonic delay-line

An electro-magnetic wave in free space travels 300 metres (i.e., 0·186 miles) in 1 μs, or 64 × 300 = 19,200 metres in 64 μs. By comparison, a sound wave in air travels only 331 metres (i.e., 1100 ft) in one second and hence only approximately 2·1 cm (i.e., 0·85 in) in 64 μs.

To delay the r.f. chrominance signal by 64 μs it is first converted into an ultrasonic wave and this is then propagated along a solid glass block. The velocity of the ultra-sonic wave along the block in the type of glass normally used, is typically 2750 metres per second or 2·75 mm per μs. This implies that the block length must be (64 × 2·75) mm = 17·6 cm for a 64 μs delay. A similar transducer at the receiving end reverses the process and the chrominance signal is recovered as an electro-magnetic signal. The wave propagated along the glass delay-line has the same form as a 'sound' wave and for this reason the line is sometimes described as an 'acoustic' delay-line. The word acoustic is however, a misnomer when applied to a 4·43 MHz signal and the term 'ultrasonic' is better. Figure 12.1(a) illustrates the basic structure of the type of chrominance signal delay-line described.

Delay-line transducers

The transducers are simply slices of piezo-electric material mounted between two metal plates usually called electrodes. These units have the properties (so widely used in other devices such as crystal microphones and pick-ups) of producing an e.m.f. between the electrodes if the piezo-electric material is mechanically deformed, or, conversely, of showing mechanical deformation when an e.m.f. is applied to the electrodes.

The chrominance signal is applied to the plates of such a transducer fixed at one end of the delay-line. The vibration of the piezo-electric slice then sets up an ultra-sonic wave which travels along the glass block. Upon reaching the end it sets up a vibration of the piezo-electric material in the receiving transducer. This in turn re-establishes the chrominance signal in an electrical form as an e.m.f. between the transducer plates. There is naturally a power loss in this process and typically the

194

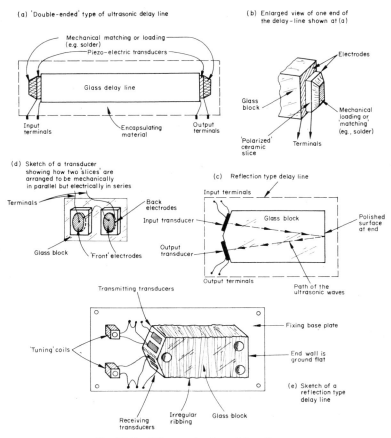

Fig. 12.1 *Ultrasonic glass delay-lines*

Diagrams illustrating the structure of the 'one-line' (i.e., 64 μs) chrominance signal delay-lines used in PAL-D receivers.

overall loss of the delay-line is of the order 12 dB. Compensation for this loss is necessary before the electrical summation of the direct and delayed signals.

For many years quartz crystals were used whenever piezo-electric properties were sought. Piezo-electric ceramics are now widely used instead of quartz, e.g., in PAL delay-lines lead-zirconate-titanate is often employed. Such materials offer better electrical characteristics and are cheaper to produce and process.

Each transducer has one electrode in intimate contact with an end wall of the glass delay-line. In early PAL delay-lines the outer (or non-working) electrodes were in contact with a solder mass forming a terminating mechanical load which absorbed energy without creating reflections back along the line. These formed matching terminations analogous to the characteristic impedance terminations of an electrical

195

transmission line. Later lines now in use, are simpler in construction, yet perfectly adequate in performance.

The transducer is fixed to the delay-line by evaporating solder on to both the end wall of the glass block and the 'working-plate' of the transducer. On heating, a bond is formed between the two. The piezo-electric slices are very thin in a practical transducer, typically being some 0·3 mm thick and of about 1 cm^2 surface area.

Sound waves (or in this application 'ultrasonic' waves) can be of two forms. These are categorized according to the way in which the particles of the transmitting medium (e.g., air, glass, steel, etc.) vibrate as the wave travels.

If the molecules of the medium move to-and-fro in the direction in which the wave travels, the medium undergoes successive half-cycles of compression and rarefaction along the transmission direction. Such waves are described as 'compression' or 'longitudinal' vibrations.

Alternatively, the atoms or molecules of the medium may move to-and-fro along a line which is perpendicular to the direction of travel. These are known as transverse vibrations. A useful conception of what is meant by a transverse vibration may be gained by studying a cork floating in a still pond. When a stone is dropped in the pond a wave motion spreads radially from the point of impact. When the wave passes it, the cork rides up and down (as do the molecules of water). It does *not* move off in the direction in which the wave motion is travelling.

Piezo-electric slices may be obtained which vibrate either across the slice in the direction of the applied field between the plates, or at right angles to the field. The former, if fixed to a glass rod, will induce a 'longitudinal or compression' vibration, whilst the latter will create a 'transverse or shear' vibration. The word 'shear' is used to denote a transverse vibration in a solid because the forces exerted when the material vibrates in this way are such that they create a shearing stress.

The terminology used in describing the properties of piezo-electric slices was developed in connection with quartz crystal slices. A complete quartz crystal (from which a slice is cut) is described in terms of three axes mutually at right angles to one another. The Z axis passes from end to end; an X axis passes from a corner to the opposite corner, and a Y axis passes from the centre of a flat face to the centre of the opposite face. This is illustrated in Fig. 12.2. Since the quartz crystal has six faces there are clearly three possible X axes and three Y axes.

Crystal slices cut with their faces perpendicular to a Y-axis are said to be Y-cut, whilst those cut with faces perpendicular to an X-axis are described as X-cut. The Y-axis is sometimes referred to as the mechanical axis because mechanical deformation is always along this axis. It follows that Y-cut slices are 'thickness-vibrators' and X-cut are 'shear-vibrators'.

Slices of ceramics may be treated so that they also exhibit one of the two possible characteristics displayed naturally by X- and Y-cut quartz crystal slices. The process is known as 'polarization'. This involves heating the ceramic slice in an oil bath to a temperature of about 150°C whilst simultaneously maintaining across it a potential of the order of 1 to 3 kV. If the potential is applied between the two large faces (i.e.,

196

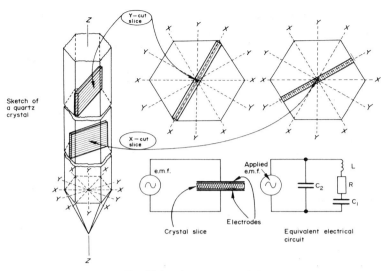

Fig. 12.2 *Quartz crystal slices*

across the narrow width of the slice) it becomes permanently polarized in such a way that it behaves as a 'thickness' vibrator (i.e., is equivalent to a Y-cut quartz crystal slice). If the potential is applied between the narrow edges then, on cooling, the ceramic slice behaves as a 'shear' (or transverse) vibrator (i.e., it is equivalent to an X-cut quartz slice). In both cases when the slice is in use its electrodes are of course on its main faces. The techniques are illustrated in Fig. 12.3.

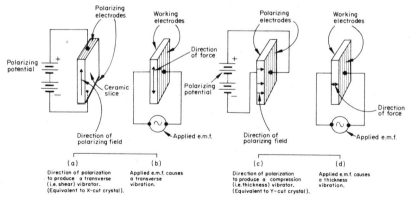

Fig. 12.3 *Showing the planes of polarization of ceramic slices (e.g., lead-zirconate-titanate) necessary to produce transverse and thickness vibrators*

Note:
(i) The slice is heated in an oil bath and the polarizing field is maintained for several minutes (e.g., temperature 150°C; electric field strength 3 kV/mm).
(ii) For a PAL-D transducer a ceramic slice has a surface area of about 1 cm^2 and is of the order of 0·3 mm thick.

Before the polarization of a ceramic slice, if mechanical deformation is plotted against the applied e.m.f. the characteristic is of parabolic form, with the nose of the parabola resting at the origin, i.e., at the zero potential point. In this condition it is a very non-linear device. After polarization, the slice behaves as though an electric field (such as would result from a permanent applied bias) is 'frozen' into it. In use it then acts as though the a.c. signal is applied in series with a d.c. bias. In effect this shifts the working point so that it lies to one side of the nose of the parabola, beneath a much more linear part of the characteristic.

Since ultrasonic waves induced by transverse vibrations have a lower velocity of propagation along the glass bar than the compression waves formed by thickness vibrators (the ratio is about 0·56 to 1). transverse (or 'shear') mode ceramic slices are preferred since the PAL delay-line is then physically shorter than it would have to be using a thickness vibrator.

The slice is 'tuned' so that at the centre operating frequency of 4·43361875 MHz it has a peak performance. To achieve this it has a surface area of a little less than 1 cm^2. Its thickness is $\lambda/2$ at 4·43 MHz, where λ is the wavelength of the signal in the glass block (i.e., $\lambda = v/f$ where f is the frequency and v is the velocity of the ultrasonic wave in the particular glass used). It should be noted that, in common with many other materials, not only does glass expand when heated but the velocity of propagation of acoustic waves through it, also increases. A material in which these two qualities change by compensating amounts is described as being *isopaustic*. The glass chosen for use in PAL delay-lines has this property and it is in this way that the propagation time is held within the close tolerances mentioned earlier.

In most current PAL delay-lines the two transducers are mounted on inclined surfaces at the same end of the glass block as shown in Fig. 12.1(e). The ultrasonic wave is transmitted by one transducer, travels along the block and is reflected off the polished end wall to travel back to the receiving transducer. By this method the required delay is obtained with a block which is only half as long as the original 'two-ended' delay-line. An important advantage of the reflection-type delay-line is that when manufactured, the precise required delay-time may be achieved by grinding the reflecting face until dynamic tests show that it is exactly correct. Clearly, to do this with a double-ended type would necessitate the constant removal and re-fitting of one of the transducers in order to grind the glass. For this reason, the original lines were fitted with external delay-time adjusting inductors but these are not so necessary in the reflection type.

Since reflection from the side walls of the glass block would cause interference with the propagated chrominance signal, the sides of the block are scored with irregular grooves. These uneven surfaces have the effect of producing random reflections which tend to cancel one another out.

Matching the PAL delay-line electrically

Typical characteristic impedances (R_0) of PAL delay-lines range from 50 Ω to 150 Ω. The higher figure is sometimes achieved by using transducers having two slices instead

198

of one. This is shown in the sketch in Fig. 12.1(d). The two ceramic slices are mechanically in parallel but electrically in series. This has the effect of increasing the impedance.

Ceramic transducers have a high input capacitance of the order 1000 pF to 2000 pF. As shown at (e), small inductors are fitted to 'tune-out' this capacitance. When this is done the parallel circuit so formed is at resonance and the transducer presents a resistive load; typically of 150 Ω. Obviously the Q factor is very low since the bandwidth is 2 MHz, centred on a frequency of 4·43 MHz. The three terminals to each transducer allow the inductors to be disconnected, replaced, or supplemented if required.

Summary of typical PAL-D delay-line specification

(a) Nominal delay time: 63·943 μs at 4·43361875 MHz
(b) 'Length' of line in sub-carrier cycles: $283\frac{1}{2}$ cycles
(c) Accuracy of delay time adjustment: $\pm 0·003$ μs at 25°C
(d) Bandwidth (between -3 dB points): 2 MHz
(e) Insertion loss: 10 dB $\pm$ 3 dB
(f) Maximum input: 25 volts peak-to-peak
(g) Operating temperature range: $-20°C$ to 70°C
(h) Required source resistance: 150 Ω
(i) Required terminating resistance: 150 Ω

Addition and subtraction of direct and delayed signals

To add the direct to the delayed signals it is merely necessary to arrange for the two signals to have their transmitted relative phases and be presented in series to a common resistor load. Similarly, to achieve the equivalent of subtraction, one of the two signals must be inverted so that when they are applied in series with one another, the net result is the difference between the two.

It is clearly necessary that the direct and delayed signals shall have equal amplitudes. There are various ways of meeting this requirement.

For example a voltage step-up transformer may be used following the delay-line.

Assuming a delay-line loss of 16 dB, this represents an input-to-output voltage ratio of:

$$16 = 20 \log_{10} (V_i/V_o)$$
$$V_i/V_o = \text{anti-log } 0·8 = 6·3 : 1$$

A compensating step-up voltage transformation ratio of 6·3:1 is needed at the output of the delay-line to make the final output voltage V_o once again equal to V_i. Similarly to compensate for a 10 dB line loss, the step-up ratio would need to be 3·2:1.

A second possibility is to attenuate the direct signal (relative to that fed into the delay-line) so that its amplitude is equal to that of the delayed signal issuing from the delay-line.

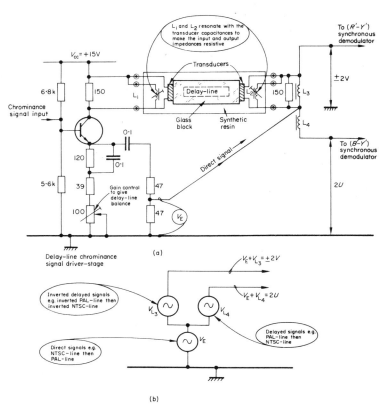

Fig. 12.4   *Addition and subtraction of 'direct' and 'delayed' chrominance signals*
The diagram shows typical 'Summation' circuitry (see also Fig. 10.1).

Figure 12.4(a) shows an example of this method. The direct signal is taken from the emitter of the delay-line 'driver' stage whilst the delay-line itself is fed with a larger amplitude anti-phase signal taken from the collector. Connected to the output terminals of the delay-line is a 1:1 auto-transformer and the direct signal is applied to the centre-tap of this winding. Since opposite ends of the winding are in anti-phase relative to the centre-tap, the required addition and subtraction is achieved. The simplified diagram of Fig. 12.4(b) depicts the direct and delayed signals as generators and allows the action of the summation process to be perceived.

Thirdly, a post-delay-line amplifier may be used to compensate for the loss due to the delay-line. This amplifier is then interposed between the delay-line and the summation circuitry. Figure 12.5(a) shows an example of this method. The gain control in the emitter of the post-delay-line amplifier Tr_4 is set to establish equality between the output at the collector of the amplifier and the input to the delay-line, i.e., to make the 'direct' and 'delayed' signals equal.

200

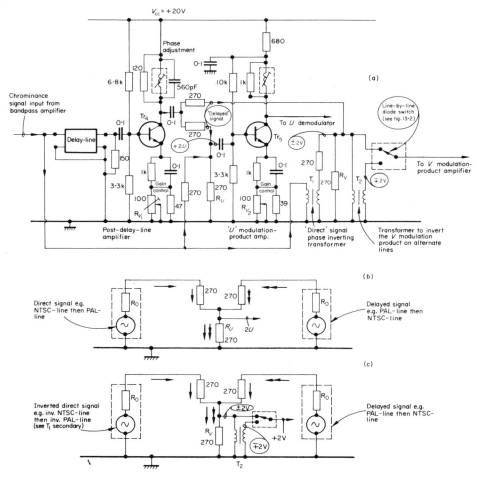

Fig. 12.5 *PAL-D chrominance signal summation circuitry*

(Associated diagrams: Figs. 11.8, 13.2, 14.3, 15.2, 17.5)

These two signals then pass to the summation circuits. The U modulation-product is obtained by adding the two signals and the V modulation-product by adding the inverted direct signal to the delayed signal.

At (b) and (c) simplified diagrams are drawn to show the arrangement of these circuits. Two generators represent the two signal sources. These are shown as having an internal impedance of R_0. Dealing first with the U circuit at (b), one generator represents the output from the chrominance amplifier emitter follower (not shown) which feeds the delay-line. The other generator represents the output from the post-delay-line amplifier Tr_4. These generators are assumed to have approximately the

201

same output impedances. Adding is accomplished by connecting the two generators via 270 Ω resistors to a common 270 Ω load resistor R_U. The voltage across R_U is proportional to the sum of the two currents and these in turn, since the circuit is resistive and completely symmetrical, are proportional to the two individual generator voltages and equal in magnitude. In this way a voltage is obtained which is directly proportional to the sum of the two signals.

To obtain the V modulation-product, the circuit is arranged to provide an output which is proportional to the sum of the inverted direct-signal and the delayed-signal. The output from the pre-delay-line amplifier is inverted by the 1:1 transformer T_1. The voltage induced in the secondary therefore has the same amplitude as the 'direct' signal into the delay-line, but is in anti-phase with it. In the simplified diagram at (c) this inverted direct-signal is shown as being developed by a generator having an internal impedance R_0. Since T_1 is of 1:1 ratio, the transformed impedance in the secondary is equal to the output impedance of the emitter-follower which feeds the delay-line and this was designated R_0 in the diagram at (b).

The inverted direct-signal and the delayed-signal generators are in a balanced circuit, sharing a common load resistor R_V. The current in this resistor—and hence the voltage across it—is proportional to the sum of the inverted direct-signal and the delayed-signal voltages.

As shown in the previous chapter, the polarity of the V modulation-product obtained by the PAL-D system changes sign on each line. This is corrected in the V synchronous demodulator by a switching circuit which is used to give line-by-line inversion of one of the two inputs to the V demodulator, i.e., either the V modulation-product delivered by the subtractor, or the sub-carrier from the reference oscillator. In this particular circuit the former method is used. The inversion is achieved by the second 1:1 transformer T_2 and the line-by-line switch selects the V modulation-product from the primary of T_2 on one line and from the secondary on the next line.

A further example of delay-line circuitry is shown in Fig. 12.6. The chrominance signal, having passed through a two-stage chrominance amplifier and a burst-blanking circuit, passes to the base of the delay-line driver transistor Tr_{10}.

This works as an emitter-follower as far as the delay-line is concerned and the component values in the emitter circuit, together with the transistor's own output impedance, establish a match into the 150 Ω input impedance of the delay-line. The output from the delay-line is applied between base and emitter of transistor Tr_{11}. The load for this transistor is the 470 Ω emitter resistor. Since the low-potential terminal of the delay-line is returned to the upper (i.e., emitter) end of this load resistor, the stage is working, not as an emitter-follower in the normal sense (i.e., where the input returns to earth so that there is 100% feedback and the gain is less than unity) but as an emitter-loaded amplifier.

The amplified output from the emitter load is of course in phase with the base input signal (contrary to a collector-loaded stage which introduces signal inversion). The delayed-signal from the emitter is taken to the V and U resistor matrixing circuits. It is convenient to refer to both of these under the heading of summation circuits.

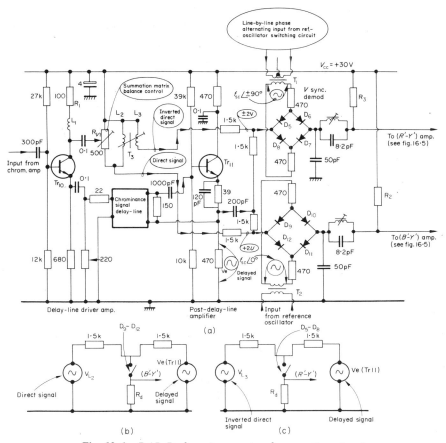

Fig. 12.6 *PAL-D chrominance signal summation circuitry*

(Associated diagrams: Figs. 13.5, 13.7, 14.1, 15.5, 16.5, 17.8, 17.10)

The direct signal for these two summation circuits is taken from the collector of Tr_{10}. The inductor L_1 provides h.f. compensation to linearize the response curve of this amplifier.[1] Across the collector load, which comprises R_1 and L_1, is a 500 Ω potentiometer. This allows an amplitude balance to be achieved, between the direct and delayed signals which are applied to the summation circuits from the collector of Tr_{10} and the emitter of Tr_{11} respectively. The direct-signal from the lower end of this potentiometer is applied to the input terminal of the U demodulator, via a 1·5 kΩ resistor. Also applied to this point is the delayed signal from Tr_{11} emitter; again through a 1·5 kΩ resistor. There is no actual load resistor connected to the junction

[1] See Video Amplifier h.f. Compensation Techniques, in *Television Receiver Theory*: Part 1, published by Arnolds of London.

203

of the two 1·5 kΩ resistors, to compare with the resistor R_U in the previous circuit. However, it is only during the time that the actual 'sampling' operation takes place, that the direct and delayed signals need to be combined. When the four-diode ring-type demodulator is switched on by the sub-carrier from the reference oscillator, the junction of the two 1·5 kΩ resistors is connected through the conductive diodes and the sub-carrier filter to the resistor R_2.

In the simplified diagram of Fig. 12.6(b) the resistance seen looking through the four-diode demodulator (when it is conductive) is shown as R_d, and the diodes are represented by a switch which closes for one half of each sub-carrier cycle. It is clear that the current through the effective load R_d is proportional to the sum of the direct and delayed signal voltages which both create currents through the demodulator. From a d.c. point of view the input and output terminals of the demodulator are held at similar potentials since both return to the V_{cc} line.

The circuit for the V demodulator is similar. However, since the phase of the delayed-signal fed to the V demodulator, is the same as that to the U demodulator, it follows that the direct-signal to the V summation circuit must be inverted. The inversion is achieved by the 1 : 1 transformer T_3. In this circuit, contrary to the previous one, it is the reference sub-carrier to the V demodulator which is inverted by the line-by-line switch and not the V component. The actual switching circuit is studied in the next chapter.

It is perhaps true that the absence of matrix 'load' resistors, corresponding to R_U and R_V in the previous diagram, makes this circuit a little more confusing. If such resistors were shown connected from the earth line to the junctions of the pairs of 1·5 kΩ resistors, then the modulation-products of U in the one case and $\pm V$ in the other, could be seen to be present at the inputs to the $(B' - Y')$ and $(R' - Y')$ demodulators respectively. These voltages would then be considered to be sensed once per sub-carrier half-cycle and transferred through the then conductive four-diode demodulators via the low-pass filter circuits to the input terminals of the $(B' - Y')$ and $(R' - Y')$ colour-difference signal amplifiers.

However, these resistors are electrically unnecessary since no U and V modulation-products are needed when the diodes are 'off', and when they are 'on' the required loads for the two matrixes are, as stated, effectively switched into position by the diodes.

Adjustment of delay-line balance controls

For the proper operation of the PAL-D system, the direct and delayed signals applied to the summation circuits must be of equal amplitude. Receivers make provision for obtaining this equality by placing a variable control somewhere in the circuit to allow the amplitude of one or the other of the two signals to be adjusted.

In Fig. 12.6 it is the direct signal's amplitude which is adjustable by the 500 Ω potentiometer R_{v1}. Conversely in Fig. 12.5 the adjustment is in the delayed-signal's path. Here the post-delay-line amplifier's gain is variable (see R_{v1} in the emitter circuit of Tr_4).

There is a simple technique for setting this adjustment. If there is no line-by-line switched $(R' - Y')$ component in the chrominance signal, the output from the V signal 'subtractor' circuit is zero. It follows that if a continuous sine-wave at 4·43361875 MHz is fed into the delay line circuitry, the algebraic sum of the direct and delayed signals from the subtractor will be zero, provided that they are both of equal amplitude. This is obvious when it is remembered that the V component is in practice produced by adding an inverted delayed signal to the direct signal (or vice versa), and when the signal is a simple continuous sine-wave this process must yield zero output.

The necessary sine-wave is available from the receiver reference oscillator but it is imperative that the frequency be exactly correct. For this to be so the receiver must be locked to an incoming colour transmission.

The method of adjustment is as follows:

(a) Tune in a colour signal.
(b) Remove the chrominance signal input to the delay-line driver stage.
(c) Replace this input by a sub-carrier frequency signal applied by a suitable cross connection (e.g., via a 100 pF capacitor) from the reference oscillator output circuit to the input of the delay-line driver amplifier. (*N.B.* If the delay-line driver amplifier does *not* also feed a *direct* signal to the delay-line output summation circuitry, the sub-carrier must be applied to the chrominance amplifier which precedes the driver stage.)
(d) Connect an oscilloscope via a high-impedance probe to the output terminal of the subtractor circuit (i.e., the input terminal of the V synchronous demodulator) and adjust the delay-line balance control for minimum amplitude of the r.f. signal displayed on the oscilloscope.

Not only must the direct and delayed signals be of equal amplitude, but their relative phases must also be correctly set. Cancellation of the V component at the adder and of the U component at the subtractor, only takes place if the components which are supposed to cancel out, are truly in antiphase.

Provision for a delay-line phase balance adjustment is sometimes included, by placing a pre-set control in either the direct or the delayed signal paths. The same procedure as described for amplitude balancing, may be used to adjust this pre-set. If the amplitude control is presupposed to be correctly set, then the phase adjustment has the effect of 'moving along' one of the sine waves until it is exactly in antiphase with the other at the V component (i.e., the subtractor) output terminal.

In practice therefore, both adjustments may be made together, to establish zero (or very nearly zero) output, at the V terminal.

A number of service generators, some of them of sophisticated and ingenious design, include amongst their various test signals, special provision for delay-line circuitry balance adjustments.

13

PAL-D Decoder Techniques: V-Channel
Switching Circuitry

Of the two inputs to the V synchronous demodulator, *either* the V modulation-product *or* the reference sub-carrier, must be inverted in phase by a switching circuit which operates during the line blanking period at the end of each active picture line.

It is usual to employ two semiconductor diodes to carry out the actual switching operation. Each diode has to go 'on' for one line and 'off' for the next. To achieve this a square wave at half the line frequency fed in anti-phase to the two diodes, is needed. The square wave has to complete $15,625/2 = 7812\frac{1}{2}$ cycles in one picture period.

A component at this frequency is present in the incoming signal because of the phase modulation of the 4·43 MHz sub-carrier burst transmitted in the back-porch period. The burst phase is switched line-by-line by $\mp 45°$ about its mean phase of $180°$, to allow the receiver to identify the alternate 'NTSC-' and 'PAL-lines' of the PAL signal. On 'NTSC-lines' the burst phase is $135°$ and on 'PAL-lines' it is $225°$. Since one complete swing of the burst phase takes place every two lines, the cyclic frequency of the 'swinging' burst-phase is half the line frequency, i.e., 7·8125 kHz. This is normally quoted approximately as 7·8 kHz and referred to as the IDENT signal.

Figure 13.1 shows in simplified form, the basic principle of a diode switching circuit. The necessary line-by-line inversion of one of the two inputs to the V-demodulator is brought about by connecting the signal to opposite halves of the primary of transformer T_1 on alternate lines so that the voltage induced in the secondary is of the required phase on every line.

The 7·8 kHz square wave switching signal to the diodes may either be derived directly from the swinging burst, or it may be generated by a bistable multivibrator which is triggered once per line by pulses from the line timebase and synchronized by the 7·8 kHz IDENT signal.

An example of the first method is shown in Fig. 13.2. As is described in chapter 15 the burst signal is gated out of the composite video signal and fed to an automatic phase control circuit which also receives a signal from the receiver's reference oscillator.

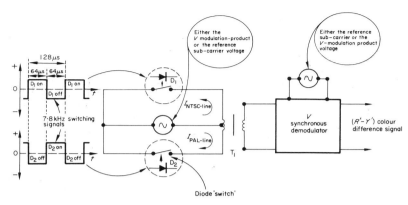

Fig. 13.1 *Showing the basic principle of a V-channel diode switching circuit*

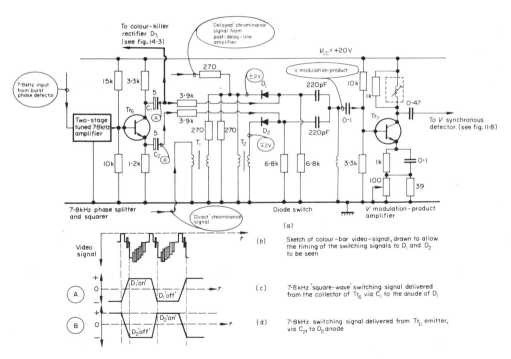

(a)

(b) Sketch of colour-bar video-signal, drawn to allow the timing of the switching signals to D₁ and D₂ to be seen

(c) 7·8kHz 'square-wave' switching signal delivered from the collector of Tr₆ via C₁ to the anode of D₁

(d) 7·8kHz switching signal delivered from Tr₆ emitter, via C₂, to D₂ anode

Fig. 13.2 *PAL-D V-component line-by-line switching circuit*
(Associated diagrams: Figs. 11.8, 12.5, 14.3, 15.2, 17.5)

207

The purpose of this circuit is to lock the receiver's reference oscillator to the correct sub-carrier frequency, as represented by the burst.

It is from this A.P.C. circuit that the 7·8 kHz component borne by the burst signal is taken off. In the receiver now being studied, the 7·8 kHz component passes through two tuned amplifiers which develop a roughly sinusoidal waveform. This is passed to the squarer stage Tr_6 shown in Fig. 13.2. This transistor is driven hard by the waveform so that it alternately 'bottoms' and is 'cut-off' on the positive and negative half-cycles respectively. Anti-phase 7·8 kHz squared waveforms appear at its collector and emitter, and these are a.c. coupled to the anodes of the two switching diodes D_1 and D_2, so switching them on and off alternately. The waveforms at (c) and (d) illustrate this and the colour-bar signal waveform at (b) allows the timing of the switching action to be related to the incoming video signal. Each diode is on for one half-cycle only of the 7·8 kHz signal which means that it is on for one picture line and off for the next; the switch-over taking place during the 12 µs line-blanking period.

The summation circuitry by which the V component is obtained by adding currents derived from the inverted direct signal and the delayed signal, was described under Fig. 12.5 in the previous chapter. The V modulation-product is taken via D_1 from the primary of T_2 on one line but via D_2 from the secondary of T_2 on the next. Since the signal at the secondary of T_2 is in anti-phase with that at the primary, it follows that by switching from the primary to the secondary on alternate lines, the line-by-line alternation of the V component at the transmitter is countered and the input to the pre-demodulator V-component amplifier Tr_7 is of the same phase on NTSC- and PAL-lines. This signal then goes forward, together with an unswitched (i.e., constant phase) reference sub-carrier to the $(R' - Y')$ demodulator shown in Fig. 11.8.

The second method, using a bistable multivibrator, is, however, more widely used. Before looking at examples of complete circuits, it is useful to summarize the basic principles of bistable multivibrators.

Basic bistable multivibrator circuits

In a bistable multivibrator which uses two transistors of the same form (i.e., two p-n-p or two n-p-n transistors) one transistor is always fully ON whilst the other is OFF, at any one time. It is 'stable' in either of the two possible states (e.g., with Tr_1 ON and Tr_2 OFF, or with Tr_1 OFF and Tr_2 ON), hence the description 'bistable'. The circuit remains in one of these states until an applied trigger-pulse causes it to switch over to its alternate state where it again rests until the next trigger-pulse returns it to its original condition.

Bistable multivibrators which employ a complementary pair of transistors (i.e., one n-p-n and one p-n-p), again have two stable states but here both go ON and OFF together.

Figure 13.3 shows various circuits using two n-p-n transistors. The circuit at (a)

208

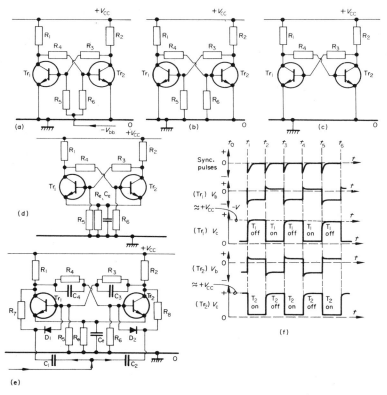

Fig. 13.3 *Bistable multivibrators using two n-p-n transistors*

forms a logical introduction. If Tr_1 is assumed ON, its collector voltage will be almost zero, e.g., at $+200$ mV. Under this condition R_4 and R_6 form a potential divider connected virtually between 'earth' and $-V_{bb}$. This places the junction of R_4 and R_6 at a negative potential relative to earth, hence placing a back-bias on the base-emitter junction of Tr_2 which holds this transistor completely cut-off. Clearly the circuit will rest indefinitely in this condition if no other influence is brought to bear upon it. A positive pulse to Tr_2 base, of sufficient amplitude to overcome the back-bias, will, however, cause Tr_2 to conduct and this in turn drives the base of Tr_1 negative so cutting Tr_1 off. With Tr_1 OFF its collector voltage is at $+V_{cc}$. Resistors R_1, R_4, and R_6 are now connected between $+V_{cc}$ and $-V_{bb}$. The resistor values are so chosen that this makes the junction R_4, R_6 positive to earth by the amount necessary to provide Tr_2 with a suitable forward bias. Once switched on therefore, Tr_2 stays on until a positive pulse to Tr_1 base causes Tr_1 to go ON and Tr_2 OFF again.

Instead of applying a positive trigger pulse direct to the OFF transistor, a common method is to provide a smaller amplitude pulse of opposite polarity to the base of the

209

ON transistor. The ON transistor works as an 'amplifier'—passing an amplified but inverted pulse to the OFF transistor, so switching it ON and in turn being itself switched OFF as a result. Hence, if Tr_2 is OFF a negative pulse to the conductive Tr_1 gives rise to a positive pulse at Tr_1 collector. This is passed on by the d.c. coupling network to Tr_2 base so switching Tr_2 ON. When Tr_2 goes ON it puts Tr_1 OFF.

The circuit at (a) has the disadvantage of requiring both positive and negative supply voltages. At (b) the resistors R_5 and R_6 are returned to earth instead of to a negative potential. Clearly, it is now not possible for the base of either transistor to be negative to its emitter, hence neither can be completely cut-off. However, if—for example—Tr_1 is fully ON, its collector is very nearly at zero potential and this small potential (say of 200 mV) is all there is across the potential divider R_4R_6. This leaves the base of Tr_2 only slightly positive to its emitter and this very small forward bias leaves the collector current of Tr_2 at a very low level. Conversely, with such a low current through R_2, the collector voltage of Tr_2 is only a little below $+V_{cc}$. This provides a positive forward bias on the base of Tr_1, at the junction of R_3 and R_5. The circuit is less incisive in its action than (a) but is perfectly adequate for many applications and will be found in some PAL-D receivers.

At (c) still another economy is made, by leaving out the earth return resistors R_5 and R_6. Again, if Tr_1 is ON, its collector voltage is almost zero and the forward bias current provided by R_4 to the base of Tr_2 is very low. Conversely, the collector voltage of Tr_2 is almost at $+V_{cc}$ and R_3 provides the base-emitter junction of Tr_1 with a strong forward bias current.

One disadvantage of both (b) and (c) is that the lack of an actual 'back-bias' on the OFF transistor makes the circuit responsive to smaller noise pulses than would trouble circuit (a).

The circuit at (d) has the advantages of (a) without the need for the $-V_{bb}$ supply rail. This is achieved by the use of the common emitter-bias circuit R_eC_e. The time constant R_eC_e is long compared with the periodic time of the multivibrator, which is assumed to be regularly triggered as it is in the PAL-D application.

If Tr_1 is ON its steady emitter current maintains a positive voltage across R_eC_e, and this same voltage is present at Tr_2 emitter. But the collector voltage of Tr_1 is almost at this same potential and resistors $R_4 R_6$ may be regarded as being connected across R_eC_e. The ratio of R_4 to R_6 is chosen to make the base of Tr_2 well negative to its emitter so that Tr_2 is cut-off. The circuit has a greater noise immunity than (b) or (c). It is redrawn at (e) with the following additions:

(i) *Steering diodes*

A regular succession of negative-going trigger pulses is assumed to be applied to the junction of C_1 and C_2. Each pulse needs to be routed to the ON transistor, to be passed on as an amplified positive-going pulse to switch on the OFF transistor. This is achieved by the use of the steering diodes D_1 and D_2 with their associated resistors R_7 and R_8. Each diode is cut-off completely when the transistor to which it is connected is OFF. This is because its cathode returns to the collector which rests at $+V_{cc}$

210

when the transistor is off, whilst its anode returns to the base which is only slightly positive to earth. Conversely, when a transistor is ON the associated diode is conductive since its cathode (like the transistor's collector) is virtually at emitter potential, whilst its anode is at the almost equal positive base potential. When Tr_1 is ON, the next pulse to arrive is blocked by D_2 but passed by D_1 to the base of Tr_1. The resulting positive-going pulse delivered from the collector of Tr_1 to the base of Tr_2, causes Tr_2 to switch hard on and Tr_1 then goes off. The next trigger pulse is blocked by D_1 but passed by D_2 to the base of Tr_2. This reaches Tr_1 as a positive pulse so switching Tr_1 ON again and Tr_2 off.

(ii) *Speed-up capacitors*

The input impedance of a transistor has a capacitive element. Referring to circuit (b), when Tr_2 is OFF, R_6 may be regarded as being shunted by a capacitor formed by the back-biased base-emitter 'diode' connected across it. When a positive trigger pulse appears at Tr_1 collector, the base of Tr_2 cannot immediately switch to the level dictated by the potential divider $R_4 R_6$. Some time must elapse whilst the shunt capacitor charges via the coupling resistor, R_4. This delays the switch-over of the circuit. Treating the ON transistor as an amplifier, the presence of the shunt capacitance degrades the response curve, causing the overall gain/frequency characteristic to fall off at higher frequencies. This prevents the 'amplifier' from handling the step-function without 'distortion'.

To overcome this, the amplifier coupling circuit must be made aperiodic, i.e., unaffected by frequency. This may be accomplished by shunting the series coupling resistor with a capacitor having a value such that the time-constant of these two components equals the time constant of the input impedance of the next stage. Because these capacitors improve the rate at which the circuit can switch over states, they are called speed-up capacitors. In Fig. 13.3(e), C_3 and C_4 serve this purpose. If $C_{(i)}$ is the input capacitance to Tr_2 when it is OFF, then C_4 should have a value such that $R_4 C_4 = R_6 C_{(i)}$.

Waveforms

The waveforms for the basic circuit of Fig. 13.3(a) are shown at (f). Normally, for most applications and for PAL-D use, the circuits are symmetrical, i.e., $R_1 = R_2$, $R_4 = R_3$, $R_5 = R_6$, etc. Ideally the collector voltage waveforms would be square waves, moving between the limiting values of $+V_{cc}$ and 0 V, as the transistors switch OFF and ON. In practice, the presence of capacitance across the input and output circuits, together with the phenomenon of 'charge-storage' in the base material of the transistors, causes curvature; particularly on the rising edges of these waveforms.

For circuit (e), the collector voltage waveforms descend not to the near-zero level reached in circuits (a), (b), and (c), but to the steady emitter potential across $R_e C_e$, and the negative excursions of the base voltages (i.e., the extent of the back-bias) is less. Otherwise the waveforms have the same 'shape' as those shown. (*N.B.* The

211

effect of speed-up capacitors cannot be shown on such small scale diagrams. This would, however, show up on an 'expanded' oscilloscope trace.)

Complementary bistable multivibrator circuits

The circuits in Fig. 13.4 show the basic form of bistable multivibrators using complementary pairs of transistors. The circuit at (a) needs positive and negative supply

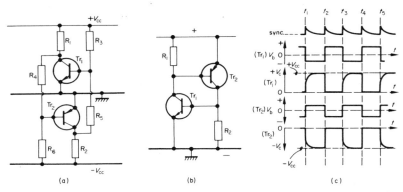

Fig. 13.4   *Bistable multivibrators using complementary transistors (i.e., one n-p-n and one p-n-p)*

voltages. As stated earlier, both transistors go ON and OFF together. If, for example, Tr_1 is assumed OFF then the junction of R_1 and R_4 is virtually at $+V_{cc}$. This causes the potential at the junction of R_4 and R_6 to be positive to 'earth' so ensuring that Tr_2 (which is of p-n-p type), is also OFF. Meanwhile the junction of R_2 and R_5 is at $-V_{cc}$ and this causes the potential at the junction of R_3 and R_5 to be negative to earth, so that the base of the n-p-n transistor Tr_1 is negative and Tr_1 is held cut-off.

If, say, a positive trigger pulse is applied to Tr_1 base to over-ride the back-bias, then Tr_1 will switch on and this in turn drives the base of Tr_2 negative so that it, also, switches on. Both now remain ON until another pulse (e.g., a positive pulse to Tr_2 base) switches one—and hence the other—off again.

The routing of successive positive trigger pulses, first to Tr_1 and then to Tr_2, may be achieved by the use of steering diodes. Circuit waveforms are shown at (c).

A complementary circuit has the advantage that a steep-fronted positive-going step is obtainable from one collector and a similarly steep-fronted negative-going step is available at the other. Two n-p-n transistors on the other hand (as in Fig. 13.3) produce at *both* collectors, steep negative-going but rounded positive-going steps, whilst two p-n-p transistors yield steep positive-going but rounded negative-going edges. A further point of comparison is that 'normal' multivibrators take a constant current because one transistor is on and one is off in both states, but complementary-pair circuits take either a comparatively heavy current or none at all, as they move from 'state' to 'state'.

The simpler circuit shown at (b) does not require both positive and negative

212

power supplies. When Tr_1 is ON the voltage drop across R_1 makes the base of the p-n-p transistor Tr_2 negative to its emitter, so that Tr_2 is also ON. In turn the voltage drop across R_2 makes the base of the n-p-n transistor Tr_1 positive to its emitter and Tr_1 is held ON.

If either transistor is switched off by a trigger pulse which back-biases its base–emitter junction, the other is also switched off.

Bistable multivibrators in V-channel switching circuits

A bistable multivibrator which is triggered regularly at the end of each picture line by a pulse from the line timebase, completes one cycle of operation every two lines. Present at the collectors of the two transistors therefore, are 7·8 kHz square waveforms which are mutually in anti-phase. These are ideally suitable for application to the two diodes in the V-channel switch. If no other synchronizing information were applied to the multivibrator, however, the V-channel switch would stand an even chance of being out of step with the transmitter's PAL-switch.

Synchronization is achieved by feeding an IDENT signal to the bistable multivibrator. As before, this is derived from the swinging-burst at the A.P.C. circuit. Examples of practical circuits are now studied.

In Fig. 13.5 the four-diode $(R' - Y')$ synchronous demodulator $(D_{5–8})$, is fed with the V modulation-product from the delay-line 'subtractor' circuit. The subcarrier from the reference oscillator has its phase switched by $\pm 90°$ at line repetition frequency by the diode switching circuit D_3 and D_4. The sub-carrier is fed via C_3 and C_4 to the anodes of D_3 and D_4 respectively. On any given picture line, one of these diodes is conductive and one non-conductive. When D_3 is ON the sub-carrier current is routed through the top half of the primary of the sub-carrier coupling transformer T_1, and on the next line when D_3 is OFF and D_4 is ON, the current passes through the lower half. The effect of this is to cause the phase of the reference sub-carrier voltage induced in the secondary, to be inverted at the end of each line (i.e., it switches from $+90°$ on one line to $+90° + 180° = +270°$ on the next line).

The diodes are switched on and off by the bistable multivibrator Tr_1, Tr_2. Both diodes have their cathodes held at a potential of approximately $+8$ V relative to earth by the potential divider $R_{12}R_{13}$.

R_{13} is shunted by C_2 which provides a return path to earth for the sub-carrier current in T_1 primary and also removes from the cathode bias any component at 7·8 kHz.

The anodes of D_3 and D_4 are connected to the collectors of Tr_1 and Tr_2 respectively. Since the collectors alternate between potentials of $+V_{cc}$ and Ve as the transistors go OFF and ON, each diode goes ON when the transistor it is strapped to goes OFF. Thus when Tr_1 is OFF, D_3 anode is connected via R_{14} (560 Ω) and R_1 (1 kΩ) to $+30$ V whilst D_3 cathode is at $+8$ V, so that D_3 is strongly forward biased. Meanwhile Tr_2 is ON and D_4 anode is at $+Ve$ while its cathode is at $+8$ V so that D_4 is back-biased and of high resistance.

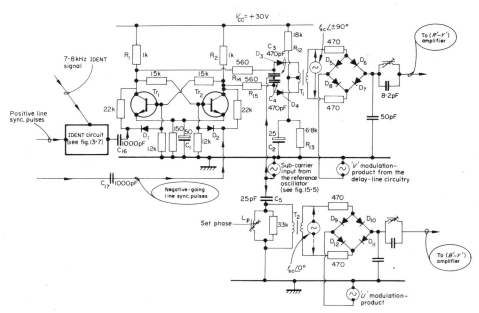

Fig. 13.5 *Example of a practical sub-carrier switching circuit and diode-ring synchronous demodulator in a PAL-D decoder*

(Associated diagrams: Figs. 12.6, 13.7, 14.1, 15.5, 16.5, 17.8, 17.10)

It is important that the back-bias on the OFF diode substantially exceeds the peak value of the applied reference sub-carrier voltage so that the diode is not pulsed into conduction by the positive peaks of this signal. In this same way, the ON diode must be forward biased sufficiently to ensure that the whole of the sub-carrier signal falls beneath the I_a/V_a curve and partial rectification of the signal is avoided. These two requirements are illustrated in Fig. 13.6. If the back-bias and forward-bias are of approximately double the peak amplitude of the applied reference sub-carrier, the circuit works with a good safety margin.

The two 560 Ω resistors stand-off the shunt capacitance of the multivibrator circuit so that the sub-carrier current is directed through D_3 and D_4.

Negative-going line pulses are fed via the steering diodes D_1 and D_2 to the bases of Tr_1 and Tr_2 respectively. The function of the 7·8 kHz IDENT signal in this and similar circuits, is simply to 'knock-out' one out of every two of the line pulses to *one* of the transistors; in this circuit to Tr_1. In the absence of the IDENT signal a continuous succession of line pulses reaches both steering diodes and upon first switching on it is a matter of chance which one of two successive pulses happens to switch on Tr_1. When the IDENT signal is present, only one out of every two line pulses gets through to trigger Tr_1. This puts the synchronization of the bistable multivibrator under the command of the incoming signal from which the IDENT waveform is derived.

214

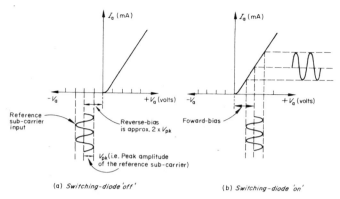

(a) *Switching-diode 'off'*   (b) *Switching-diode 'on'*

Fig. 13.6 *Showing the bias conditions for the V-channel switching diodes in the* OFF *and* ON *states*

The circuitry which develops and combines the line-triggering and IDENT signals is shown in Fig. 13.7.

Positive-going line pulses from the line timebase are fed to the base of the clipper and phase-splitter transistor Tr_3. This has no fixed forward bias and conducts only during the line pulses when the base is driven positive to emitter. In between pulses the discharge current from C_6 through R_{16} creates a negative back-bias on the base–emitter junction so that Tr_3 is cut-off.

The 30 V positive-going input pulses cause Tr_3 to bottom and squared negative-going line pulses from the collector are fed via C_{17} to the cathode of steering diode D_2 (Fig. 13.5).

Smaller amplitude positive-going pulses are simultaneously produced at Tr_3 emitter and these are fed via R_{19}, C_{14}, and C_{15} to the base of Tr_7. In the absence of an IDENT signal, these each give rise to a negative-going line pulse at the collector of Tr_7 which pass via C_{16} to the cathode of the steering diode D_1. During a normal colour transmission, however, every other one of these is eradicated by the negative half-cycle of a 7·8 kHz square IDENT waveform passed to the base of Tr_7 from the collector of Tr_6. Since Tr_7 has no fixed bias, it only conducts on the positive part of the net input signal which is a.c. coupled to its base. This input signal is the algebraic sum of the positive-going line pulses from Tr_3 emitter and the 7·8 kHz square wave from Tr_6 collector. Seen on an oscilloscope the waveforms present in the circuit are as shown below the diagram. Line pulses which coincide with the positive half-cycle of the IDENT square wave ride on the top of this flat-topped waveform and their tips are flattened by base current which charges C_{15}. The next line pulse coincides with the negative half of the IDENT signal and the greater amplitude of the latter prevents these alternate line pulses from driving the base of Tr_1 positive. Under normal conditions therefore, negative-going trigger pulses appear at Tr_7 collector only once every two lines and in this way synchronization of the PAL switch is achieved.

The squared IDENT signal is produced by the action of Tr_5 and Tr_6. The 7·8 kHz

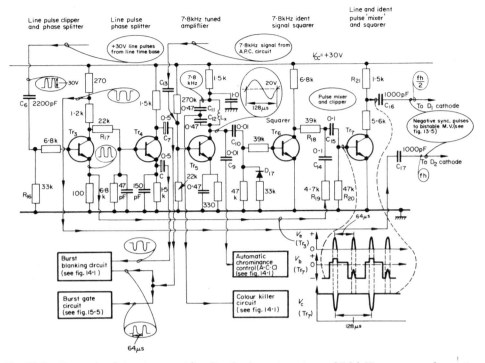

Fig. 13.7 *Example of circuitry providing line-by-line triggering and 7·8 kHz* IDENT *synchronizing pulses for the bistable multivibrator which controls the diode-switch in a PAL-D decoder (see Fig. 13.5). The circuit also provides output pulses to control the four other facilities shown in the blocks*

(Associated diagrams: Figs. 12.6, 13.5, 14.1, 15.5, 16.5, 17.8, 17.10)

'swinging-burst' component is taken from the A.P.C. circuit and coupled via C_{13} to the base of the tuned amplifier Tr_5. The roughly sinusoidal waveform from Tr_5 collector is a.c. coupled to the squarer stage Tr_6. This has no fixed bias but a small positive auto-bias is produced by D_{17} which partially rectifies the signal to produce a positive charge on the right-hand plate of C_{10}. Tr_6 delivers the required squared 7·8 kHz IDENT waveform to the base of Tr_7, as described. The 7·8 kHz signal from Tr_5 collector is used for two other purposes; for the 'colour-killer' and the 'automatic chrominance control' circuits. These are described in chapter 14 and shown in Fig. 14.1. The phasing of the 7·8 kHz square wave relative to the line-pulses, may be altered by adjustment of the core of inductor L_x in the collector tuned circuit.

It will be noticed that the negative-going line pulses from Tr_3 collector, are also fed to the base of a line-pulse phase splitter Tr_4. This transistor develops positive and negative line pulses at its collector and emitter respectively and these are used to operate chrominance amplifier burst-blanking and burst amplifier burst-gating

216

circuits. The action of these is described in chapter 14 (Fig. 14.1) and chapter 15 (Fig. 15.5) respectively.

Referring back to Fig. 13.5, the U synchronous demodulator is also included in the diagram to draw attention once again to the relative phases of the reference sub-carrier input voltages to the U and V demodulators. Inductor L_p introduces a lagging angle to the voltage applied to T_2 primary, to give T_2 secondary voltage a phase angle of $0°$ compared with the T_1 secondary voltage, which has a phase angle of $+90°$ on NTSC-lines and $-90°$ on PAL-lines.

Figure 13.8 shows a second example of a diode switching circuit driven by a bistable multivibrator. The reference sub-carrier for the V demodulator, is applied via C_1 to L_2 which forms half of the primary of transformer T_1. The transformer circuit is redrawn at (b) in a simplified form to allow its action to be studied more easily.

The centre-tap of the primary of T_1 is earthed. If V_B is the sub-carrier voltage applied to L_2, then the e.m.f. V_A induced in L_1 as a result of the current in L_2, is equal to—but in anti-phase with—V_B. The corresponding secondary voltages V'_B and V'_A are also equal in magnitude but opposite in phase. The diode switching circuit (D_3 and D_4) simply selects these voltages in turn on alternate lines, for application to the primary of the V-demodulator sub-carrier input transformer T_2.

This produces across T_2 secondary, for application to the V-demodulator ($D_5 \rightarrow D_8$), a reference sub-carrier voltage having a phase angle of $+90°$ on NTSC-lines and $+270°$ on PAL-lines. The 4·43 MHz tuned circuit connected across T_2 secondary improves the waveform by reducing the second-harmonic distortion caused by the switching action.

Before looking in more detail at the switching circuit it is interesting to note from (b) and (c) how the correct sub-carrier phase is obtained for application to the U demodulator. The 1·5 kΩ resistor R_2 is connected in series with the parallel combination C_2 and C_3, across the whole of T_1 primary. The trimmer C_3 is set to make the voltage V_C equal to V_R, ($N.B.$ At 4·43 MHz a capacitor of 25 pF presents a reactance of approximately 1·5 kΩ). V_R and V_C are at $90°$ to one another and since the voltage applied to the series combination is ($V_A + V_B$), the phasor diagram at (c) may be drawn. The voltage between earth and the junction of R and C is then represented by the phasor V_U, and this is at $90°$ to both V_A and V_B. But V_U is the voltage applied to the primary of the U-demodulator sub-carrier input transformer T_3 and it follows that across T_3 secondary the sub-carrier voltage V'_U is at $90°$ to the voltages V'_A and V'_B which form the alternately selected sub-carrier voltages for the V demodulator which are developed at T_1 secondary.

Referring now to the switching diodes D_3 and D_4, these work in a different way from those of the previous circuit. The anodes are returned to a positive potential of approximately 10 V and the cathodes return to the collectors of Tr_8 and Tr_9 respectively. Unlike the previous circuit therefore, each diode goes ON when the transistor it is strapped to is ON, i.e., when the collector voltage drops to 0 V, making the diode's cathode negative to its anode. When the transistor is OFF its collector voltage rises to

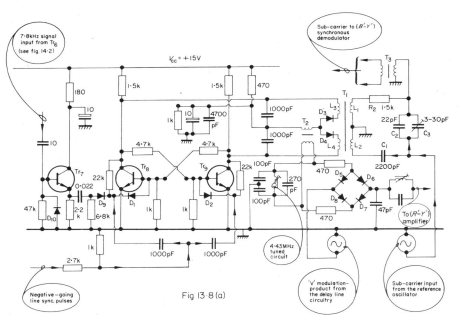

Fig 13·8 (a)

Fig. 13.8(a) *Further example of a PAL-D V-signal demodulator in which a bistable multivibrator drives a diode sub-carrier switching circuit*

(Associated diagrams: Figs. 13.8(b), 14.2)

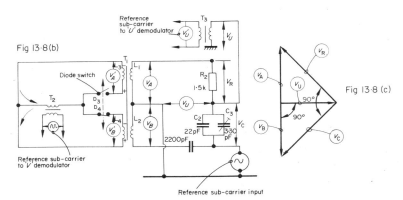

Fig. 13.8(b) *Simplified diagram of the switching circuit of Fig. 13.8(a)*

Fig. 13.8(c) *Phasor diagram showing the relative phases of the voltages in the T_1 primary circuit*

218

$+V_{cc}$ so carrying the diode cathode some 5 volts positive with respect to its anode.

As before, the bistable multivibrator is triggered at the end of each line by negative-going line pulses which are routed to Tr_8 and Tr_9 alternately by the steering diodes D_1 and D_2. The IDENT circuit once again provides a 7·8 kHz square-wave which takes out one in every two negative line trigger pulses to Tr_8 to establish synchronism with the transmitter PAL switch. The 7·8 kHz IDENT square-wave is obtained from the emitter of the squarer stage Tr_7. This is driven by an approximately sine-wave shaped signal which is a.c. coupled to its base from a 7·8 kHz tuned amplifier stage (see Tr_6 in Fig. 14.2). Tr_7 is auto-biased by the bias rectifier D_{10} which produces a positive charge on the 'lower' plate of the 10 μF base coupling capacitor. The square wave at the emitter is a.c. coupled to the anode of the IDENT diode D_9. On positive half cycles D_9 is conductive and the positive half cycle of the 7·8 kHz square-wave over-rides the negative line trigger pulse and prevents it from triggering the bistable multivibrator.

V-channel switch: effects of fault conditions

In the absence, due to fault conditions, of the IDENT signal to the bistable multivibrator in a *V*-channel switch, there is an even chance that the switch will be out-of-step with the transmitted signal. The *V* component bears either positive or negative $(R' - Y')$ information and the effect upon the picture of this fault condition is greatest on hues where the magnitude of $(R' - Y')$ is large, i.e., on reds, magentas, greens, and cyans.

Figure 13.9 illustrates what happens when red is present. When the switch is in synchronism, the *V*-component (or alternatively the reference sub-carrier) to the *V* demodulator is inverted on PAL-lines but 'left-alone' on NTSC-lines. A positive $(R' - Y')$ voltage is then correctly recovered from the demodulator on each line. If the switch is out of step, however, it is now the NTSC-line which is *inverted* and the PAL-line is left-alone. This gives rise to a negative $(R' - Y')$ voltage on both lines. The *U* demodulator gives the correct negative $(B' - Y')$ voltage whether the switch is in step or not. It follows that the fault manifests itself by all red areas of a scene being reproduced as green. The converse is also clearly true so that the observed symptoms of an out-of-step *V*-channel switch may be described as those of green-faces and red-grass!

On a colour-bar signal, the most noticeable effect is that the red and green bars appear to change places. The actual red and green hues in these wrongly placed bars are not however identical to the true primaries of the normally produced bars. A study of the chrominance signal phasor diagram Fig. 3.4 in chapter 3 shows why this is so. With the *V*-channel switch out-of-step, the *V*-components on all bars are inverted so that the hues reproduced correspond to the 'mirror-image' (dotted) phasors shown. On what should be the red bar, a green corresponding to a phasor of angle 257° is displayed, while on what should be the green bar a red appropriate to a phasor of angle 119° is seen.

Details when the transmitted hue is RED	Receiver V-channel switch IN-STEP with transmitter		Receiver V-channel switch OUT-OF-STEP with transmitter	
	NTSC line	PAL-line	NTSC-line	PAL-line
Incoming chrominance signal	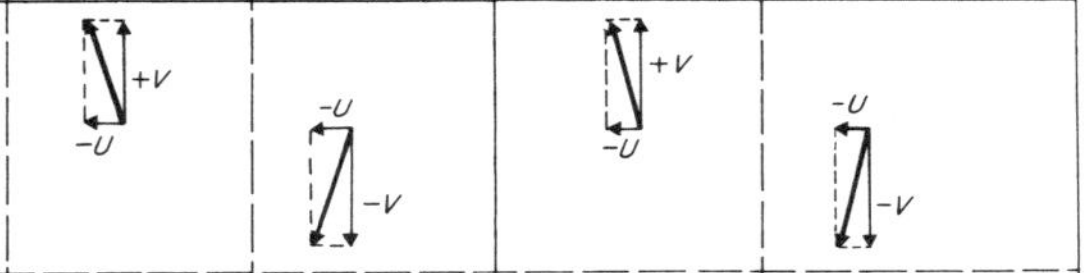 $+V$, $-U$	$-U$, $-V$	$+V$, $-U$	$-U$, $-V$
V-component produced by the post delay-line subtractor	$+V$	$-V$	$+V$	$-V$
V-component after action of the V-channel switch	$+V$ (NOT inv.)	$+V$ (INV.)	$-V$ (INV.)	$-V$ (NOT inv.)
Nature of the V-demodulator output	$+(R'-Y')$	$+(R'-Y')$	$-(R'-Y')$	$-(R'-Y')$
Nature of the U demodulator output	$-(B'-Y')$	$-(B'-Y')$	$-(B'-Y')$	$-(B'-Y')$
Hue reproduced on the screen	RED	RED	GREEN	GREEN

Fig. 13.9 *Showing the effect in a PAL-D receiver, when the V-channel switch is out of step with the transmitter's 'PAL-switch'*

(The observed symptoms are 'green-faces' and 'red-grass')

Note: If the switch is out of action altogether, reds and greens are not produced at all, but appear as dull, flat, sepia-coloured areas.

The magenta and cyan bars also show marked changes and again it may roughly be said that these two colour-bars change places. However, the 'cyan' corresponding to a mirror-image of magenta, is distinctly bluer than the true cyan, while the magenta which appears where the cyan bar should be, is markedly redder than the true magenta.

On yellow, the inversion of the V-component causes this bar to have a greenish-yellow hue. There is little noticeable effect upon the blue bar.

It is sometimes wrongly said that when the V-channel switch is out-of-step, complementary colours are produced in the colour-bars. This is not true; a complementary hue would have to be one which, when mixed with the original hue, would yield white. For any given colour-bar, a phasor representing a complementary hue would have to lie diametrically opposite (i.e., at 180° to) the position of the colour-bar's own phasor. A phase shift of 180° can only be brought about by the inversion of *both* the V- and the U-components.

A switch which is working, but is out of synchronism, gives rise to wrong colours in some areas, but the colours are nonetheless vivid, i.e., bright reds and greens will be present, though in the wrong places.

If, however, the switch is inoperative, it may rest in either one of its two possible conditions.

The V-component (or the reference sub-carrier) to the V-demodulator will therefore either not be inverted on any line or it will be inverted on all lines. These two possible conditions each give rise to the same symptoms. Assuming colour-bars are being transmitted, on any two successive lines through a given bar, the $(R' - Y')$ voltage delivered to the c.r.t. will be equal and opposite. For example, on the red bar one line will be red and the other green. The same two lines will be green and red when they pass through the green bar. Only colours where $(R' - Y')$ is very small (e.g., blues) are therefore approximately correctly reproduced, and all reds and greens merge into a flat sepia-like dull colour.

Complementary colours and complementary hue errors

Some confusion arises because the word *complementary* is used for two different purposes in colour television studies.

(i) In the additive mixing of coloured lights, two colours are said to be *complementary* if together they produce white (see chapter 1, page 15).

(ii) Two hue errors produced on a pair of successively scanned raster lines are said to be *complementary* if, when 'averaged' (e.g., by the eye), they produce a hue which is the same as that of the original (error-free) hue (see chapter 9, page 150).

The effect produced by an 'out-of-step' V-channel switch, falls into neither of these categories.

14

Chrominance Amplifiers and Associated Circuitry

In this chapter the circuitry between the chrominance signal take-off point and the delay-line, is studied.

The primary function of this section of the receiver is to extract the chrominance signal from the composite video signal and amplify it to a level suitable for application to the delay-line and summation circuitry. The chrominance signal is centred upon a frequency of 4·43 MHz and has a bandwidth of ±1 MHz. To handle a signal of such a low carrier-frequency to bandwidth ratio a broad-band amplifier is needed and resistance-capacitance coupling is largely used.

The gain-frequency response curve is sensibly flat over the 3·4 MHz to 5·4 MHz pass-band, with attenuation slopes on each side of this region, provided by the rising reactance of series coupling capacitors at the l.f. end and by shunt capacitance together with 6 MHz trap circuits at the h.f. end.[1]

Included in this section of a colour-receiver are some or all of the following ancillary circuits:

COLOUR KILLER. The purpose of this circuit is to close down the chrominance amplifier path on monochrome transmissions so that video signal components which fall within the chrominance signal spectrum do not give rise to random colour effects on the screen.

BURST BLANKING. In a similar way the chrominance amplifier is shut down during the period of the back-porch sub-carrier burst to prevent this signal from reaching the demodulators and giving rise to an unwanted output during the flyback period. The mean burst phase of 180° corresponds to a chrominance signal bearing greenish information. If visible the burst would appear as greenish vertical striations, towards the left of the picture.

AUTOMATIC CHROMINANCE CONTROL (A.C.C.) For correct reproduction of the transmitted picture, the original relative amplitudes of the chrominance and luminance

---

[1] For a full treatment of R.C. coupled wide-band amplifiers see *Television Receiver Theory*: Part 1, by G. H. Hutson, published by Arnolds of London.

signals must be maintained. It is possible during the reception of a programme for this ratio to be incorrect. One cause of this may be tuner-unit oscillator drift, or an inaccurate setting of the fine-tuner. The chrominance information is positioned towards the upper edge of the vision signal bandspace. If the oscillator frequency happens to be lower than it should be the chrominance signal will fall under the lower attenuation slope of the vision i.f. response curve and therefore reach the chrominance amplifiers at lower than normal amplitude.[1] The repercussions of this are minimized by making the gain of one of the chrominance amplifier stages inversely proportional to the amplitude of the chrominance signal (cf. simple a.g.c.). A control voltage is needed, which is proportional to the amplitude of the chrominance signal. This control voltage cannot be derived from the actual chrominance signal during the active picture line since this varies in amplitude as the colour information itself changes. However, the sub-carrier burst should be of unvarying amplitude and monitoring this offers a convenient way of determining the way in which the chrominance signal is being treated in the receiver. The a.c.c. voltage is therefore derived by sensing the amplitude either of the burst itself or of the 7·8 kHz component borne by the burst.

MANUAL SATURATION (OR COLOUR) CONTROL. A manual control of the gain of one of the chrominance amplifiers allows the user to set the intensity of colour reproduction when first switching on. This is normally adjusted to give what are judged to be correct flesh tints.

INTER-CARRIER SOUND REJECTOR. Because the upper edge of the chrominance signal extends to the edge of the video signal bandspace (i.e., to 5·5 MHz) the low selectivity broad-band chrominance amplifiers will pass any component present at the inter-carrier sound i.f. of 6 MHz. To eliminate this, one or more 6 MHz traps are fitted in the chrominance amplifiers.

There are various ways of achieving these facilities. Some examples are now studied.

Figure 14.1

(i) A.C.C. The chrominance signal is selected by a 4·43 MHz tuned circuit from the composite video signal recovered at the vision detector, and applied to the emitter follower Tr_{12}. The forward transfer ratio of this stage, which is always of course less than unity, depends upon the forward bias on the base–emitter junction.

In the absence of a colour signal, this positive forward bias is determined by the setting of the 100 kΩ 'SET A.C.C.' control, the adjustment of which forms part of a specified service procedure. When a colour signal is being received the net forward

---

[1] It must be remembered that the upper sideband of the incoming r.f. vision signal, becomes the lower sideband of the vision i.f. signal. (See vision i.f. response curves, Fig. 2.5 page 22, of *Television Receiver Theory*, Part 1, by G. H. Hutson, published by Arnolds of London.)

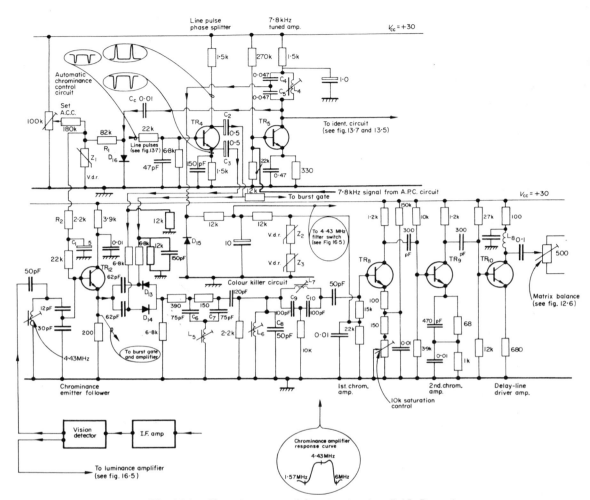

Fig. 14.1   *Chrominance amplifier circuitry in a PAL-D receiver*

(Associated diagrams: Figs. 12.6, 13.5, 13.7, 15.5, 16.5, 17.8, 17.10)

bias is reduced by a negative a.c.c. voltage obtained by rectifying the 7·8 kHz signal from the tuned amplifier Tr_5. The 7·8 kHz signal is a.c. coupled by C_c to the rectifier diode D_{16}. On the positive half cycles D_{16} conducts and C_c is charged with its left-hand plate negative. On the negative half-cycles the discharge current from C_c reduces the positive voltage across the 5 μF capacitor C_1.

The network R_1, R_2, Z_1 (v.d.r.) and C_1 provides a smoothing circuit to remove any 7·8 kHz ripple from the net bias to Tr_{12}.

A fall in amplitude of the chrominance signal is normally accompanied by a corresponding decrease in the burst amplitude. This leads to a reduction in amplitude

224

of the 7·8 kHz component which is extracted from the swinging burst at the a.p.c. circuit, with the result that the negative voltage output of D_{16} is less. The increase in positive forward bias on Tr_{12} causes the forward transfer ratio to be higher (i.e., nearer to unity) so giving partial compensation for the fall in chrominance signal amplitude.

(ii) BURST BLANKING. The chrominance signal passes from the emitter of Tr_{12} to the base of the first chrominance signal amplifier Tr_8. Diodes D_{13}, D_{14}, in series with the signal path, form the burst blanking circuit. One diode connected in this way, would—by rectification—seriously distort the sine-wave signal. By using a second diode in parallel with the first but connected the opposite way round, the distortion is eliminated since the two diodes pass alternate half-cycles. During the line blanking period, however, a positive-going pulse from Tr_4 collector—and a negative-going pulse from Tr_4 emitter—are applied to D_{13} cathode and D_{14} anode respectively. These pulses are timed to bridge the back-porch period and cut-off the two diodes so preventing the burst signal from passing from Tr_{12} to Tr_8.

(iii) CHROMINANCE RESPONSE CURVE. The tuned circuits between the burst-blanking circuit and Tr_8 are for shaping the chrominance amplifier response curve.

The parallel circuit L_6, C_8, is tuned to 4·43 MHz. This makes the shunt impedance across the coupling path maximum at the centre of the chrominance signal passband.

The second parallel tuned circuit L_7, C_9, C_{10} is tuned to the inter-carrier sound i.f. of 6 MHz. This is in series with the signal path and offers a high attenuation at 6 MHz, so 'pinning down' the response curve at this frequency.

L_5 forms part of a 1·57 MHz series tuned circuit connected in shunt with the signal path to attenuate any component present at this frequency. 1·57 MHz is the difference between the 6 MHz inter-carrier and the 4·43 MHz sub-carrier frequencies. The simultaneous presence of these two frequencies in a non-linear device such as the vision demodulator, gives rise by the normal mixing process to a difference frequency component of 1·57 MHz which is close to the chrominance amplifier's passband and must be attenuated in receivers where its amplitude is sufficient to be troublesome.

(iv) COLOUR KILLER. The 7·8 kHz component across C_4 in the collector tuned circuit of the tuned amplifier Tr_5, is applied to the cathode of D_{15}; the colour-killer diode. D_{15} rectifies the roughly sinusoidal signal to produce a positive voltage output which is smoothed and stabilized by the 12 kΩ resistors, the 10 μF capacitor and the two v.d.r.'s Z_2 and Z_3. This positive voltage provides forward bias for the base-emitter junction of the first chrominance amplifier Tr_8.

On a monochrome signal there is no 7·8 kHz input to the colour-killer rectifier and hence no positive bias at the base of Tr_8. The emitter of Tr_8 is held slightly positive by a potential divider between $+V_{cc}$ and earth. The transistor is therefore back-biased and cut-off, so closing down the chrominance signal path.

(v) CHROMINANCE AMPLIFIERS. Tr_8 and Tr_9 form a two-stage chrominance amplifier and Tr_{10} acts as the delay-line and summation circuitry driver stage. The user's manual saturation control adjusts the gain of the first stage Tr_8 by variation of the resistance in the emitter circuit. The amplifiers are R.C. coupled and in addition to the action of the tuned circuits discussed above, the response curve is further shaped by the coupling capacitors, the shunt input capacitances of the transistors, and the negative feedback due to the emitter circuits which are not fully decoupled.[1] The circuitry associated with the driver stage Tr_{10} was explained in chapter 12 (see Fig. 12.6).

Figure 14.2

(i) A.C.C. The chrominance signal is extracted from the composite video signal, by a 4·43 MHz tuned circuit in the emitter of a phase splitter following the vision demodulator, and applied to the base of the first common-emitter chrominance amplifier stage Tr_3. In the absence of a colour signal, the forward bias on the base of this transistor is determined by the 'SET A.C.C.' pre-set control.

When a colour signal is being received, the amplified burst signal from the burst amplifier is rectified by the a.c.c. diode D_{16} which produces a negative voltage output. This decreases the net forward bias on Tr_3 base-emitter junction to a level suitable for normal operation of the stage.

Should the chrominance signal amplitude now diminish, the burst input to D_{16} gets less and in turn the net positive forward bias on Tr_3 increases. This causes a rise in the gain of Tr_3 which compensates for the drop in chrominance signal amplitude.

(ii) MANUAL COLOUR (I.E., SATURATION) CONTROL. This is provided by D_{13} and D_{14} which form a variable attenuator in series with the chrominance signal path from Tr_3 to Tr_4. The diodes are connected back-to-back with their cathodes returned to earth by 2·7 kΩ resistors. Their anode potentials are determined by a potential divider, one end of which is at -20 V and the other at a small positive potential set by the slider of the saturation control potentiometer.

One biased diode in series with the signal path would cause distortion, but two connected back-to-back give a substantially linear impedance. Since the diodes face opposite ways, when the cathode of one is moved in the positive direction by the applied signal—hence increasing the diode's resistance—the anode of the other also moves positive so decreasing its resistance by a similar compensating amount, leaving the net resistance virtually unchanged.

Adjustment of the colour control changes the fixed bias and varies the attenuation of the two diodes.

This control is linked, by a 22 kΩ resistor to the contrast control in the emitter of the emitter-follower which feeds the luminance amplifier. The object is to provide tracking between the contrast and colour controls. Turning up the contrast control—which increases the amplitude of the luminance signal—also increases the positive

---

[1] See 'H.F. Compensation' in *Television Receiver Theory*: Part 1, by G. H. Hutson, published by Arnolds of London.

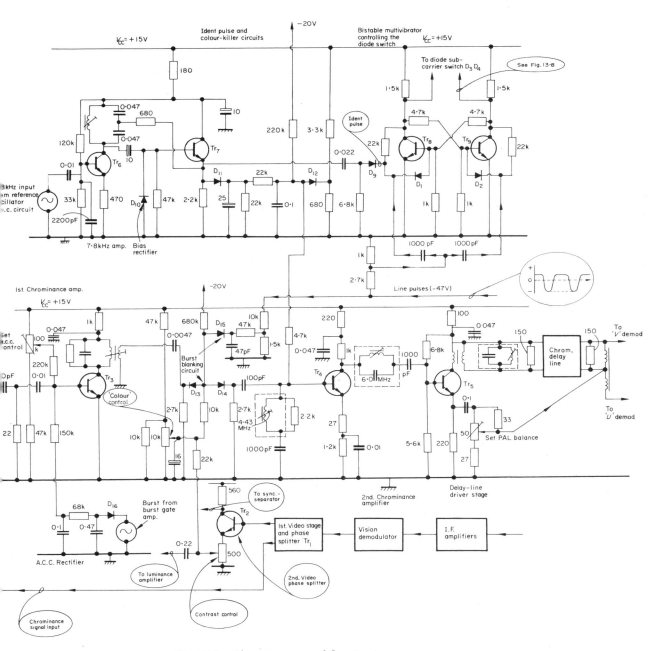

Fig. 14.2 *Chrominance amplifier circuitry*

(Associated diagrams: Figs. 13.8(a), 13.8(b))

227

potential at the colour control slider, so causing a rise in the bias on D_{13} and D_{14}. This results in the chrominance signal amplitude rising in step with the luminance signal.

(iii) BURST BLANKING. In the active line period diode D_{15} is of high resistance since its cathode is driven more positive than its anode which is at the same potential as D_{13} and D_{14} anodes. During the line blanking period, however, a negative-going line pulse, timed to bridge the back-porch, is applied to the cathode of D_{15} so making it conductive. This causes the negative line pulse to reach D_{13} and D_{14} anodes and its amplitude is such that the diodes are heavily back-biased, so causing a sharp rise in their resistances. This introduces a high degree of attenuation in the chrominance signal path and prevents the burst signal from passing through.

(iv) COLOUR KILLER. The second common-emitter chrominance amplifier Tr_4 depends for its forward bias upon the presence of the 7·8 kHz signal. When a colour signal is being received, the 7·8 kHz component is taken from the a.p.c. circuit and applied to the base of the tuned amplifier Tr_6. The amplified 7·8 kHz signal is a.c. coupled to Tr_7. Diode D_{10} conducts on the negative half-cycles and charges the right-hand plate of the 10 μF capacitor positive. The discharge current from this capacitor provides a forward bias for the squarer stage Tr_7. The emitter of Tr_7 is coupled back via a 680 Ω resistor to the tuned circuit in the collector of Tr_6. This provides positive feedback and has the effect of improving the 'Q-factor' of the tuned circuit.

The colour-killer diode D_{11} rectifies the square-wave output from the emitter of Tr_7, producing across its cathode smoothing circuit a positive voltage which serves as a source of forward-bias for the chrominance amplifier Tr_4. Diode D_{12} is switched on by this bias, so clamping the voltage to that produced at D_{12} cathode by the potential divider across the $+V_{cc}$ line.

On a monochrome signal there is no 7·8 kHz input to the colour-killer diode D_{11} and no positive voltage is developed at its cathode. Both D_{12} and the base-emitter-junction of Tr_4 are now back biased by the -20 V potential to which D_{12} anode returns via a 220 kΩ resistor. The chrominance amplifier path is therefore closed down.

(v) IDENT CIRCUIT. The 7·8 kHz square wave from Tr_7 is a.c. coupled to the anode of D_9, the IDENT diode. D_9 conducts on the positive half-cycles and the positive voltage at its cathode overrides one in every two of the negative-going line trigger pulses to steering diode D_1, so synchronizing the multivibrator and its associated V-channel switch.

(vi) CHROMINANCE AMPLIFIER RESPONSE CURVE. The low-Q tuned circuits in the collector of Tr_3 and base of Tr_4 are tuned to 4·43 MHz and provide some measure of selectivity. A parallel circuit tuned to 6 MHz is included in series with the coupling circuit between the second chrominance amplifier Tr_4 and the delay-line driver stage Tr_5, so removing any inter-carrier sound i.f. component which may be present.

The delay-line driver stage is of the form described in Fig. 12.4.

228

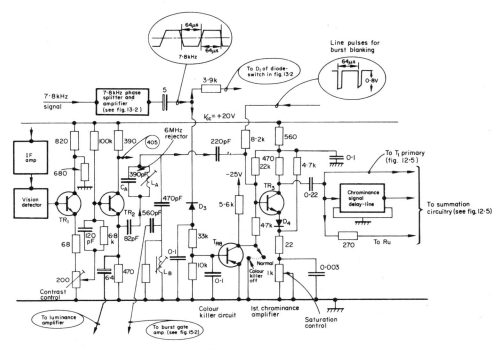

Fig. 14.3 *Chrominance amplifier circuitry*

(Associated diagrams: Figs. 11.8, 12.5, 13.2, 15.2, 17.5)

Figure 14.3

(i) Tr_1 AND Tr_2. The composite video signal from the vision detector is applied to the base of the emitter-follower Tr_1. The proportion of the total emitter output voltage passed on to the next stage may be varied by adjustment of the 200 Ω potentiometer which forms part of the emitter load resistance. This provides a very simple method of contrast control.

On the negatively modulated 625-line signal Tr_2 works as a second emitter-follower. When switched to the positively modulated 405-line signal, however, the output is taken from Tr_2 collector. Tr_2 therefore provides the luminance amplifier with video signals of the same polarity on both standards.

(ii) CHROMINANCE RESPONSE CURVE. The 6 MHz parallel tuned circuit $L_A C_A$, is in series with the signal from Tr_2 emitter to the base of the chrominance amplifier Tr_3. This presents a high impedance to the 6 MHz inter-carrier i.f. component and prevents it from reaching Tr_3.

Shunt inductor L_B is adjusted at 3·4 MHz to give a lift in the response curve towards the lower limit of the chrominance signal frequency spectrum.

The 82 pF capacitor coupling Tr_2 emitter to $L_A C_A$, offers an increasing reactance at lower frequencies and therefore helps to shape the l.f. attenuation slope below the chrominance pass-band.

(iii) COLOUR KILLER. In the presence of a colour transmission the 7·8 kHz signal is rectified by diode D_3 to provide at its anode a negative voltage which forward-biases the p-n-p transistor Tr_8. When Tr_8 is switched hard on, its collector is virtually at earth potential. This effectively earths the lower end of the 4·7 kΩ resistor which forms part of the base bias potential divider of the chrominance amplifier Tr_3. This stage then functions normally.

On a monochrome transmission no 7·8 kHz signal is present and D_3 does not provide a forward bias for Tr_8. But when Tr_8 is non-conductive its collector potential is almost at -25 V. This in turn makes the base of the n-p-n transistor Tr_3 negative to emitter so that the stage is shut-down.

The colour-killer circuit may be 'disabled' by the switch shown. This is necessary during service adjustments of the delay-line balance control (see R_{V_1} in emitter circuit of Tr_4 in Fig. 12.5), and of the reference oscillator frequency control (discussed under Fig. 15.2 in the next chapter).

(iv) SATURATION CONTROL. This is achieved by varying the total Tr_3 emitter resistance by the 1 kΩ potentiometer.

The diode D_4 improves the range of the control since its through resistance changes as the voltage drop across it varies. Instead of the gain varying sharply over a small section only of the range of the 1 kΩ potentiometer, a smooth continuous control is obtained.

15

Sub-Carrier Reference Oscillators and Associated Circuitry

Before making a detailed study of this section of the receiver it is helpful to take an overall look at the organization of the whole decoding and picture signal processing circuitry in a typical PAL-D receiver. The block diagram, Fig. 15.1, is intended to provide a logical presentation of the main circuits involved. The sections of the receiver so far discussed should be identified and particular attention paid to cross connections between the main circuit sections.

The majority of receivers follow a similar pattern. The greatest single difference is likely to be in the matrixing of the colour difference and luminance signals. Here this is shown to be achieved by the c.r.t. itself, with the colour difference signals going to the control grids and the luminance signal to the cathodes. Instead of this, the matrixing is sometimes carried out in a separate circuit, in which event the three cathodes receive straightforward R', G', and B' (in fact $-R'$, $-G'$, and $-B'$) drives.

By the use of integrated circuits whole sections of the receiver are currently being developed as single units and these sophisticated techniques are likely to make an increasing impact on receiver design in the future. Whilst this will place whole sections of the receiver detailed circuitry out of reach of the engineer, there is nonetheless no better way of gaining an understanding of receiver principles than by a close study of the discrete component circuitry which the integrated circuits will at length often largely replace.

Reference oscillator and a.p.c.

In this chapter, the circuitry associated with the left-hand column of blocks in Fig. 15.1 is examined. The primary purpose of this section is simply to produce a sub-carrier of precisely the correct frequency to replace the sub-carrier suppressed in the two chrominance signal balanced modulators at the transmission encoder.

Not only must the generated sub-carrier be of exactly the right frequency but it must also be as nearly as possible of the same phase reference as the original sub-carrier. As described in earlier chapters, two outputs are in fact required, which are mutually in quadrature; one for the U and one for the V synchronous demodulators.

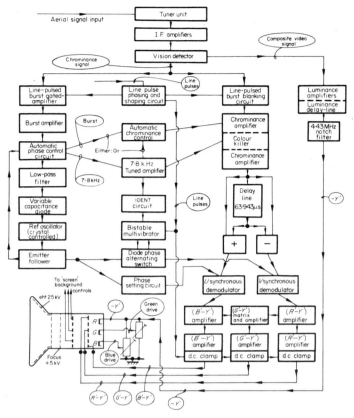

Fig. 15.1 *Block diagram showing typical circuit organization in the decoder and chrominance signal processing sections of a PAL-D receiver*

A crystal oscillator is used in the receiver and this is compelled to work at the correct frequency by the action of an automatic frequency and phase controlling circuit (usually called the a.p.c. circuit). This is achieved by including in the oscillator circuit a variable reactance device such as a variable capacitance diode. The effective capacitance of the diode is varied by a control voltage provided by a phase detector circuit. The latter receives two inputs; the locally generated reference sub-carrier and the transmitted burst. When the sub-carrier is of exactly the correct frequency and phase, the control voltage is zero and the variable capacitance element has its mean value. If the sub-carrier tries to run at the wrong frequency the phase detector recognizes this as an error in the phase of the reference oscillator relative to that of the burst. A control voltage is produced which pulls the oscillator frequency back to its correct value. To hold it there, a small phase error has to be allowed to persist.

An important point should now be noted. It is imperative that the sub-carrier

232

frequency be precisely correct. If the error-correcting control voltage were to be developed in a *frequency* discriminating circuit, then to hold the oscillator at the correct frequency when its natural tendency was to work at a slightly wrong frequency, would require the maintenance of a control voltage which in turn could only be produced if a residual frequency error persisted. This is a vicious circle. To escape from it the frequency discriminator must be replaced by a phase discriminator. The correction voltage is then maintained by allowing a phase error to persist between the reference oscillator and the incoming burst. The frequency of the sub-carrier may now be made absolutely correct at the expense of a small, but tolerable, phase error. Exactly the same conditions exist in a line timebase flywheel synchronization circuit. Obviously the line frequency must be exactly right (not just nearly right!) and this is achieved by a control voltage which is maintained by the existence of a residual phase error between the line timebase flyback pulses and the incoming line sync. pulses.

A sub-carrier *frequency* error would result in the synchronous demodulator 'sampling-points' being different on each successive line. A very small error would give rise to a slow drift of sampling-points along the V and U modulation-product sine-waves, causing continuously changing colours to appear in the picture. On a colour-bar signal, these 'rainbow' patterns can become stationary when the frequency error has certain fixed numerical relationships with the line frequency. This may be seen when the free-running reference oscillator frequency is being adjusted with the a.p.c. circuit inoperative.

Conversely, phase error in a PAL-D receiver merely results in a loss of saturation, since the colour-difference signal outputs from the two demodulators are of smaller amplitude than they should be. Normally this is not sufficient to notice. If, however, colours *do* appear to be lacking in intensity, the user will increase the saturation by an adjustment of the manual colour (i.e., chrominance amplifier gain) control.

Burst amplifiers

Returning to the block diagram, the burst present in the back-porch is separated from the chrominance signal by a line-gated burst amplifier. This is simply a tuned 4·43 MHz amplifier which is switched on by a line pulse for a brief period only, during the back-porch, to allow the burst to pass through. The amplifier is shut-down during the remainder of the line period. The burst is then amplified in a second tuned amplifier.

Because the signal handled by these amplifiers consists of short bursts of some 10 cycles occurring once per 64 µs line period and not a continuous 4·43 MHz signal, their bandwidth has to be wider than might be expected. A continuous signal could be handled by high-Q narrow bandwidth circuits, but to reproduce the bursts without distortion the response curve needs to have a bandwidth of some 600 kHz.

In effect, the signal fed to the burst amplifiers is 4·43 MHz carrier wave, 100% modulated by a line frequency square wave having a mark-to-space (i.e., burst ON to burst OFF) ratio of approximately 1 to 28. The frequency spectrum of such a signal is the 4·43 MHz carrier with upper and lower sidebands corresponding to a whole series of harmonics of the line frequency (i.e., 4·43 MHz $+ f_h$; $\pm 2f_h$; $\pm 3f_h$, etc.).

In addition the 7·8 kHz component due to the swinging burst phase, gives rise to side frequencies of $\pm\frac{1}{2}f_h$, $\pm\frac{3}{2}f_h$, etc. Due to the interruption of the bursts during the field blanking period, the spectrum also includes components at harmonics of the field frequency.

A satisfactory reproduction of the bursts is assured if side-frequencies extending to those corresponding to $20f_h$ are included. This constitutes a bandwidth of (2 × 20 × 15·625) kHz = 625 kHz.

Typical examples of circuitry found in the section of a receiver under discussion are now to be studied.

Figure 15.2

(i) BURST AMPLIFIERS. Tr_9 is the burst gate amplifier. Its emitter has a small permanent positive bias of about 300 mV, developed across a 470 Ω resistor forming part of a potential divider connected between the +20 V V_{cc} line and earth. Except when line pulses are present there is no positive voltage on the base, because D_4 is cut-off, leaving $V_b = 0$ V. The n-p-n transistor is therefore back-biased since the emitter is positive to the base and the chrominance signal, which is a.c. coupled to the base, produces no output at the collector.

During the line blanking period, 60 V positive-going line pulses, timed to bridge the back porch, are applied to D_4 anode. D_4 switches on and becomes of very low resistance, so that the 3·3 kΩ resistor and 1 kΩ potentiometer, form a potential divider between $+ V_{cc}$ and earth. Tr_9 base is then positive by an amount determined by the slider of the 1 kΩ 'set burst-gate bias' control and the two 10 kΩ resistors. This switches on Tr_9 and the burst gives rise to an output across the damped broad-bandwidth tuned circuit in the collector. Viewed on an oscilloscope at the base, the bursts appear to ride on flat-topped pulses, well positive of the active-line part of the chrominance signal. The waveform at the collector consists of the bursts only.

Positive line pulses would still gate Tr_9 into conduction if D_4 were removed, but its presence has the effect of clamping the peaks of the pulses to +20 V, so making Tr_9 base-potential constant during the burst period. Some receivers do, however, use a pulse only, with no potential divider across the V_{cc} line.

Tr_{10} further amplifies the burst, which is a.c. coupled to its base. The input from Tr_9 does in fact cause Tr_{10} to bottom on positive half cycles and cut-off on negative half cycles. A sinusoidal burst is, however, produced across the collector load, since this is a tuned circuit which resonates at 4·43 MHz. The tuned circuit has a centre-tapped inductor to provide anti-phase inputs to the phase detector diodes D_5 and D_6.

(ii) PHASE DETECTOR. The centre-tap on L_2 returns to $+ V_{cc}$; i.e., is earthed to a.c. Since one end of L_2 is connected to D_5 anode and the other to D_6 cathode, the two diodes conduct simultaneously on equal burst input voltages. Emitter-follower Tr_{11}

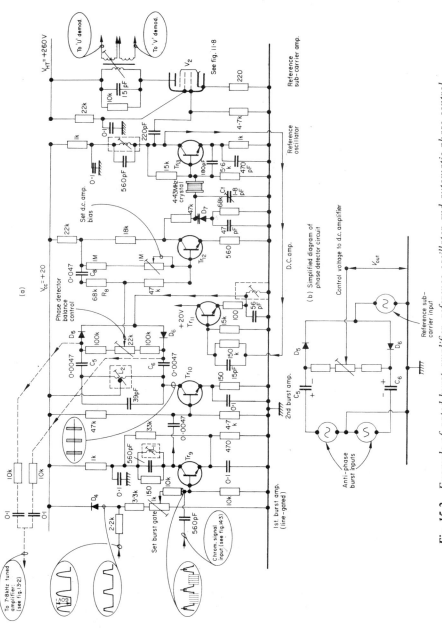

Fig. 15.2 *Example of gated burst amplifier, reference oscillator and automatic phase control (a.p.c.) circuitry*

(Associated diagrams: Figs. 11.8, 12.5, 13.2, 14.3, 17.5)

235

feeds a sample of the locally generated sub-carrier from the reference oscillator Tr_{13}, to D_5 cathode and D_6 anode. The effective circuit is shown in simplified form in Fig. 15.2(b).

As a starting point in studying the action of the circuit, let the reference oscillator input be shorted out, leaving only the burst input to the two diodes. C_5 and C_6 now charge up equally with the polarities shown. The discharge time constant for these capacitors is $(0.0047 \times 10^{-6} \times 111 \times 10^3 \times 10^6)$ μs = 522 μs. This is very long compared with the periodic time (approximately 0.225 μs) of the 4.43 MHz burst signal, hence the capacitors remain charged and the diodes only conduct for a small part of each cycle to replace the charge lost during the remainder of the cycle, i.e., the angle of flow is very small. Assuming the circuit is perfectly balanced and the slider of the balance control is at the centre, the output voltage measured at the slider will be zero since the capacitor voltages facing it are equal and opposite.

The effect of a reference oscillator input to the common connection may now be considered. If the oscillator's free-running frequency is exactly correct, the reference input to the phase detector is arranged to be in quadrature with the incoming burst signals to the two diodes. This is illustrated in Fig. 15.3(a). It follows that the charges on the two capacitors will remain equal, since the reference signal passes through zero potential half-way through the time interval during which the diodes are pulsed into conduction by the peaks of the burst signals. If the angle of flow were 30° for example, then, with the phases shown in Fig. 15.3(a) D_5 would be favoured for the first 15° and D_6 for the second 15°. Over the 30° period the average currents are equal.

The line-by-line phase alternation of $\mp 45°$ about the 180° axis of the burst signal, does not affect the circuit balance because the mean phase is still 180°. To attempt to show this 'swinging burst' in Fig. 15.3 would unnecessarily complicate the diagram. The effect may be visualized by imagining the sine waves at (i) and (iii) to be shifted by 45° to the right on one line and by 45° to the left on the next. These conditions favour D_5 on one line and D_6 on the next, by equal amounts, so that the mean output voltage is still zero.

There is however, always a 7.8 kHz a.c. component superimposed upon the mean level output voltage. This is taken off for IDENT and other purposes (as previously described), but is not passed on by the d.c. amplifier to the reference oscillator control element, because the frequency response of the circuit is kept very low, for reasons discussed later.

The dotted sine-wave in Fig. 15.3(a) (ii) shows what happens if the oscillator tries to run at a higher than normal frequency. The reference signal to the common connection now passes through zero ahead of the centre of the time interval when the burst pulses the two diodes. During the conduction period, the reference sub-carrier is positive to earth for more than half the time and the net input to D_6 greater than that to D_5. The charge on C_6 now exceeds that on C_5 and the net voltage output at the slider of the 22 kΩ resistor is positive to earth. This positive output is amplified and inverted by the d.c. amplifier Tr_{12}. The negative-going output from Tr_{12} reduces the back-bias on the cathode of the variable-capacitance diode D_7 with the result

236

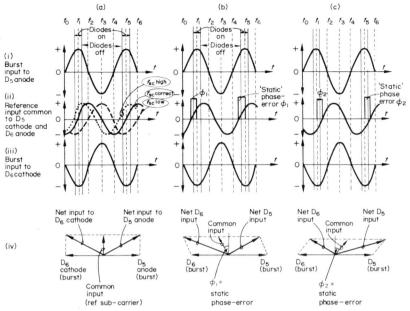

Fig. 15.3 *Showing the action of the phase detector circuit of Fig. 15.2*

Notes:

(a) Shows the inputs to D_5 and D_6 when the free-running frequency is exactly correct and no control voltage is developed. (But at (ii) the dotted and dashed sine-waves show in exaggerated form what would be the condition when first switching on, if the free-running frequency were high and low respectively.)

(b) Shows the condition when the a.p.c. circuit is holding the oscillator frequency correct, against a tendency for it to run high.

(c) Shows the condition when the a.p.c. circuit is holding the frequency correct against a tendency to run low.

that the capacitance of D_7 increases. This in turn reduces the oscillator frequency. When the frequency is at length correct, the necessary correction voltage from the a.p.c. circuit is sustained by the persistence of a phase error in the reference signal. Instead of the two inputs to each diode being in quadrature, as they are when there is no inherent frequency error at all, the reference signal is less than 90° out of phase with the burst to one diode but more than 90° out of phase with the burst to the other diode. This is the condition portrayed in Fig. 15.3(b).

If the oscillator tries to run at a lower than normal frequency, the reference signal passes through zero after the centre of the diode conduction period. The 'dashed' sine-wave in Fig. 15.3(a) (ii) illustrates this. D_5 is now favoured instead of D_6, since the reference voltage is negative for more than half the conduction period. The output voltage at the slider is then negative and this gives rise to a positive voltage change at the collector of the d.c. amplifier. In turn this decreases the capacitance of D_7 and increases the oscillator frequency. Figure 15.3(c) portrays the condition when such an error is being corrected by the persistence of a phase error of opposite sign to that shown in Fig. 15.3(b).

237

It is evident that when the receiver is first switched on there must be a brief period—perhaps lasting for a few seconds—during which the a.p.c. circuit gets a grip on the oscillator frequency and pulls it to the correct value. In this period, the oscillator may hunt 'to and fro' as it moves towards the correct value but the nature of the circuit finally compels the frequency to stabilize exactly equal to that of the burst, provided the original error does not exceed a certain limit which places it beyond the corrective range of the a.p.c. circuit.

Further insight into the behaviour of a.p.c. circuits may be gained by the following considerations. If the control voltage from the a.p.c. circuit is disconnected and the free-running frequency of the oscillator is, say, 60 Hz above the burst frequency, then the output from the a.p.c. circuit will be a sine-wave voltage at the difference (or 'beat') frequency of 60 Hz. When this a.p.c. control voltage is connected to the d.c. amplifier which controls the variable capacitance diode, the positive half-cycles cause a slowing down of the oscillator so that during this half cycle the effective beat note is less than 60 Hz. During the negative half cycles the oscillator is speeded up and the beat note is higher. But a half cycle of the lower frequency lasts longer than a half cycle of the higher. The control voltage from the a.p.c. circuit is therefore no longer sinusoidal and there is a net d.c. component in favour of the lower frequency condition. This positive d.c. component moves the error downwards below 60 Hz and the movement continues until the oscillator frequency is correct. Because of the a.c. component in the control voltage, if the instantaneous frequency were plotted on a time scale extending through the correction period, the curve would show ripples, i.e., the oscillator tends to 'hunt'. The situation is analogous to a ball which runs down a steep hill but passes up and down a series of minor hills on its way down.

If the free-running frequency is low instead of high, a similar argument shows that a net negative d.c. component is produced and this increases the frequency until it is correct.

The maximum oscillator frequency error an a.p.c. circuit can correct when first switched to an incoming signal is known as its 'pull-in' range. This is typically of the order of ± 400 Hz. The receiver is adjusted to make the free-running frequency as accurate as possible. On switching on, the a.p.c. circuit locks-in the oscillator very quickly. The phase angle which then persists between the reference signal and the burst (to maintain the necessary control voltage) is known as the 'static phase error'.

For brief periods the phase error may be different from this, due, for example, to spurious interference or noise causing the burst phase to vary. This temporary condition gives rise to a 'dynamic phase error'. The circuit is designed to minimize such errors so that the reproduced saturation in PAL-D receivers, is little affected by noise.

It is of academic interest to note that if the widest possible hold-in range *were* sought (and as stated, it is *not*), the limit would have to be less than half the separation between the sub-carrier and the first strong side-frequency present in the burst sidebands. The 7·8 kHz swinging burst creates strong side-frequencies at 4·43361875 MHz $\pm$ 7·8 kHz. Hence the maximum theoretical hold-in range has to be less than˙

± 3.9 kHz, otherwise 'side-lock' might occur, i.e., the reference oscillator could lock-in to a side-frequency instead of the centre frequency, if its free-running frequency were nearer to the former than to the latter.

It is theoretically possible for the oscillator frequency to be exactly correct but $180°$ out of phase with the required phase. Reference to Fig. 15.3(a) (ii) shows that if the sine-wave were moved along by $180°$ it would make no difference to the balance of the phase detector. However, the condition cannot occur in practice because it is one of extreme electrical instability. The slightest deviation in frequency would produce a control voltage of polarity such that the frequency error would be increased; not decreased. The a.p.c. action would then finally cause the oscillator to return to its correct frequency and proper phase, with the loop then resting in its only stable state.

The a.p.c. circuit thus responds to the $180°$ phase error by making the frequency wrong and then right again. In this way the a.p.c. circuit controls phase as well as frequency. If, for example, the phase of the burst were to be slightly changed, the a.p.c. circuit would respond by altering the frequency slightly (making it momentarily wrong), and then locking it in again to preserve the same quadrature relationship as before, between the burst and reference oscillator input to the phase detector.

The block diagram of Fig. 15.1 shows a low-pass filter between the a.p.c. circuit and the variable capacitance diode. It is this circuit which determines the width of the pull-in range. The longer the time-constant the narrower is the pull-in range and the greater is the immunity to noise. If the circuit were fast acting, random noise would modulate the control voltage and affect the oscillator. With high stability crystal controlled oscillators, a pull-in range of between ± 300 Hz and ± 500 Hz ensures that the oscillator will lock-in when first switched on and remain virtually immune from spurious noise effects. This is analogous once again to flywheel sync. circuits where a compromise between noise immunity and pull-in range is necessary.

In Fig. 15.2 the same effect as a low-pass filter is achieved by a high degree of a.c. feedback in the d.c. amplifier, from collector to base via $C_8 R_8$. The 0.47 μF capacitor ensures a high level of negative feedback and therefore a low gain to all but low frequencies and d.c.

Once locked the a.p.c. circuit is able to compensate for wider frequency errors than those at the limits of the pull-in range. Its maximum error-correcting ability once locked, is referred to as the hold-in range. This may be say ± 900 Hz for an a.p.c. circuit with a pull-in range of ± 300 Hz. However, an extended hold-in range is not a design objective. The main aim is to limit the inherent frequency error so that the static sub-carrier phase shift implicit in the existence of an error-correcting voltage, is minimized. The crystal controlled oscillator is designed, and adjusted, so that it runs at almost exactly the right frequency with the a.p.c. circuit disconnected. The static phase error when the a.p.c. circuit is brought into operation, is then very small. Finally, the oscillator long term stability is made as high as possible so that the a.p.c. circuit does not have to go on increasing its control voltage (with a correspondingly increasing static phase error) to hold-in a drifting oscillator.

(iii) REFERENCE OSCILLATOR AND VARIABLE-CAPACITANCE DIODE. Tr_{13} in Fig. 15.2 is a crystal controlled oscillator of the inverted Colpitts type, i.e., with the 'tuned circuit' (which in this circuit is a crystal), connected between base and emitter. Nominally, the total external capacitance required across the crystal to make the oscillator work at 4·43361875 MHz is about 20 pF. The trimmer C_t and the variable capacitance diode D_7 provide this. The collector is loaded by a 4·43 MHz tuned circuit to cut-down the harmonic content in the oscillator's output. Oscillation is further encouraged by feedback from collector to base through the transistor's own internal impedance. From the collector the 4·43 MHz signal is a.c. coupled to the grid of pentode V_2 which amplifies the sub-carrier and passes it on to the U and V demodulators (see Fig. 11.8). Tr_{13} also feeds the reference signal to the emitter follower Tr_{11} to provide the input to the a.p.c. circuit, as discussed above.

The capacitance against reverse voltage characteristic of a typical variable-capacitance diode (i.e., a varactor) is shown in Fig. 15.4. When reverse biased any semiconductor diode is essentially capacitive. The reverse bias drives charge carriers away from the junction region, leaving a 'depletion-zone' which is of very low conductivity and hence behaves as a dielectric material. The 'p-' and 'n-' type zones are, however, very conductive and the diode therefore takes on the character of a capacitor, with two conductive 'plates' separated by an insulator. Increasing the

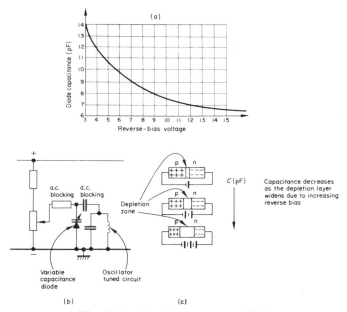

Fig. 15.4 *Variable capacitance diodes*

(a) Typical diode-capacitance against reverse-bias curve.
(b) Basic circuit for controlling the frequency of an oscillator.
(c) Showing that the fall in capacitance with increasing reverse bias, is due to a widening of the depletion zone.
(*N.B.* With zero *applied* reverse bias, there is still a very narrow depletion zone due to the barrier potential at the junction.)

240

reverse bias widens the depletion zone. This is equivalent to making the dielectric thicker and so the capacitance gets less. The standing reverse bias on the diode is arranged to give it an optimum control range.

(iv) ADJUSTMENT OF REFERENCE OSCILLATOR FREQUENCY. The reference signal input to the a.p.c. circuit is removed by shorting the tuned circuit in Tr_{11} emitter. Alternatively, the burst input to the a.p.c. circuit may be removed by shorting the base of Tr_{10} to earth. With only one input signal to the phase detector, its output should be zero. This may be achieved by adjustment of the 'balance control' to give the same voltage at Tr_{12} collector as exists when the second input to the a.p.c. circuit is removed.

The 'set d.c. amp. bias' control is next adjusted to give a specified voltage at the collector of Tr_{12} (e.g., $+6$ V). With a colour-bar signal fed to the receiver, the trimmer C_t is then adjusted to give vertical bars, each of uniform colour but with the colours drifting horizontally. Finally, the short on the input to the a.p.c. circuit is removed and the colour-bar signal will lock-in to give a normal display.

Reference back to Fig. 14.3 will show that neither the colour-killer nor the PAL-D switch, can operate normally until the 7·8 kHz signal is present. When the a.p.c. circuit is rendered inoperative during the adjustment of the oscillator frequency, there is no 7·8 kHz signal produced and both these functions are therefore put out of action. To make the chrominance amplifier work during this procedure, the colour-killer must be switched off. It is also evident that in this particular receiver (but not in *all* colour receivers) the bars where $(R' - Y')$ is large cannot register normal colour until the a.p.c. circuit is in use because the *V*-channel switch is not working. C_t is therefore adjusted for 'uniform' colour in any one vertical bar, but not for a normal colour-bar signal which cannot be resolved. In the majority of receivers it *is* possible to see normal colours during this adjustment procedure.

Figure 15.5

(i) BURST AMPLIFIERS. Tr_{13} is the burst-gate amplifier. Unlike the previous circuit it has no potential divider derived forward bias on its base and no fixed bias on the emitter. Positive-going line gating pulses are a.c. coupled to the base during the back-porch period. These forward-bias the n-p-n transistor, allowing the burst signal through the amplifier. A long time constant (1·88 ms) auto-bias circuit in the emitter develops a positive voltage which holds Tr_{13} cut-off between the line gating pulses, so that the 52 µs active-picture part of the chrominance signal applied to the base, is ignored. The positive gating pulses are obtained from the line-pulse phase splitter shown in Figs. 13.7 and 14.1.

Tr_{13} collector load is a 4·43 MHz tuned circuit. The collector inductor is tuned by self and stray capacitance. The burst is a.c. coupled to the second amplifier Tr_{14}, which is loaded with the untuned primary of the a.p.c. burst input transformer T_3.

(ii) A.P.C. AND REFERENCE OSCILLATOR CIRCUITS. The four diodes D_{18-21} form the phase detector. The diodes are switched on once per burst cycle and the reference

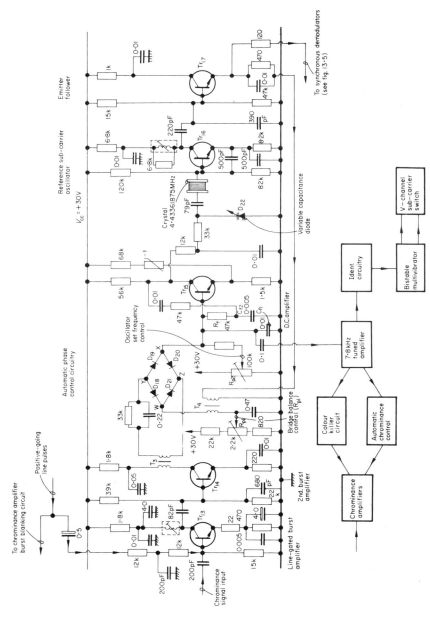

Fig. 15.5 *Further example of gated burst amplifier, reference oscillator and a.p.c. circuitry*

(Associated diagrams: Figs. 12.6, 13.5, 13.7, 14.1, 16.5, 17.8, 17.10)

242

sub-carrier voltage presented to point W from the secondary of transformer T_4, is transferred over to the low-pass filter circuit C_{f1}, C_{f2}, R_f connected between point X and earth. In series with the burst input to the diodes is an R.C. auto-bias circuit which limits the angle of flow to the tips of the half-cycles which drive point Y positive to Z. The time constant of this circuit is $(33 \times 10^3 \times 0.22 \times 10^{-6} \times 10^6)\,\mu s =$ 7·26 ms.

When the free-running frequency is exactly 4·43361875 MHz the phase of the reference input to point W is in quadrature with the burst so that the sine-wave at W passes through zero in the middle of the diode conduction period. This results in zero control voltage output across the low-pass filter at X. If the oscillator now tries to run at a higher frequency the reference sine-wave at W is positive for more than half the diode conduction period and this results in a positive control voltage at X. The d.c. amplifier Tr_{15}, amplifies and inverts this voltage to produce a negative movement in the reverse-bias on the cathode of the variable-capacitance diode D_{22}. This increases the diode's capacitance (because the depletion zone gets narrower) and the oscillator frequency is reduced.

The d.c. amplifier has a high degree of a.c. negative feedback from collector to base via the 0·01 µF capacitor and 47 kΩ resistor. This stabilizes the circuit, and in particular prevents the transfer to the variable capacitance diode, of the 7·8 kHz component which is present across the low-pass filter.

Like the previous circuit the oscillator is an inverted Colpitts, with the crystal connected between the base and emitter circuits. The collector of the oscillator transistor Tr_{16} is loaded with a 4·43 MHz tuned circuit and the sinusoidal sub-carrier output signal is a.c. coupled to the base of emitter follower Tr_{17}. This drives the synchronous demodulators (shown in Fig. 13.5) and also feeds the primary of T_4. Included in the connection to T_4 is a parallel RC network which adjusts the phase of the reference input to the phase detector, so that it has the required quadrature relationship with the burst.

(iii) ADJUSTMENT OF THE REFERENCE OSCILLATOR FREQUENCY. It will be noticed that there are potential-divider-derived positive potentials at terminals W and X of the phase detector. The d.c. amplifier has to have a steady forward bias to establish at its collector a suitable mean reverse bias on the variable-capacitance diode. A similar potential at the other side (point W) of the phase detector removes any d.c. bias from the diodes. Unlike the previous circuit, there is no trimmer in the oscillator circuit. Instead of this, the mean bias on the d.c. amplifier is adjusted until the diode D_{22} tunes the oscillator to the correct frequency. In practice the potential at Tr_{15} is of the order of 6·2 V when the circuit is tuned. The sequence of adjustments for the two potentiometers is as follows:

(a) Since the a.p.c. circuit will be out of action and the 7·8 kHz signal therefore not present, the colour-killer forward bias to the first chrominance amplifier (see Fig. 14.1) must be replaced. This may be achieved by connecting a 3 V battery across D_{15} (positive to cathode). Alternatively, instead of using a battery, a suitable potential is available across the emitter auto-bias circuit in the bistable multivibrator shown in Fig. 13.5.

(b) The connection between point X of the phase detector and the base of Tr_{15} is open-circuited. A link is provided for the purpose on this chassis.

(c) On a colour-bar signal, the reference oscillator frequency is adjusted by means of the potentiometer R_{p_2} until the colours down each bar are uniform, although 'drifting' slowly horizontally (e.g., a bar may be yellow, changing across its width slowly before returning to yellow). It should be noted by reference to Fig. 13.5 that the PAL-D switch is still working in this receiver but may or may not be in synchronism, since the IDENT signal is missing when point X is disconnected. Hence the colour-bar pattern may or may not drift through its normal colour sequence. This is unimportant; the object is to arrive at colour-bars which— although in a different sequence—are nonetheless each of uniform colour from top to bottom at any given instant.

(d) The voltage at Tr_{15} collector is measured, using a high resistance voltmeter.

(e) Point X is re-connected.

(f) The burst input from Tr_{13} is removed by shorting the base to earth, and the bridge balance control R_{p_1} is then adjusted to make the voltage reading at Tr_{15} collector the same as before.

(g) Normal receiver operation is now restored by removing both the short from Tr_{13} base and the supplementary bias to the chrominance amplifier. The colour-bar signal then locks-in.

Passive regenerator sub-carrier circuits

It is possible to obtain the sub-carrier *direct* from the burst, instead of from an active oscillator the frequency of which is *controlled* by the burst, through an a.p.c. circuit.

Such circuits have been used successfully in NTSC receivers. They may equally well be employed in PAL receivers but it is first necessary to remove the line-by-line phase change from the burst, since a sub-carrier of constant phase is needed to work the demodulators. It does not matter what this phase is initially, since—once having obtained a sub-carrier of correct frequency and constant phase—it is then easy to phase-shift this to the axes needed for the U and V demodulators.

A diode switch, driven by the bistable multivibrator already present in the V-channel, may be used to remove the phase modulation of the PAL 'swinging burst'. This is conveniently done by making the switch advance by 90° the phase of the 'NTSC-line' burst, from 135° to 225°, so that it has the same phase as the alternate 'PAL-lines'.

When this has been done the waveform arrived at is equivalent to an a.m. signal having a carrier frequency of 4·43361875 MHz, 100% modulated by a line-frequency square wave. This is depicted in Fig. 15.6(a). Since approximately 284 sub-carrier cycles can take place in 64 µs, and the burst is nominally of 10 cycles, the mark-to-space ratio of the square wave is about 28:1.

244

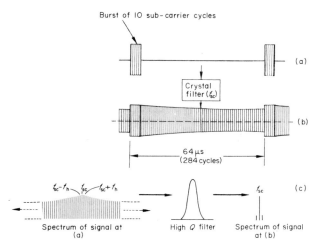

Fig. 15.6 *Showing the effect of passing the gated-out burst waveform through a crystal filter of high selectivity (e.g., Q = 10,000)*

An analysis of such a modulated wave shows a carrier component of frequency f_{sc}, with upper and lower sidebands consisting of side-frequencies representing harmonics of the line frequency f_h. The spectrum of frequencies present in the signal thus contains components at f_{sc} $(f_{sc} \pm f_h)$, $(f_{sc} \pm 2f_h)$, etc. These extend up to the limits of the passband of the gated burst amplifier(s) through which the burst signal has passed.

It is interesting to note that if all of these individual frequency components were drawn as sine-waves, having the relative amplitudes shown by the analysis (the amplitudes actually diminish progressively, the higher the harmonic of f_h), and then added graphically, the waveshape of Fig. 15.6(a) would be arrived at.

It is also true, but less obvious, that if the complex signal of Fig. 15.6(a) is passed through a bandpass filter, having a passband so narrow that all of the side-frequencies are rejected, then the signal at the filter output will be a continuous sine-wave at the sub-carrier frequency.

This is the basis of passive regenerator circuits. The block diagram of Fig. 15.7 shows the basic principle.

To accept a frequency of 4·43361875 MHz, but reject all side frequencies, the filter circuit must be highly selective, and crystal filters are used.

The filter is required to give a high degree of rejection to the nearest side-frequencies but must accommodate the normal variations of the sub-carrier frequency allowed by the transmitter tolerances. In practice a bandwidth of a few hundred cycles is aimed at and this involves the use of a crystal filter having an effective Q-factor of the order of 8000 to 10,000.

A simple filter of the type used is shown in Fig. 15.8. The equivalent circuit of a crystal is a high-Q series tuned circuit shunted by a capacitor. The latter represents

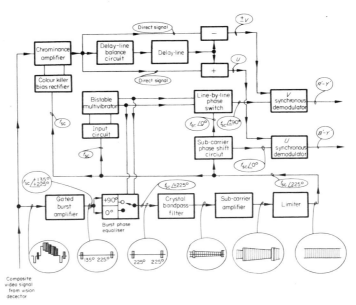

Fig. 15.7 *Block diagram of a PAL-D decoder circuit in which the reference sub-carrier is derived from the burst by a passive regenerator*

the capacitance formed by the two mounting plates, with the crystal itself as the dielectric. It is necessary to neutralize the effect of the shunt capacitance, otherwise some of the side-frequencies will be transmitted through the filter, via this route.

In practical circuits the sub-carrier sine-wave may show a fall in amplitude between the bursts, but by passing the signal through an amplifier and a limiter, a constant sub-carrier may be obtained. Tuned circuits are then used to present appropriately phased versions of this sub-carrier to the demodulators, which in this way receive stable sine-wave inputs.

There are useful by-products of this system of sub-carrier derivation.

Since there is no sub-carrier output at all from the circuit when the incoming signal bears no burst, the colour-killer may conveniently be driven by a bias developed by rectifying the output from the limiter. This bias may be made to open the chrominance amplifier when a colour transmission is being received, and its absence then closes down the chrominance path.

In addition synchronization of the *V*-channel switch is possible, because the bistable multivibrator which drives it, also drives the switch which removes the phase modulation from the burst. If the bistable is 'out-of-step', then instead of moving the NTSC-line burst forward by 90°, it moves the PAL-line phase from 225° to $(225 + 90)° = 315°$. This places the burst exactly in antiphase with the NTSC-line burst which is at 135°. The net result is that there is no output at all from the sub-

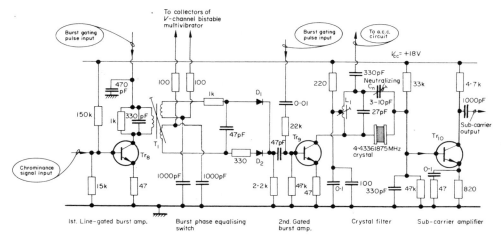

Fig. 15.8 *Showing an example of a passive sub-carrier regenerator circuit in a PAL-D receiver*

(Associated diagrams: Figs. 16.8, 17.12)

carrier passive regenerator. The absence of output may be made to inhibit the bistable multivibrator and bring it into step.

The way in which the various circuits are interconnected is illustrated in Fig. 15.7. The bistable multivibrator is designed so that it does not run in the absence of a bias output derived from the sub-carrier output from the limiter.

When first switched on the burst phase equalizing switch is therefore not working and a normal PAL 'swinging burst' signal is passed to the filter. The output from the filter is then much smaller than it is when a burst of constant phase is applied to it, but sufficient output is present from the limiter to create a bias to switch on the bistable multivibrator. If this starts in the right phase, the burst phase equalizing circuit switch is started with the correct phase and the burst passed to the filter then becomes constant at 225°. A short period later the increased output from the limiter produces a bias from the colour-killer rectifier, and the chrominance amplifier switches on. The receiver now works normally.

If however, when first switching on, the initial output from the limiter starts the bistable in the wrong phase, the burst phase equalizing switch is now switched with the wrong phase, and the net burst output passed to the filter becomes zero (as explained above). The bias from the limiter now disappears and the bistable stops. Immediately this happens, the normal PAL swinging burst signal passes through to the filter to produce an output bias from the limiter, i.e., the circuit 'tries again'. This on-off sequence could theoretically repeat several times until at length the circuit starts up with the bistable correctly synchronized.

The time constant in the bistable bias circuit is shorter than that of the colour-killer bias circuit, so that the latter holds the chrominance signal path switched off until synchronism is established. The period taken to establish synchronism is very

247

short and in practice a normal colour picture appears on the screen very soon after the receiver is switched on, i.e., as soon as the c.r.t. 'warms up'.

In the circuit of Fig. 15.8, Tr_8 is switched on by a line gating pulse during the back porch, and the burst is passed from the tuned primary of the r.f. transformer T_1, to the two secondaries. The diodes D_1 and D_2 are switched on alternately by the line-by-line bistable multivibrator which works the diode sub-carrier phase switch in the V-channel demodulator circuit. The diodes are connected to the collectors of the n-p-n transistors in the multivibrator. Each diode goes on when the transistor it is strapped to goes off, since the collector is then at the supply rail potential of $+18$ V.

In this way the burst is taken from one secondary on the 'NTSC-line' and the other on the 'PAL-line', to achieve the constant-phase burst signal referred to above.

Tr_9 forms a second gated-amplifier stage, which drives the crystal filter. The output from Tr_9 is developed across the centre-tapped tuned inductor L_1. Since opposite ends of L_1 are in antiphase, it is possible to adjust C_n so that the current it passes to the base of Tr_{10} is in antiphase to that passed as a result of the crystal's shunt capacitance. The circuit is similar to the highly selective crystal filters used in the i.f. stages of c.w. receivers.

At 4.43361875 MHz the crystal behaves as a series tuned circuit at resonance, and its losses at this frequency are negligibly small, so that the collector of Tr_9 may be regarded as being connected directly to the base of Tr_{10} at this frequency. From Tr_{10} the sub-carrier passes via an emitter-follower to the U and V synchronous demodulator circuits. The emitter-follower also feeds a p-n-p amplifier stage from which the sub-carrier is taken to the colour-killer and the bistable multivibrator circuits.

The sub-carrier from L_1 is also coupled via a 330 pF capacitor to a rectifier which produces a positive bias for an n-p-n emitter-follower. This drives another transistor which provides a.c.c. bias for the first chrominance signal amplifier stage.

16

Colour-Difference and Luminance Amplifiers

The three c.r.t. electron beams must be modulated by the gamma corrected R', B', and G' voltages. These have to be derived by the addition of the colour-difference and luminance signals. Thus:

$$(R' - Y') + Y' = R'$$
$$(B' - Y') + Y' = B'$$
$$(G' - Y') + Y' = G'$$

This addition can be carried out in a matrix and the inverted colour voltages, $-R'$, $-G'$, and $-B'$, applied to the c.r.t. cathodes.

Alternatively, as indicated in the previous chapter in block diagram Fig. 15.1, it may be achieved in the c.r.t. itself, by applying the colour-difference signals to the control grids and a negative luminance signal ($-Y'$) to the cathodes. Applying $-Y'$ to the cathodes is equivalent to $+Y'$ to the grids so that the c.r.t. performs the algebraic operation shown in the above formulae.

It is necessary to remember that a given voltage input to the cathode of a c.r.t. gives rise to a greater change of beam current than the same input to its control grid.[1] This is because as the cathode is driven less positive, the effective voltage between the first anode and the cathode becomes more positive. This in itself creates an increase of beam current, in addition to that due to the voltage change between cathode and control grid. An input to the control grid on the other hand, leaves the effective first anode to cathode voltage unchanged. Cathode drive gives an increase of the order of 30% in the sensitivity of a c.r.t. compared with grid drive, i.e., the dynamic 'g_m' is some 30% greater.

The practical result of this when the c.r.t. matrixing is used is that to make the Y' factors inside and outside of the bracket in the above equations, produce equal and opposite changes in beam current (so that the net changes are due to the colour voltages only), the input to the grids must be greater than that to the cathode.

---

[1] See 'Grid and cathode modulation of the c.r.t.' (page 140 et seq.), in *Television Receiver Theory: Part 1*, by G. H. Hutson, published by Arnolds of London.

To illustrate this, suppose that on a 100% amplitude video signal, peak white is produced by a drive of 100 V to the three cathodes. Ignoring the difference in phosphor sensitivities for the moment, this means that since the three colour-difference signals are zero (on white), the only input to each gun is the 100 V to its cathode. To establish the same beam current using grid drive would require about $100 \times 130/100 = 130$ V input to the grids. It follows, that to produce the same intensity of illumination of, say the red phosphor, on a 100% saturated, 100% amplitude pure red signal, must require a net input to the red gun of the c.r.t. which is equivalent to 100 V at the cathode. But, on a non-white signal, the net beam currents of the three guns are due to both a luminance drive to the cathodes and colour-difference signals to the grids. The amplitudes of these input signals may now be deduced.

If $Y' = 100$ V on white, then on red:

$$Y' = \{0 \cdot 3R' + 0 \cdot 59G' + 1 \cdot 11B'\} \times 100$$
$$= \{0 \cdot 3(1) + 0 \cdot 59(0) + 0 \cdot 11(0)\} \times 100 = \mathbf{30\ V}$$

The amplitudes of the corresponding colour-difference signals are:

$$(R' - Y') = (1 - 0 \cdot 3) \times 100 = +70\ \text{V}$$
$$(B' - Y') = (0 - 0 \cdot 3) \times 100 = -30\ \text{V}$$
$$(G' - Y') = (0 - 0 \cdot 3) \times 100 = -30\ \text{V}$$

Each gun must now be considered in turn. The net input to the red gun has to be the same as -100 V to the cathode. This will not be given by -30 V to the cathode and $+70$ V to the red grid. The input to the red grid will need to be $+(70 \times 130/100) = +91$ V.

The blue and green guns must each receive a net input of 0 V. But the blue and green cathodes, like the red cathode, receive a -30 V input on the red signal. To cancel this involves an input to the grids, not of -30 V, but of $-(30 \times 130/100) = -39$ V.

On a saturated cyan signal the net inputs to the blue and green guns must each be equivalent to -100 V to their cathodes, whilst the net input to the red gun must be 0 V. But, on cyan, the luminance signal to the cathodes (again for 100% saturation, 100% amplitude) is:

$$-Y' = -\{0 \cdot 3R' + 0 \cdot 59G' + 0 \cdot 11B'\} \times 100$$
$$= -\{0 \cdot 3(0) + 0 \cdot 59(1) + 0 \cdot 11(1)\} \times 100$$
$$= -\{0 \cdot 59 + 0 \cdot 11\} \times 100 = -\mathbf{70\ V}$$

The relative amplitudes of the corresponding colour-difference signals are:

$$(R' - Y') = (0 - 0 \cdot 7) \times 100 = -70\ \text{V}$$
$$(B' - Y') = (1 - 0 \cdot 7) \times 100 = +30\ \text{V}$$
$$(G' - Y') = (1 - 0 \cdot 7) \times 100 = +30\ \text{V}$$

To produce the equivalent of a net cathode input of -100 V to the blue and green guns, the $(B' - Y')$ and $(G' - Y')$ signals have to be increased from $+30$ V to $(30 \times 130/100) = +39$ V.

250

To give a net input to the red gun of 0 V, the $(R' - Y)$ signal to the red grid must be, not -70 V but $-(70 \times 130/100) = -91$ V.

Starting from the assumption therefore, that for peak beam current a 100 V drive to the cathode is required, it emerges that on pure red and pure cyan, the $(R' - Y')$ signal to the red grid has to be $+91$ V and -91 V respectively. This shows that the final $(R' - Y')$ stage has to handle a signal whose maximum peak-to-peak amplitude is 182 V.

A similar approach for the other two primaries and their corresponding complementaries, for 100% amplitude 100% saturated colours, yields the maximum peak-to-peak signal amplitudes which the $(B' - Y')$ and $(G' - Y')$ final amplifiers would have to handle under the specified conditions (i.e., when white produces 100 V input to the three cathodes).

On blue, $(B' - Y')$ would be $+(89 \times 130/100)V = +116$ V and on yellow $(B' - Y')$ would be $-(89 \times 130/100)V = -116$ V. This shows a peak-to-peak maximum amplitude of 232 V for $(B' - Y')$.

Similarly on green $(G' - Y')$ would be $+(41 \times 130/100)V = +53$ V and on magenta $(G' - Y') = -(41 \times 130/100)V = -53$ V. This shows a maximum peak-to-peak amplitude of 106 V for $(G' - Y')$.

In practice, however, the efficiencies of the three phosphors differ and it would be necessary to take this into account to make a more accurate assessment of the comparative maximum peak-to-peak colour-difference signals to be handled in the three channels. For example, under typical working conditions a given c.r.t. may require cathode drives of -100 V, -95 V, and -90 V, for the red, green, and blue guns respectively, to yield peak amplitude white. This implies that the red phosphor is the least (and the blue phosphor the most) efficient for this particular tube. To adjust for this difference the peak-to-peak grid input voltages could be assessed by taking the proportions $100:95:90$ respectively, of the $(R' - Y')$, $(G' - Y')$, and $(B' - Y')$ voltages referred to above.

Such calculations are merely useful in indicating the approximate order of magnitudes involved. From them it is possible to arrive at a rough assessment of the gain requirements between the synchronous detectors and the c.r.t. For example, if the peak-to-peak output from the V demodulator is assumed to be 600 mV (i.e., $+300$ mV on red and -300 mV on cyan) the total gain needed in the $(R' - Y')$ channel is of the order $(182/600 \times 10^3) = 303$. If, at the same time, the vision detector yields a video signal which shows an excursion of 2·5 V from black to peak-white the luminance channel gain would need to be $100/2·5 = 40$.

In some receivers, wideband r.f. amplifiers are used between the delay-line summation circuitry and the U and V synchronous demodulators. In this event the gain in the colour-difference signal amplifiers is correspondingly less because the synchronous demodulators yield a greater output.

Other numerical factors which must be considered in this section of a receiver are the U and V weighting factors and the method of derivation of the $(G' - Y')$ from the $(R' - Y')$ and $(B' - Y')$ signals.

251

Influence of the U and V weighting factors

Between the delay-line and the c.r.t. it is necessary to compensate for the modulation-product weighting factors of 0·877 for the V and 0·493 for the U components, introduced at the transmitter to restrict the amplitudes of the chrominance signal. Correction merely involves arranging for the gains in the $(R' - Y')$ and $(B' - Y')$ paths to differ by an appropriate amount. The U component suffers a greater attenuation than the V and hence there must be a greater gain in the $(B' - Y')$ channel. The ratio of the U to the V weighting factors is $0·493/0·877 = 0·56$. Clearly, the gains in the paths between the summation circuits and the c.r.t. must be the inverse of this ratio, i.e., the total $(B' - Y')$ gain has to be $0·877/0·493 = 1·78$ times the $(R' - Y')$ gain. Expressed the other way round, the $(R' - Y')$ gain needs to be only 0·56 of the $(B' - Y')$ gain.

Using the example discussed above, where a gain of 303 was found to be needed in the $(R' - Y')$ amplifiers, the corresponding $(B' - Y')$ gain would need to be $303 \times 1·78 = 539$.

Although provision is often made for an adjustment of gain in both channels, it is possible to make do with only one of the two variables, since this still allows the relative gains to be correctly set. However, in setting-up receivers for optimum performance, it is often advantageous to have both channels under control. This is in addition to the $(G' - Y')$ amplifier gain which has not yet been discussed.

The 'de-weighting' operation is sometimes carried out in pre-demodulator U and V r.f. amplifiers instead of in the post-demodulator colour-difference amplifiers.

When studying how the $(G' - Y')$ signal is obtained it is necessary to note whether or not the $(R' - Y')$ and $(B' - Y')$ signals have been de-weighted before application to the $(G' - Y')$ matrix.

The $(G' - Y')$ matrix

The proportions of the $(R' - Y')$ and $(B' - Y')$ colour-difference signals which are necessary to obtain the third $(G' - Y')$ signal are easily established as follows:

$$(1)\, Y' = 0·30R' + 0·59G' + 0·11B'$$
$$(0·30 + 0·59 + 0·11)Y' = 0·30R' + 0·59G' + 0·11B'$$
$$0·30Y' + 0·59Y' + 0·11Y' = 0·30R' + 0·59G' + 0·11B'$$
$$0·30(R' - Y') + 0·59(G' - Y') + 0·11(B' - Y') = 0 \qquad (1)$$
$$+0·59(G' - Y') = -0·30(R' - Y') - 0·11(B' - Y')$$
$$(G' - Y') = -\frac{0·30}{0·59}(R' - Y') - \frac{0·11}{0·59}(B' - Y')$$
$$\mathbf{(G' - Y') = -0·51(R' - Y')}$$
$$\mathbf{-0·186(B' - Y')} \quad (2)$$

Since the required $(R' - Y')$ and $(B' - Y')$ amplitudes are both less than unity they may be derived using simple resistor attenuators across the respective signal paths at points where the signals have the required polarities, i.e., where they are negative if $+(G' - Y')$, or positive if $-(G' - Y')$ is needed.

It is of interest to note that if $(G' - Y')$ were one of the two transmitted signals then *gain* would be required in the matrix. Thus, from eq. (1) above, it follows that:

(a) If $(R' - Y')$ were the missing signal, then the matrix would have to be based upon the formula:

$$(R' - Y') = -0.59/0.3(G' - Y') - 0.11/0.3(B' - Y')$$

The factor $0.59/0.3 = 1.97$ implies gain in the matrix.

(b) If $(B' - Y')$ were missing, the matrix formula would be:

$$(B' - Y') = -0.59/0.11(G' - Y') - 0.3/0.11(R' - Y')$$

The factors $0.59/0.11 = 5.4$, and $0.3/0.11 = 2.7$ both imply gain.

This shows that it would be technically less convenient to use $(G' - Y')$ to modulate one of the two quadrature components of the chrominance signal. Also, in many scenes, the amplitude of $(G' - Y')$ is small. Examination of colour-bar signal waveforms shows that $(G' - Y')$ is either the smallest of the three colour-difference signals, or is at most only equal to the smaller of the other two. The small amplitude, together with the need for gain in the matrix, would make noise problems greater than they are using the chosen $(R' - Y')$ and $(B' - Y')$ signals.

Figure 16.1 shows a schematic diagram of the colour-difference amplifiers and $(G' - Y')$ matrixing arrangements for a receiver employing the widely used system discussed above, where the colour-difference and luminance signals are combined by the c.r.t. itself.

It is assumed that there are no r.f. amplifiers between the summation circuitry and the synchronous demodulators, so that the $(R' - Y')$ and $(B' - Y')$ signals delivered by the demodulators are still 'weighted'.

De-weighting is achieved by arranging for the gains P and Q of the first $(R' - Y')$ and $(B' - Y')$ amplifier stages, to be in the ratio 0.56 to 1.0 (i.e., $P = 0.56Q$).

The inputs to these amplifiers are shown as being of the order of mV, whilst the outputs are labelled *volts*. The second stages then deliver to the c.r.t. red and blue grids, signals whose maximum peak-to-peak amplitudes are of the order deduced above, i.e., 182 V and 230 V for $(R' - Y')$ and $(B' - Y')$ on 100% saturated, 100% amplitude red and blue signals respectively.

Since positive-going signals are needed at the c.r.t. grids, the inputs to the final amplifiers have to be negative-going and the inputs to the first stages positive-going.

The $(G' - Y')$ amplifier is also shown as having two stages. The first of these is required to deliver to the $(G' - Y')$ final stage, a negative-going signal to match the other two channels. Hence a positive-going $(G' - Y')$ input is needed to the first amplifier. But, as shown by the $(G' - Y')$ matrix equation above, to produce a positive $(G' - Y')$ signal, the fractions 0.51 and 0.186 of *negative* $(R' - Y')$ and $(B' - Y')$ signals respectively, are needed. These negative-going signals are available from the outputs of the $(R' - Y')$ and $(B' - Y')$ first amplifiers. If the gain of the first

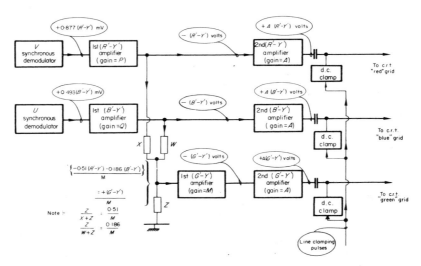

Fig. 16.1 *Showing, in schematic form, a typical arrangement of colour-difference amplifiers, with* $(G' - Y')$ *matrixing*

$(G' - Y')$ amplifier were unity, then the potential divider X, Z, would be calculated so that $Z/(X + Z) = 0.51$. Similarly W and Z would be such that $Z/(W + Z) = 0.186$. Since, however, the first $(G' - Y')$ amplifier is shown as having a gain of M, then resistors are chosen so that

$$\frac{Z}{X + Z} = \frac{0.51}{M} \quad \text{and} \quad \frac{Z}{W + Z} = \frac{0.186}{M}$$

It will be noticed that the resistor Z provides a common shunt load in both the $(R' - Y')$ and $(B' - Y')$ paths and hence there is an apparent danger of crosstalk between these two signals. To obviate this Z needs to be as small as possible compared with X and W. If the gain of the first $(G' - Y')$ stage is unity then the ratio of these resistors is entirely dictated by the matrix equation and Z cannot be very small compared with the other two resistors. But, if the amplifier has a gain of M the situation is better. This is shown, for the $(R' - Y')$ attenuator, by the two simple equations for Z shown below:

(a) If the first $(G' - Y')$ amplifier gain $= 1$

$$Z = 0.51(Z + X)$$
$$Z(1 - 0.51) = 0.51X$$
$$Z = \frac{0.51X}{0.49}$$

254

(b) If the first $(G' - Y')$ amplifier has a gain $= M$

$$MZ = 0.51(Z + X)$$
$$Z(M - 0.51) = 0.51X$$
$$Z = \frac{0.51X}{(M - 0.51)}$$

This reduces the value of Z to a much lower figure. It is, however, important to realize that in a practical circuit the value of Z is not to be taken as the value of the resistor connected between the control grid and earth, if the first $(G' - Y')$ amplifier is a valve, or between the base and earth if it is a transistor. The value for Z is the net input impedance Z_{in} of the stage. When, as is often the case, shunt-fed negative feedback is employed, the net input impedance is substantially less than the value of the wired-in input resistor.

In both (a) and (b) above, it was assumed that the value for X was known and Z was then obtained in terms of X. If this were so then W would now have to be found in terms of the calculated value for Z. Thus, for (a):

$$\frac{Z}{W + Z} = 0.186 \quad \text{therefore} \quad W = \frac{Z(1 - 0.186)}{0.186}$$

and for (b):

$$\frac{Z}{W + Z} = \frac{0.186}{M} \quad \text{therefore} \quad W = \frac{Z(M - 0.186)}{0.186}$$

In practice, since Z is common to both attenuators, it would be more logical to choose a suitably low value for the net input impedance Z_{in} of the $(G' - Y')$ amplifier and then to calculate both X and W in terms of the chosen Z_{in}. Then, assuming a gain M for this amplifier:

$$X = \frac{Z_{in}(M - 0.51)}{0.51} \quad \text{and} \quad W = \frac{Z_{in}(M - 0.186)}{0.186}$$

D.C. clamps

To use d.c. coupled amplifiers would involve difficulties; especially in maintaining a constant 'no-colour' voltage level at the c.r.t. grids. It is usual to a.c. couple the colour-difference signals and then to establish a constant no-colour level by employing d.c. clamps. These are driven during the line-blanking period by pulses derived in the line timebase. At the beginning of each active picture line therefore, the d.c. level is set and the discharge time-constants of the a.c. coupling networks are arranged to be too long for this level to change significantly between the beginning and end of one active line period.

Examples of typical circuitry are now studied.

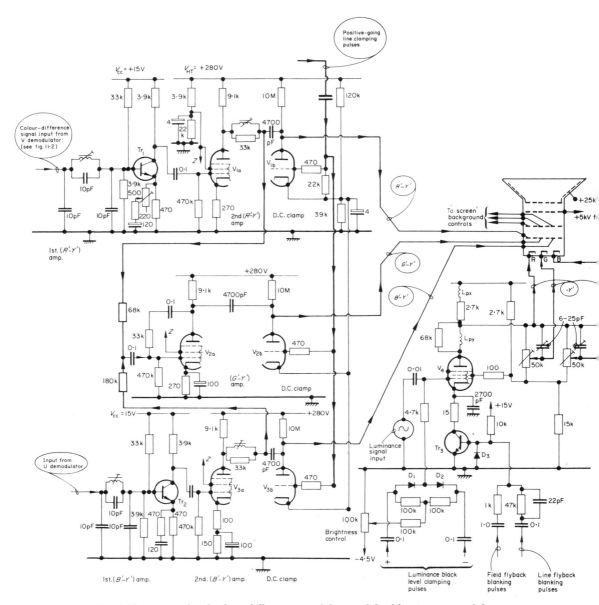

Fig. 16.2   *Example of colour-difference amplifiers and final luminance amplifier circuitry*

(Associated diagram: Fig. 11.2)

Figure 16.2

(i) COLOUR-DIFFERENCE AMPLIFIERS AND $(G' - Y')$ MATRIX. Tr_1 and Tr_2 are the first $(R' - Y')$ and $(B' - Y')$ amplifiers receiving their inputs from the V and U demodulators respectively. The gain of Tr_2, the $(B' - Y')$ amplifier, is not adjustable. A series R and C combination in shunt with the emitter resistor, gives differential negative feedback to provide an adequate frequency response.

A pre-set potentiometer, in series with a similar network across the emitter resistor of Tr_1, allows the relative gain of the $(R' - Y')$ amplifier to be adjusted. There are no U and V amplifiers between the delay-line and the demodulators in this receiver, so that the inputs to Tr_1 and Tr_2 must still be weighted.

It will be seen that the $(G' - Y')$ matrix is fed from the final $(R' - Y')$ and $(B' - Y')$ stages. These two deliver positive-polarity signals to the c.r.t. grids so that matrixing appropriate proportions of them yields a $(G' - Y')$ signal of negative polarity. This is amplified by the single stage $(G' - Y')$ amplifier to drive the green grid with a signal of positive polarity.

Since the $(G' - Y')$ matrix is fed from the output terminals of the $(R' - Y')$ and $(B' - Y')$ stages, it is evident that the two signals to the matrix are already de-weighted. This means that the proportions of the two need to be those indicated by the $(G' - Y')$ equation.

Comparing the resistor matrix in this circuit with the general case discussed above, it will be seen that X is here represented by the 68 kΩ resistor and W by the 180 kΩ. Z is the input impedance of the $(G' - Y')$ amplifier. There is strong negative feedback on this stage, shunt fed from the anode circuit, so that Z is substantially less than the 470 kΩ value of the grid resistor.

It will be noticed that the cathode circuits and hence the gains of the $(R' - Y')$ and $(B' - Y')$ final stages differ. This again indicates that it is not until the anode signals are compared that the two signals have their correct relative amplitudes.

(ii) D.C. CLAMP CIRCUITS. The three colour-difference signals are a.c. coupled via 4700 pF capacitors to the c.r.t. grids. Shunted across each signal path is a triode which acts as a driven d.c. clamp. The three triodes are biased-off during the active picture line by a potential divider across the H.T. line, which provides a common cathode cut-off bias of approximately $+70$ V.

During each line blanking period, a positive-going line pulse to their control grids drives the three triodes into anode current saturation. In effect the triodes are changed from a very high to a very low resistance state and the anodes may be regarded as being strapped to the cathodes for the duration of the pulse. The right-hand plate of each 4700 pF coupling capacitor is therefore connected to the $+70$ V cathode potential whilst the left-hand plates are at the 'no-colour' potential present at the anodes of the pentodes. This is of the order of $+140$ V. During this period the charging time constant of each capacitor is fast since the total resistance in series with each is a 9·1 kΩ anode load resistor and the low resistance of a saturated triode. When the triodes switch off at the end of the line pulse, the right-hand plates of the capacitors are left at $+70$ V, and this is the potential level to which the c.r.t. grids are clamped. With the triodes off, the time constants for the 4700 pF capacitors are very long since the 10 MΩ anode resistors now provide the only d.c. connection to the right-hand plates. There is no significant change of potential during the active line period and hence the colour-difference signals presented to the c.r.t. swing the grids about a constant 'no-colour' level of some $+70$ V.

(iii) LUMINANCE OUTPUT STAGE. The luminance signal is a.c. coupled from an emitter follower to the grid of V_4, the luminance output stage. During the line blanking period the diodes D_1 and D_2 are switched on and the right-hand plate of the grid coupling capacitor is clamped to a negative potential set by the brightness control. D_1 and D_2 are so connected that D_1 is switched on by a positive pulse to its anode and D_2 by a negative pulse to its cathode. When they are both conductive the net pulse potential at their common connection is zero and the net voltage due to the equal and opposite charges on the two capacitors is also zero. Hence the 0.01 μF grid coupling capacitor is connected via the 4.7 kΩ resistor and the 100 kΩ resistors to the brightness control slider potential, and its charge is not influenced by the balanced switching circuit. When the clamping pulses end, the diodes are cut-off by the charges on their feed capacitors. Without the d.c. clamp the charge on the grid capacitor would vary with the d.c. content of the luminance signal and black level would change as the mean level of the signal varied.

With the clamp, black-level is held constant because the positive-going video signal input to V_4 'sits' upon a fixed negative voltage provided by the permanent charge which is maintained on the coupling capacitor by the clamp circuit.

Line and field retrace blanking is achieved by switching off V_4 in the flyback periods so that its anode, and hence the c.r.t. cathodes, rise to the full H.T. voltage. This cuts-off the beam currents. V_4 is switched by transistor Tr_3 which is in series with the cathode earth connection. Tr_3 is forward biased by the 10 kΩ resistor which returns to $+15$ V. It therefore offers negligible resistance between emitter and collector during the active line period. On field and line flyback, however, negative pulses to D_3 cathode switch the diode on and Tr_3 base is grounded. This removes the forward bias and Tr_3 cuts-off, so effectively open-circuiting V_4 cathode.

To allow for the different phosphor sensitivities provision is made for varying the luminance drive to two out of the three c.r.t. cathodes. Normally the red cathode receives full drive but the green and blue cathodes receive rather less. The 50 kΩ drive potentiometers are connected between the anode take-off point and V_4 screen grid. The screen potential is arranged to equal the anode black-level potential which means that whatever setting the sliders have the black-level voltages to the cathodes are always the same. This voltage is approximately $+200$ V and since the c.r.t. grid d.c. clamp level is about $+70$ V, the no-signal grid-to-cathode bias on the c.r.t. guns is of the order of -130 V.

The h.f. response of the amplifier is improved by the inclusion of series (L_{py}) and shunt (L_{px}) peaking coils.[1]

[1] See chapter 6 on 'Video Amplifiers; H.F. Compensation Techniques', page 98 et seq. in *Television Receiver Theory*, by G. H. Hutson, published by Arnolds of London.

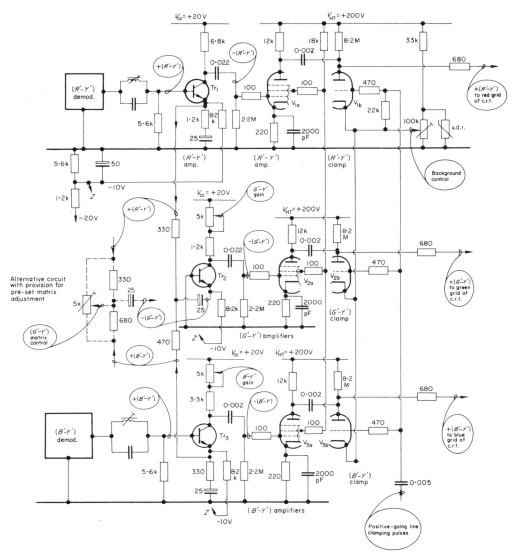

Fig. 16.3 *Example of colour-difference amplifiers with emitter circuit matrixing of the $(G' - Y')$ signal*

(Associated diagram: Fig. 5.11)

Figure 16.3

(i) COLOUR-DIFFERENCE AMPLIFIERS. In each of the three channels the final pentode amplifier stages are identical. This indicates that de-weighting is carried out earlier. It is achieved by giving different gains to the first $(R' - Y')$ and $(B' - Y')$ amplifiers, Tr_1 and Tr_3.

The main adjustment of relative gain is provided by a 5 kΩ pre-set potentiometer forming part of the collector load of the $(B' - Y')$ amplifier.

There is also more negative feedback on the $(R' - Y')$ than on the $(B' - Y')$ stage. The undecoupled emitter load for Tr_1 is essentially 1·2 kΩ whilst that for Tr_3 is 330 Ω. These loads are a.c. coupled by 25 μF capacitors, which are needed for d.c. blocking since forward bias is arranged—not in the normal way by connecting the base to a positive potential—but by returning the emitters to a negative potential via 8·2 kΩ resistors. The d.c. feedback across the 8·2 kΩ resistors gives a high degree of stabilization against variations such as the changing level of leakage current with temperature. This bias arrangement has the merits of removing a positive voltage from the synchronous demodulators which are directly coupled to Tr_1 and Tr_3 bases and also of allowing the base of the first $(G' - Y')$ stage Tr_2 to be connected directly to earth so reducing the input impedance to a very low level.

As in the previous circuit, the final stages are a.c. coupled to the c.r.t. grids and the no-colour potential on the grids is set by triodes working as driven clamps. In this circuit, however, the common cathode potential for the triodes, may be adjusted by a 150 kΩ potentiometer which is referred to as a *background control*. This effectively sets the no-colour steady potential on the c.r.t. grids to an optimum value. The adjustment is carried out as part of the grey-scale tracking procedure.

(ii) THE $(G' - Y')$ MATRIX. Unlike the previous circuit, where the $(G' - Y')$ matrix was fed with de-weighted signals from the final $(R' - Y')$ and $(B' - Y')$ amplifiers, in this example the matrix is fed with weighted signals from the emitters of the first stages. Although the different $(R' - Y')$ and $(B' - Y')$ emitter resistors do make a difference to the ratio of the $(R' - Y')$ and $(B' - Y')$ signals (as compared with their ratio at the bases of the transistors) the emitter signals may—as a first approximation—still be regarded as bearing their original relative weightings.

The $(G' - Y')$ equation discussed earlier is true for de-weighted signals. But de-weighting involves establishing the demodulated $(R' - Y')$ and $(B' - Y')$ signals in the ratio of 0·56 to 1·0.

To assemble $(G' - Y')$ from the weighted signals therefore, involves adding 0·51 of 0·56$(R' - Y')$ to 0·186 of $(B' - Y')$. The ratio of the $(R' - Y')$ to the $(B' - Y')$ contributions, is therefore 0·2856 to 0·186 = 1·54 to 1.

The polarity of the $(G' - Y')$ signal to Tr_2 emitter has to be negative because a

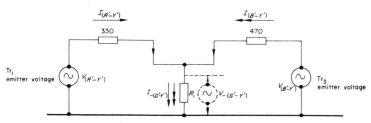

Fig. 16.4 *Simplified diagram of the emitter $(G' - Y')$ matrixing circuit in Fig. 16.3*

negative signal is needed at the collector to feed the grid of the final stage. Tr_2 is in the grounded base mode which gives no phase change, or—more strictly—no signal inversion, between emitter and collector.

The object of the matrix is to drive the base–emitter junction of Tr_2 with a $(G' - Y')$ current compounded of two currents of appropriate proportions derived from the emitters of Tr_1 and Tr_3. To minimize cross-talk the common impedance through which the two currents pass must be as small as possible compared with the series feed resistors from Tr_1 and Tr_3 emitters. The common impedance is the input resistance to Tr_2 and this is essentially the low resistance of the forward-biased base–emitter junction.

Figure 16.4 shows in simplified form the effective matrixing arrangement.

Here $I_{(R' - Y')}$ and $I_{(B' - Y')}$ are the two components of the input current to Tr_2, and R_i is the input resistance of Tr_2. If the Tr_1 and Tr_3 emitter voltages, shown as $V_{(R' - Y')}$ and $V_{(B' - Y')}$, are assumed to bear the original weighting factors, and to be presented by generators of very low impedance, then it is required that:

$$\frac{I_{(R' - Y')}}{I_{(B' - Y')}} = \frac{1 \cdot 54}{1}$$

but

$$I_{(R' - Y')} = \frac{V_{(R' - Y')}}{330 + R_i} \quad \text{and} \quad I_{(B' - Y')} = \frac{V_{(B' - Y')}}{470 + R_i}$$

therefore

$$\frac{I_{(R' - Y')}}{I_{(B' - Y')}} = \frac{V_{(R' - Y')}}{V_{(B' - Y')}} \times \frac{(470 + R_i)}{(330 + R_i)}$$

Suppose $R_i = 30$ then

$$\frac{I_{(R' - Y')}}{I_{(B' - Y')}} = \frac{V_{(R' - Y')}}{V_{(B' - Y')}} \times \frac{1 \cdot 4}{1}$$

The chief reason why this ratio differs slightly from the theoretical value of $1 \cdot 54 : 1$ is that the emitter load on Tr_1 is somewhat greater than that on Tr_3, which still further increases the weighting factor in favour of $(R' - Y')$.

Although not included in this receiver, a potentiometer is sometimes fitted to allow the $(G' - Y')$ matrix to be adjusted for an optimum value, as judged by inspection of the $(G' - Y')$ waveform on a colour-bar signal.

The arrangement is shown by the dotted circuit alongside Tr_2 in Fig. 16.3.

Figure 16.5

This provides an example of the R', G', and B' drive system. Instead of the colour-difference and luminance signals being added by the c.r.t., the *matrixing* operation is carried out externally and the c.r.t. is driven by the reconstituted colour signals, applied with negative polarity as $-R'$, $-G'$, and $-B'$ to the respective cathodes.

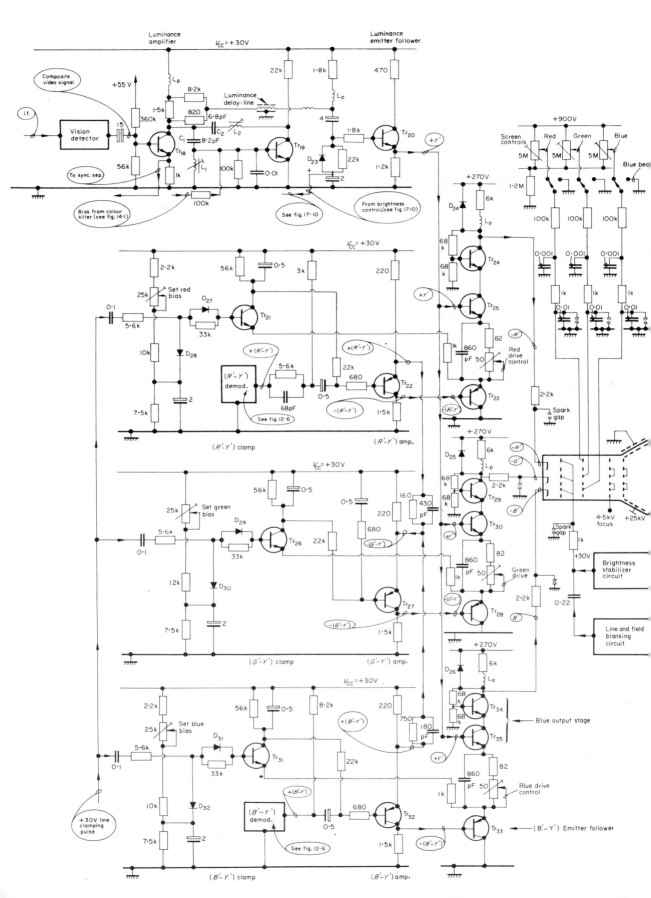

(i) R', G' AND B' OUTPUT STAGES. These are identical in each channel. Using the red channel as an example, the output stage consists of the two n-p-n transistors Tr_{24} and Tr_{25}. Two series connected transistors are used to enable the output stage to operate on an h.t. supply of 270 V. This permits the required maximum peak-to-peak signal swing of 160 V at the output terminal to be handled. The mean Tr_{24} collector potential is typically 190 V, implying a voltage drop of 80 V across the 6 kΩ collector load. This in turn shows a mean current level of 13·3 mA. Since the maximum possible positive-going voltage swing is 80 V (taking the collector of Tr_{24} up to the full h.t. voltage of 270 V and the collector current down to zero), the corresponding maximum would involve distortion and a normal practical maximum peak-to-peak output swing would be of the order of 150 V, corresponding to a peak collector current of 26 mA.

Collector currents of this order necessitate the use of power transistors, with adequate heat sinks. A similar voltage swing could of course be achieved using smaller currents with a higher value of collector load resistor. However, the bandwidth of each amplifier, for black and white detail must extend to 5·5 MHz and the h.f. droop of the gain/frequency characteristic is caused by shunt capacitance across the collector load resistance. For a given capacitance, the higher the value of the load resistor, the narrower becomes the bandwidth and it is this factor which sets a limit to the value of the collector resistor. The use of a peaking coil (L_p) improves the frequency response at the h.f. end and allows the resistor value to be somewhat higher than it could otherwise be.[1]

Each output pair has to receive two additive inputs; the Y' luminance signal and the appropriate colour-difference signal.

It will be noticed that the emitter of the lower of each output stage transistor pair, returns to earth via a p-n-p transistor connected in the emitter-follower mode. These provide the method of feeding the colour-difference signals to the output stages.

Referring again to the red amplifier, the emitter-follower Tr_{23}, has, in effect, the red output stage as its emitter load. The base-emitter current of Tr_{23} is modulated by the $(R' - Y')$ signal applied from the collector of the $(R' - Y')$ amplifier Tr_{22} and in turn the current passed by the output pair is modulated by an amplified version of this $(R' - Y')$ input current.

To provide the necessary negative polarity voltage drive to the c.r.t. cathode from the collector of Tr_{24}, the input to Tr_{25} emitter has to be of negative sign. Since no phase shift is introduced by the emitter-follower Tr_{23}, the input to Tr_{23} base is also of negative sign.

As each of the three emitter followers has to carry the full collector current of an output stage, these are also power transistors, fitted with suitable heat sinks.

The luminance signal is fed from the emitter of the luminance emitter-follower stage Tr_{20} to the base of the lower transistor in each output pair.

To take account of the voltage inversion between the base and collector signals,

[1] This subject is fully treated under 'Video Amplifiers' in chapters 6, 7, and 8 of *Television Receiver Theory*: Part 1, by G. H. Hutson, published by Arnolds of London.

Fig. 16.5 *Luminance amplifier, colour-difference amplifiers and R', G', and B' output stages, in a receiver in which the colour-difference and luminance signals are matrixed externally to the c.r.t.*

(Associated diagrams: Figs. 12.6, 13.5, 13.7, 14.1, 15.5, 17.8, 17.10)

the base input signal has to be positive-going (i.e., $+Y'$) to provide a $-Y'$ output.

Since each lower transistor of the output pairs receives two inputs, one (the colour-difference signal) to its emitter and the other (the luminance signal) to its base, the output collector current is in each case a function of the sum of the two inputs, i.e., the output stages perform the simple algebraic addition shown in the three formulae in the first paragraph of this chapter.

Separate pre-set gain controls are provided for the three output stages. This is achieved by including 50 Ω potentiometers, in series with fixed 82 Ω resistors, in the emitter circuits. This allows the level of negative feedback to be varied. These pre-sets are adjusted as part of the grey-scale tracking procedure; the relative gains being adjusted until a correct white is judged to be produced in the whitest bars of a stepped grey-scale luminance signal or in high contrast areas of a monochrome picture.

(ii) COLOUR-DIFFERENCE AMPLIFIERS. The p-n-p transistors Tr_{22}, Tr_{27}, and Tr_{32} are the $(R' - Y')$, $(G' - Y')$, and $(B' - Y')$ amplifiers respectively. The colour-difference signals from the V and U demodulators (shown in Fig. 12.6 of chapter 12) are a.c. coupled via 0·5 μF capacitors to the bases of Tr_{22} and Tr_{32}. De-weighting is achieved by differences in the coupling circuitry between the demodulators and the 0·5 μF capacitors. There is a series attenuating circuit comprising a 5·6 kΩ resistor shunted by a 68 pF capacitor in the $(R' - Y')$ signal path but not in the $(B' - Y')$ circuit. In addition the shunt load across which the $(B' - Y')$ signal is developed is 8·2 kΩ in the $(B' - Y')$ amplifier, but 3 kΩ in the $(R' - Y')$ circuit.

Matrixing of the $(G' - Y')$ signal is achieved in the same way as in the previous circuit, i.e., by deriving two input currents for the emitter of the $(G' - Y')$ amplifier from the emitters of the $(R' - Y')$ and $(B' - Y')$ amplifiers. Since a negative-polarity $(G' - Y')$ signal is needed at the collector of the $(G' - Y')$ amplifier Tr_{27}, it is necessary to apply $-(G' - Y')$ to the emitter. This requires appropriate proportions of $+(R' - Y')$ and $+(B' - Y')$ and signals of the correct polarity are available at the emitters of Tr_{22} and Tr_{32} respectively. The base of the $(G' - Y')$ amplifier is decoupled by a 0·5 μF capacitor in series with a 680 Ω limiting resistor.

(iii) D.C. CLAMP CIRCUITS. As described for the previously studied valve circuits, since the colour-difference signals are a.c. coupled it is necessary to provide in each channel a clamping circuit which operates during the line-blanking period to set the no-colour voltage level to a suitable datum line. Transistors Tr_{21}, Tr_{26}, and Tr_{31} provide this clamping facility. Referring to the $(R' - Y')$ amplifier Tr_{22}, it will be noted that the required forward bias for this p-n-p transistor is provided from a long time-constant circuit in the collector of the n-p-n clamp transistor Tr_{21}. This transistor is pulsed into conduction during the line-blanking period by a positive-going line pulse which is a.c. coupled via a 0·1 μF capacitor to its base. Diodes D_{27} and D_{28} are both switched on by the pulse and this in turn clamps the base to the potential present across the long time constant circuit at D_{28} cathode. This potential is fixed at a suitable level by the pre-set 25 kΩ *set-red-bias* potentiometer.

264

Since the colour-difference amplifier Tr_{22} is d.c. coupled to the output stage, the setting of the clamp bias on Tr_{21} affects the no-colour voltage level at the collector of the output transistor Tr_{24}. The practical procedure is to adjust the 25 kΩ pre-set to establish a drop of 80 V across the 6 kΩ load resistor in Tr_{24} collector circuit. The same procedure is followed for the 25 kΩ pre-sets in the other two channels.

At the end of the line pulse, D_{28} is cut-off by the positive voltage at its cathode and hence Tr_{21} is cut-off because its forward-bias is removed. D_{27} blocks from Tr_{21} base, the negative voltage spike which occurs on the trailing edge of the line pulse due to the differentiating action of the a.c. coupling network.

The clamp transistors are so connected that they provide automatic stabilization of the chosen no-colour reference potential at the collectors of the output stages. This is achieved by returning the emitters of the clamp transistors via 1 kΩ resistors to the emitters of the respective emitter followers Tr_{23}, Tr_{28}, and Tr_{33}. Should the current through an output stage rise, for example, the emitter-follower's emitter potential moves nearer to earth potential. This results in the emitter of the clamp transistor becoming less positive. It follows that when the line pulse switches on the clamp transistor, the forward bias on its base-emitter junction is greater and this causes it to conduct harder with a consequent increase in the voltage stored across the long-time constant collector circuit. This downward movement in collector potential in turn increases the negative forward-bias on the base-emitter junction of the p-n-p colour-difference amplifier transistor and makes it conduct harder, with the result that its collector potential becomes more positive. Finally, this positive-going movement carries the base of the associated p-n-p emitter-follower more positive, so cutting back its forward bias and reducing the current passing through it. But this is the output stage's current and in this way the original unwanted increase in the collector current is off-set. This clamping action is repeated during each line blanking period and stable working conditions are established.

(iv) LUMINANCE AMPLIFIER. The video signal from the vision detector is fed via a 15 μF reversible electrolytic capacitor to the base of the n-p-n luminance amplifier transistor Tr_{18}. The signal from the detector is negative-going and still bears chrominance as well as luminance information. In shunt with the collector circuit is a switched 4·43 MHz sub-carrier filter C_2L_2. When colour is present in the incoming signal, the positive bias developed by the colour-killer circuit to 'open' the chrominance amplifier path (see Fig. 14.1) is also applied to the base of the switching transistor Tr_{19}. This transistor 'bottoms' when the forward bias is applied, and the through resistance from collector to emitter is very low. The series tuned-circuit C_2L_2 is hence connected via Tr_{19} to earth so giving strong attenuation to the chrominance information borne by the video signal.

On a monochrome signal, there is no bias to switch on Tr_{19} so that the 4·43 MHz tuned circuit no longer shunts the signal path. To leave the filter in circuit, although done in many receivers, involves an unnecessary degradation in the gain/frequency response of the luminance amplifier and in this particular circuit the full 0–5·5 MHz bandwidth is available in monochrome.

The second filter C_1L_1 is tuned to 6 MHz to remove the inter-carrier sound i.f. component.

Two outputs are taken from Tr_{18}. From the emitter the video signal, with positive-going sync. pulses, is fed to the sync. separator. The collector signal, developed across a 1·5 kΩ load resistor in series with the 'shunt' peaking coil L_p is passed via a 0·65 µs luminance delay-line (see the discussion below) to the base of the luminance emitter-follower Tr_{20}. The delay-line is properly terminated at both ends by matched loads.

At Tr_{20} base, the video signal is d.c. restored by the action of the restorer diode D_{23}.[1]

The reference level on which the video signal pulses 'sit', is determined by the potential at D_{23} anode. By returning this point to the slider of the brightness control, the positive voltage on D_{23} anode—and hence the d.c. reference level—may be varied.

Increasing the voltage by turning up the brightness control makes the emitter of Tr_{20} more positive and this in turn increases the forward bias on the bases of Tr_{25}, Tr_{30}, and Tr_{35}. The corresponding increase of output stage currents decreases their collector potentials and hence moves the c.r.t. cathodes less positive. The beam currents therefore increase and the brightness level is higher.

Luminance delay lines

At the point of their combination the luminance and chrominance signals must be exactly in step. For this to be so, the times taken by the two signals to pass through their amplifiers must be equal. But the chrominance amplifier is bandwidth restricted whilst the luminance amplifier is wideband and this results in the restricted chrominance signal suffering a greater delay than the luminance signal. To compensate for this some extra delay has to be introduced into the luminance signal path. A delay-line is inserted which has a delay of the order of 0·7 µs. The precise delay needed varies with different circuit arrangements but for NTSC and PAL receivers generally it falls within the range of 0·5 µs to 1·0 µs.

Delays of this order may conveniently be introduced by using the properties of transmission lines. A coaxial cable, for example, which has distributed series inductance and shunt capacitance, introduces a finite delay to a signal transmitted along it. By making an 'artificial' transmission line, with greater inductance and capacitance per unit length, the delay is much increased and the necessary physical length becomes conveniently short (e.g., 10 cm).

Figure 16.6 shows an artificial line made of a number of L.C. sections connected in tandem. Such a device has the appearance of—and may be treated as—a low-pass filter. From d.c. up to a certain 'cut-off' frequency (f_c), the filter offers a minimum attenuation and 'looks' resistive. Above f_c the attenuation rises sharply.

[1] See 'The D.C. Restorer Diode', in chapter 5—'Vision Detectors', in *Television Receiver Theory*: Part 1, by G. H. Hutson, published by Arnolds of London.

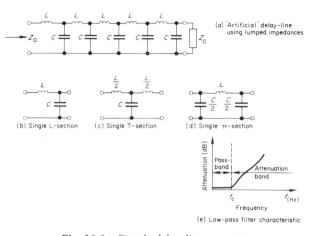

Fig. 16.6 *Simple delay-line concepts*

Note: The sections take on the form of low-pass filters

The performance parameters of the line are all functions of the inductance L and capacitance C per unit-section. As shown at (b), (c), and (d) the line may conveniently be treated as either a series of 'L-sections', 'T-sections' or 'Π-sections'. In all cases, if L and C are the values per section of series inductance and shunt capacitance respectively, the chief parameters are:

Characteristic impedance
$$R_0 = \sqrt{\frac{L}{C}} \text{ ohms}$$

Cut-off frequency
$$f_c = \frac{1}{\Pi\sqrt{LC}} \text{ Hz} \quad.$$

Phase shift (per section) $\phi = \omega\sqrt{LC}$ radians

Delay (per section) $t_d = \sqrt{LC}$ seconds

Total delay of the line $t_{dn} = n\sqrt{LC}$ (where n is the number of sections)

Instead of using a series of individual inductors and capacitors (i.e., 'lumped' impedances), a single solenoid wound over earthed metal strips may be used. This simple method provides a cheap and effective way of making a luminance delay-line. The cut-off frequency is designed to be well above the highest luminance component (e.g., say 7 MHz for the U.K. system where the video bandwidth is 5·5 MHz).

The attenuation tends to rise towards the h.f. end of the video range and to make the response more uniform, 'free' metal strips are sometimes disposed in a row along the coil. These act as bridging capacitors across sections of the inductor and provide a form of h.f. compensation. Figure 16.7(a) illustrates the construction of a typical luminance delay-line.

The delay-line must be properly terminated at each end by its characteristic

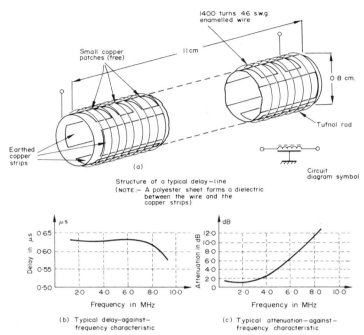

Fig. 16.7 *Showing details of the construction and performance of a typical luminance delay-line*

impedance. In many receivers, the 'sending end' is matched by making the collector load of a common-emitter luminance amplifier stage, equal in value to the R_0 of the line. A similar resistor is fitted at the receiving end. Sometimes a small variable inductor is fitted in series with the line to allow a precise pre-set adjustment of the delay.

The position of the delay-line in the luminance amplifier circuitry is not important. It is often placed in the coupling path between the penultimate and final luminance amplifier stages.

Typical performance parameters for a luminance delay-line are as follows:

Characteristic impedance	$= 1000 \ \Omega$
Nominal delay	$= 0.63 \ \mu s$
Rise time	$= 0.12 \ \mu s$
Insertion loss	$= 1.5 \ dB$
Delay variation	$= \pm 2\%$ from 0 to 7 MHz

Sketches showing approximate delay against frequency and attenuation against frequency curves for a typical luminance delay-line are shown in Fig. 16.7(b) and (c) respectively.

To assess the effect of not having equalization of the transit times in the luminance and chrominance amplifiers, a coloured bar followed by a grey bar may be considered.

268

If, at the point of combination, the luminance signal for the coloured bar 'finishes first' because the luminance amplifier transit time is faster, then the luminance signal changes from whatever level it has on the colour, to its 'grey' value. By computing the values of the colour-difference and luminance signals for any given transition, the net input to each c.r.t. gun may be deduced and it is evident that at the edge, a hue must appear which differs from that of the colour-bar. Clearly this also affects the leading edges as well as the trailing edges of all picture detail where two different hues meet and the result is a general deterioration of the whole picture. It will be observed that it is *only* the edges which are affected. In large areas of constant hue, once the chrominance signal has 'caught-up' with the luminance, the correct signals are presented to the c.r.t. and there is no visible evidence that the two signals are not in fact in step.

Adjustment of colour-difference amplifier gains and $(G' - Y')$ matrix

Assuming that grey-scale adjustments are correct it is clearly necessary to establish a method of setting the gains in the three colour-difference channels. As stated earlier, receivers vary in the number of pre-set adjustments available and one or more of the channels may have a fixed gain. However, a general adjustment procedure may be useful to note, which rests upon a subjective assessment of performance as judged from the screen using a standard colour-bar signal.

Suppose the $(B' - Y')$ gain is to be set. If the red and green guns are put out of action (or the screen viewed through a blue filter), four blue vertical stripes are seen, because full amplitude blue is present in four of the bars. These are in bar positions 1, 3, 5, and 7, corresponding to the white, cyan, magenta, and blue bars. In the white bar the c.r.t. beam current is produced by the Y' signal only, but in the remaining three bars it is determined by the sum of the Y' and $(B' - Y')$ signals. It follows that the adjustment procedure must be to set the $(B' - Y')$ and/or the U gain control(s), to the point where the bars are judged to be of equal intensity.

In a similar way, if the blue and green guns are switched off (or the tube viewed through a red filter) the $(R' - Y')$ gain may be set by looking at the four red stripes. These are in bar positions 1, 2, 5, and 6, corresponding to the white, yellow, magenta, and red bars. The $(R' - Y')$ and/or the V gain control(s) are set until the red stripes 2, 5, and 6 are judged equal in intensity to the first.

Finally, the $(G' - Y')$ gain may be set by switching off the red and blue guns (or viewing through the green filter). Stripes 1, 2, 3, and 4 corresponding to the white, yellow, cyan, and green bars, should all appear of equal intensity when the $(G' - Y')$ gain control is correctly set.

If a $(G' - Y')$ matrix adjustment is provided, this should be set to yield the correct $(G' - Y')$ waveform as viewed on an oscilloscope (see Fig. 3.5(k)), whilst the $(G' - Y')$ gain control is then adjusted by reference to the screen, as described above.

It must be noted that the EBU (European Broadcasting Union) colour-bar signal has a higher R', G', and B' content on the white bar than in the coloured-bars. For this reason, if such a signal is used when making the adjustments described, the first bar must be ignored. It is *always* correct to adjust for equality in the appearance of the *three colour bars* bearing a given primary; *whatever* the colour-bar signal in use.

The EBU colour-bar signal bears the reference 100/0/75/0. The first figure gives the amplitude of the white bar and the second the minimum level of the signal during the black bar. The third and fourth figures refer to the maximum and minimum levels respectively, of the colour signals during the colour-bars. Using this nomenclature, the 100% amplitude 95% saturated colour-bar signal described in chapter 3, bears the reference 100/0/100/25. (N.B. The minimum level of 25 corresponds to the amplitude of the 5% of white in the 95% saturated colour bars: e.g., on cyan, where $R' = 0.05$, $R' = 0.25$; as is shown in chapter 3.) It follows that when the first and third figures of a colour-bar reference are *equal*, bar 1 *may* be used in the adjustment procedure, but when these figures are *unequal*, bar 1 *must not* be used.[1]

Figure 16.8

As in the previous circuit, this receiver again uses R', G', B' drive to the c.r.t., rather than the alternative method of delivering the colour-difference signals to the grids and the luminance signal to the cathodes, with the c.r.t. itself carrying out the final matrixing operation.

The overall performance of a receiver employing a well designed R', G', B' drive can be very good, giving accurate reproduction of hues over a wide range of picture information, together with accuracy of detail outlines.

When separate colour-difference and luminance signals are fed to the c.r.t. it is essential that they should have precisely the correct timing relationship one with another. This is because the picture detail being described depends for its accurate reproduction upon the sum total of all of this information at any given instant, and any failure of the various signals to register exactly, must clearly give rise to inaccuracies of picture detail (e.g., blurring of edges and colour fringing). In addition, since both grid and cathode modulation is being employed, it is evident that the effective relative sensitivities of these electrodes would have to remain the same for all levels of input signals in order to maintain the accuracy of the matrixing operation carried out by the c.r.t.

Neither of these conditions is easy to achieve all the time in practice, because both the amplitudes and the frequencies of the signals which represent the ever-changing picture detail, create constantly changing electrical situations.

The results become easier to predict and control if each gun of the c.r.t. is presented with only one input signal, and the matrixing of the colour-difference and luminance signals is carried out at an earlier point in the receiver, close to the point at which the demodulation of the colour-difference signals takes place. This removes many of the variables which affect not only the actual light output from each phosphor at a given point in the picture, but also the registration of picture detail.

To achieve precise registration of R, G, and B information delivered to the c.r.t.

[1] At the time of writing in the UK, the BBC radiates the 100/0/100/25 colour-bar signal, but the ITA uses the 100/0/75/0 signal.

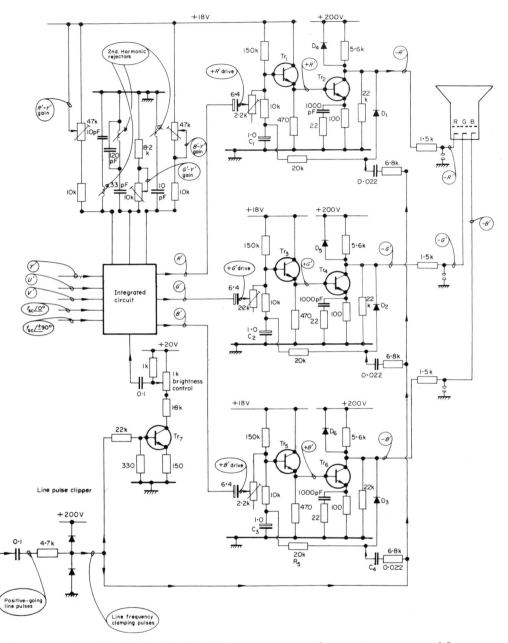

Fig. 16.8 *Example of R', G', B' drive to the c.r.t., using single transistor output amplifiers*

Note: The integrated circuit fulfils the functions of U and V synchronous demodulation, $(G' - Y')$ matrixing, and colour-difference plus luminance signal matrixing, to yield R', G', and B' drives to the emitter followers.

(Associated diagrams: Figs. 15.8, 17.12)

271

guns however, the R, G, and B signal paths between the matrix and the tube must have exactly the same bandwidths. Only when the bandwidths are equal, will the delay characteristics of the three paths be equal for *all* frequency components in the picture detail. Since there is no separate luminance path, it follows that the luminance information is carried by the three separate signals and hence the bandwidths of the three colour signal paths must be equal to the full video bandwidth of the system. For the U.K. 625-line signal the bandwidth extends from 0 to 5·5 MHz. Previous to the point of matrixing, the luminance and the colour-difference signals have their appropriate bandwidths.

A further important point which must be considered, is the maintenance of the correct black-level. When a separate luminance path is used, an efficient black-level clamping system combined with a carefully designed linear response curve over the video bandwidth, leads to an accurate maintenance of the grey-scale in monochrome information and to the proper reproduction of luminance levels in colour information, together with the clear resolution of all fine detail (which is of course in monochrome). When using RGB drive, these same ends have to be achieved through the R, G, and B amplifiers.

In seeking to compare the performance characteristics of the two systems of driving the c.r.t., it is clearly necessary to take all these relevant factors into account. At the time of writing very good results have been achieved by both methods.

Returning to Fig. 16.8, in this receiver a silicon integrated circuit (SIC), is employed to carry out several operations. These include synchronous demodulation of the U and V chrominance signal components delivered to it from the PAL-D delay-line circuitry; matrixing to produce $(G' - Y')$; amplification of the three colour-difference signals, and matrixing of these with the luminance signal to yield straightforward R', G', and B' signals for application to the three identical colour signal amplifiers. Brightness is also controlled through the SIC.

The actual SIC is very small, measuring less than one-third of a square centimetre. It is encapsulated and mounted on a bracket which forms a heat sink. The unit on the bracket measures approximately 3 cm × 1 cm and carries twenty connections (two of them earthed). These are not all shown in Fig. 16.8 which merely summarizes the essential operations of the unit by showing the input and output signals together with the external controls associated with it. Some 60 to 70 discrete components would be necessary in a conventional circuit carrying out the same functions as the SIC.

The $(R' - Y')$ demodulator uses a switched reference sub-carrier rather than a line-by-line inverted V component. The sub-carrier switching is carried out externally to the SIC, by a two-diode switch driven by a bistable multivibrator. A precise quadrature adjustment of the sub-carrier inputs to the SIC demodulators, is made possible by a trimmer in the $(B' - Y')$ sub-carrier r.f. transformer circuit.

As shown in Fig. 16.8, external series tuned circuits are fitted to remove the sub-carrier harmonics from the colour-difference signals developed by the demodulators and the $(G' - Y')$ matrix. Also fitted are $(R' - Y')$, $(B' - Y')$, and $(G' - Y')$ gain controls, which allow the three colour-difference signals to be adjusted to the correct relative amplitudes to yield the true R', G', and B' colour signals at the output terminals.

The three colour signals from the SIC are applied to emitter followers. In series with the input connections to the emitter-followers, are $2\cdot2$ kΩ potentiometers, which allow the R', G', and B' drives to be adjusted. These three controls are set as part of the grey-scale adjustment procedure, to give the correct white (i.e., D_{6500}) in high-contrast areas of the picture (or in the white bar of a stepped grey-scale test-signal).

The emitter-followers are d.c. coupled to the single transistor output stages. These work from a 200-volt supply line. The three channels are identical in every respect. They have a gain of the order of fifty and are very simple and stable. Each has a 1000 pF capacitor in series with a 22 Ω resistor, connected in shunt with the emitter resistor. This, by the progressive removal of negative feedback at higher frequencies, provides a compensating increase of gain to offset the h.f. shunting of the signal path by the input capacitance of the c.r.t.[1]

Clamping of the no-signal output voltage level is achieved by feeding line pulses during the line blanking period, to the three clamp diodes D_1, D_2, and D_3. When these diodes are switched on by the positive-going clamping pulses, the three $1\cdot0$ μF capacitors (one in each of the base bias circuits of the emitter-followers), are re-set in potential. The d.c. conditions of both transistors in each pair are maintained constant from one line to another, by the action of these circuits.

The factors which control the d.c. levels are the clipped constant-amplitude positive-going clamping pulses from the line output stage, and the back-porch potential present at the R, G, B amplifier collectors at the moment of arrival of the pulses.

Referring to the B amplifier, on arrival of the clamping pulse, D_3 becomes conductive. The current it passes, depends upon the difference between the amplitude of the positive part of the a.c. coupled clamping pulse input to its anode, and the positive potential at its cathode (i.e., the collector potential of the amplifier).

When D_3 conducts, electrons flow into the coupling capacitor C_4 making its left-hand plate negative. After the pulse ends, C_4 partially discharges through R_5 and this current into C_3 makes its top plate less positive. This in turn makes Tr_5 conduct less and its emitter voltage falls. The amplifier Tr_6 then takes less current and its collector voltage rises.

The action of the circuit is therefore such that the difference voltage present across D_3 during the positive line pulses is progressively reduced when the circuit is first switched on, until the collector potential of Tr_6 is virtually clamped to the amplitude of the positive excursion of the a.c. coupled clamping pulse. This places the collector—and hence the c.r.t. cathode—at about 120 volts positive to chassis. Any tendency for the black-level potential at Tr_6 collector to drift, has an immediate repercussion on

[1] See 'H.F. Compensation Techniques', in *Television Receiver Theory*, Vol. 1, by G. H. Hutson, published by Arnolds of London.

the amount by which D_3 conducts and this alters the forward bias on the emitter-follower Tr_5. This change is subjected to the gain of the amplifier and the collector voltage is held virtually constant.

The same clamping pulses are fed to the pulse inverter Tr_7, and a.c. coupled to the integrated circuit. Here they provide flat-topped pulses, the amplitude of which may be varied by the brightness control in the collector circuit of Tr_7. These pedestal pulses are matrixed with the luminance signal, which in turn is matrixed with the colour-difference signals. In this way the d.c. level of the colour signals as present at the colour amplifier collectors during the moment of clamping, may be varied by the brightness control.

In conventional circuits, brightness control is achieved by varying the static bias between the grid and cathode of the c.r.t. The application of the video signal then causes the negative voltage between grid and cathode to grow progressively less than the fixed bias level, as the luminance level of the picture information increases.

Brightness control circuits of the type described above for Fig. 16.8, are sometimes referred to as 'offset luminance'. The effect of offset luminance in *RGB* drive colour receivers, is to vary the potential to which the c.r.t. cathodes are set, by the d.c. clamping operation carried out during the line blanking period. By adding a pedestal pulse to the video signal during the line blanking period, the effect is to shift the voltage level on which the 'active line' part of the video signal rests, either above or below the actual black level of the incoming video signal. The luminance information is therefore offset from the original datum line (i.e., from the original 'back-porch' level). When the luminance information is subsequently matrixed with the colour-difference signals, the 'offset' is reflected in a change of level of the *R*, *G*, and *B* signals during the line blanking period, when clamping takes place, and this in turn changes the overall brightness of the reproduced picture.

Fault conditions

(1) *Loss of a colour-difference signal*

It is instructive to consider the effect upon a displayed colour-bar signal, of the reduction to zero of one of the colour-difference signals. As a starting point, consider the effect of the loss of a colour-difference signal upon a 100% saturated, 100% amplitude, colour-bar display. It is characteristic of 100% saturated hues that either one—or two—of the c.r.t. guns have to receive zero input. All three phosphors cannot be emitting light at the same time, since—by definition—no white is present.

To reduce the net input of a given gun to zero, the appropriate colour-difference signal must cancel the luminance signal. It follows that if, as a result of a fault condition a colour-difference signal is reduced to zero, the primary concerned will be present in areas where it should not appear at all. Conversely, but perhaps more obviously, the primary will be of reduced amplitude in areas where it should be present at full amplitude.

Reference to Table 3.2 allows the effect of removing one of the colour-difference signals, to be studied.

Suppose that there is no $(B' - Y')$ drive to the c.r.t. Two possibilities exist: $(B' - Y')$ may be lost *after* the point in the circuit where $(G' - Y')$ is matrixed, in which event $(G' - Y')$ will *not* be affected by the fault; or the loss may occur *ahead* of the matrix, when $(G' - Y')$ also, will be of incorrect amplitude.

If it is supposed that the fault is *after* the matrix, then the effect of the loss of $(B' - Y')$ only, may be considered. Using Table 3.2, the net input to the blue gun on each colour-bar, may be deduced from the sum of the Y' and $(B' - Y')$ signals. The values for R', G', and B' show the relative inputs under normal operation. (For the present purpose it is assumed that the phosphor efficiencies are equal and that the three guns are identical.)

Reducing $(B' - Y')$ to zero, leaves Y' as the net input to the blue gun. On yellow, green, and red, where blue should be absent, the uncancelled Y' input to the blue gun now causes the emission of blue light on these bars. The yellow-bar will now appear as near-white; the green-bar as a greenish-blue, and the red as a reddish-purple.

Conversely, on cyan, magenta, and blue, where blue should be present at full amplitude (i.e., the relative blue-gun input should be 1·0), the inputs are now 0·7, 0·41, and 0·11 respectively. This causes the cyan-bar to appear greener than usual; the magenta-bar redder, whilst the blue bar is almost extinguished.

The corresponding effects of reducing $(R' - Y')$ to zero, may also be seen from Table 3.2. On cyan, green, and blue, where no red should be present, the uncancelled Y' input to the red gun causes the cyan-bar to appear as near-white and the green-bar to become a greenish-yellow. There is however, very little noticeable effect upon the blue bar because the normal $(R' - Y')$ signal is only $-0·11$. The Y' input of $+0·11$ to the red gun still leaves the blue bar with virtually the same appearance, since the amount of red light added to the blue is very small.

On yellow, magenta, and red, where red should be present at full amplitude (i.e., at 1·0), the removal of $(R' - Y')$ causes very little change on the yellow-bar but more marked changes on magenta and red. On yellow, the $(R' - Y')$ signal is only of $+0·11$ amplitude. Most of the input to the red gun is from the Y' signal which is of $+0·89$ amplitude. The removal of $(R' - Y')$ therefore leaves the yellow bar virtually unchanged because the red gun input only falls from 1·0 to 0·89. On magenta, the red gun input falls from 1·0 to 0·41, causing this bar to appear as a bluish purple. On the red-bar the input to the red gun falls from 1·0 to 0·3 and this causes a very marked drop in the light output from this bar. It is still of course purely red, but very dark; almost black if the brightness control happens to be set low.

The BBC colour-bar test signals are at less than 100% saturation, so that under normal operating conditions no beam is cut-off altogether in any of the bars because the desaturating white demands a contribution from all three phosphors. It is instructive to consider the waveforms and data shown in Fig. 3.5, for a 95% saturated, 100% amplitude colour-bar signal.

The removal of a colour-bar signal, clearly has its most marked effects upon those colour-bars where the given signal has its greatest amplitude. The $(B' - Y')$ wave-form at (i), shows that a $(B' - Y')$ fault has its greatest effect upon the blue and yellow bars; a fairly pronounced effect upon the magenta and green bars, but a less apparent effect upon red and cyan.

Reducing $(R' - Y')$ to zero affects red and cyan most; with a quite marked effect also upon green and magenta. Blue and yellow are, however, only very little changed in appearance since on these bars $(R' - Y')$ has a very small amplitude. The net input to the red gun on the yellow bar falls from 1·0 to 0·92 whilst on the blue bar it rises from 0·25 to 0·33.

A $(G' - Y')$ fault is the least obvious to see on the screen because the low ampli-tude of this signal implies that its removal causes a comparatively small visual effect. It is greatest on green and magenta; smaller—but just visible—on red and cyan, but yellow and blue remain virtually the same.

Colour-difference signal faults are best looked for by studying the colour-bar which displays the primary associated with the colour-difference signal, together with the bar which displays the complementary hue, i.e., look at red and cyan for $(R' - Y')$; at blue and yellow for $(B' - Y')$, and at green and magenta for $(G' - Y')$.

A fault in the $(R' - Y')$ or $(B' - Y')$ circuits, ahead of the matrix, will also cause the $(G' - Y')$ colour-difference signal to be of the wrong value. This alters the green contribution on each colour-bar, so that two of the three phosphors are then incorrectly energized. If, for example, $(R' - Y')$ is reduced to zero ahead of the matrix, then the expression $(G' - Y') = -0·51(R' - Y') - 0·186(B' - Y')$ yields a value for $(G' - Y')$ of $-0·186(B' - Y')$. The effect of this upon each colour-bar, may be deduced in turn by working out the net relative inputs to the three guns under these conditions. To simplify the working, 100% saturated, 100% amplitude colour-bars may be considered. This gives a good indication of what is to be expected at lower levels of saturation.

As an example, suppose that magenta is considered.

(i) *Under normal operation*

$$\text{Red gun input} = (R' - Y') + Y' = (1·0 - 0·41) + 0·41 = \mathbf{1·0}$$
$$\text{Blue gun input} = (B' - Y') + Y' = (1·0 - 0·41) + 0·41 = \mathbf{1·0}$$
$$\text{Green gun input} = (G' - Y') + Y'$$
$$= \{-0·51(R' - Y') - 0·186(B' - Y')\} + 0·41$$
$$= \{-0·51(+0·59) - 0·186(+0·59)\} + 0·41$$
$$= -0·301 - 0·11 + 0·41 = \mathbf{0}$$

(ii) *With $(R' - Y')$ reduced to zero, before the matrix*

$$\text{Red gun input} = (R' - Y') + Y' = 0 + 0·41 = \mathbf{0·41}$$
$$\text{Blue gun input} = (B' - Y') + Y' = 0·59 + 0·41 = \mathbf{1·0}$$
$$\text{Green gun input} = (G' - Y') + Y'$$
$$= -0·51(R' - Y') - 0·186(B' - Y') + 0·41$$
$$= 0 - 0·186(+0·59) + 0·41$$
$$= 0 - 0·11 + 0·41 = \mathbf{+0·30}$$

Under the fault condition, all three phosphors are energized, so that there is some white light present in the displayed hue, which is now predominantly blue in character. Instead of a fully saturated magenta, a somewhat desaturated and distinctly bluish colour-bar is seen.

(2) *Loss of the luminance signal*

On a monochrome signal this fault obviously removes the picture altogether. On a colour-signal, it takes out all grey and white picture detail and only coloured areas give rise to some light output from the screen. Again, it is instructive to consider the 95% saturated, 100% amplitude colour-bar signal of Fig. 3.5.

As shown at (h), the bars are arranged in descending order of luminance, from left to right. As would be expected therefore, the absence of the Y' signal has its greatest effect upon bars on the left of the screen and its least effect upon those on the right.

On yellow, the inputs of 1·0 to both the red and green guns, are derived from a Y' contribution of 0·92, with $(R' - Y')$ and $(G' - Y')$ having amplitudes of only +0·08. With $Y' = 0$, this leaves only inputs of 0·08 to the red and green guns, so that the yellow bar is virtually blacked out.

A study of the three colour-difference signals at (i), (j), and (k), shows that the contributions made by these signals (in the colour-bars where their associated primaries are needed to give the bar its particular hue), grows greater from left to right, i.e., their positive amplitudes increase as Y' decreases. As an example, the contribution which $(B' - Y')$ makes to the net blue gun input of 1·0 on those bars where blue is necessary, is +0·23 for cyan, +0·44 for magenta, and +0·67 for blue. Of the six colours, blue is affected least by the absence of Y'.

It is evident that a drop in the gain of the luminance amplifier causes the reproduced picture to be lacking in yellows and greens and under some conditions it is possible wrongly to attribute this to incorrect grey scale adjustments. The inadequacy of the luminance signal is immediately apparent on a monochrome transmission, and—if the colour gain control is turned down—equally so on a colour transmission.

17

E.H.T. Systems
and Receiver Design and Development

The final anode voltage for a shadow-mask tube is normally 24 kV to 25 kV and on full brightness the total e.h.t. current (i.e., the sum of the three beam currents) is of the order of 1·2 mA to 1·5 mA. This combination of very high voltage and (for a c.r.t.) high maximum current loading, raises problems of stability.

Design problems in e.h.t. circuitry are much affected by the internal impedance of the e.h.t. system itself and by the stability of its supply voltages.

Conventional television e.h.t. systems derive the e.h.t. voltage from an overwind on the line output transformer. Line output stages employing valves, are inherently of high impedance. Conversely, recently developed circuits using semiconductors instead of valves, are of very much lower internal impedance. This substantial difference in impedance results in marked changes in the form of the e.h.t. circuitry.

The high internal impedance of the conventional systems aggravates the stability problem. Variations ranging from 0 to 1·4 mA in the current demanded of the system, would clearly give rise to large variations in the e.h.t. voltage. These voltage variations cannot be permitted since they would seriously degrade the picture. A drop in e.h.t. voltage causes a decrease of electron velocity and an increase in deflection sensitivity which in turn causes the raster to grow bigger. As the e.h.t. voltage falls and rises, the picture grows and shrinks, giving the symptoms sometimes described as 'breathing'. It is found in practice that this is by far the most serious effect of lack of e.h.t. stability. Other factors such as focus, convergence, purity, and light output all remain acceptable for e.h.t. voltage changes which are not too severe (i.e., do not exceed say 2 to 3 kV).

To prevent voltage changes, many e.h.t. systems employ stabilizing circuits which are designed to hold the e.h.t. voltage constant and virtually independent of all normal beam current changes.

One logical way to obtain a constant e.h.t. voltage is to make the load imposed upon the system constant, i.e., to demand the same current from it all the time. This involves placing a second current path (referred to as a shunt stabilizer) in parallel with the c.r.t., designed so that as the beam current rises the shunt current falls and vice versa. To achieve this the effective resistance of the shunt stabilizer must be made

278

to vary automatically, under the command of a control voltage. The control voltage may be developed by sensing either voltage or current changes.

Figure 17.1 shows two basic arrangements. At (a) the control voltage is derived by sensing the e.h.t. voltage. The circuit must act in such a way that as the e.h.t. voltage tends to fall the control voltage biases back the shunt stabilizer so that it takes less current and so eases the load on the system. A rise in e.h.t. has the opposite effect.

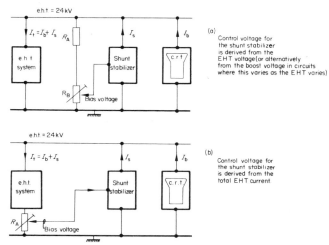

Fig. 17.1 *Showing the basic principles of e.h.t. voltage stabilization by the use of a shunt stabilizer*

When the a.c. input to the e.h.t. rectifier is taken from an overwind on the line output transformer, the control voltage for the stabilizer is sometimes derived from a potential divider across the boost h.t. line. This system has been widely used in the U.S.A. but is not suitable for British receivers which employ a stabilized line output stage. In unstabilized line output stages, a change in the e.h.t. loading causes a change in the boost h.t. and this voltage may therefore be used in the e.h.t. control loop. With stabilized line output stages, however, the boost voltage is already maintained sensibly constant by a voltage feedback loop which increases or decreases the bias on the line output stage as the output circuit flyback voltage rises or falls respectively. This prohibits the use of the boost h.t. as a control voltage for the e.h.t. stabilizer, since the two loops would interact.

At (b), the control voltage is derived by monitoring the total e.h.t. current. If the e.h.t. current tends to rise, the control voltage biases back the shunt stabilizer so that it passes less current. When the current tends to fall (i.e., during dark parts of the picture) the control voltage changes in the opposite direction so causing a corresponding increase in the shunt current.

The e.h.t. system shown in Fig. 17.2 differs substantially from the more con-

279

ventional methods of Fig. 17.1(a) and (b). Here the line output stage does not form part of the e.h.t. system. A separate generator stage is driven by the same line drive waveform as is used to drive the line output stage.

The generator stage is simply an inductively loaded transistor amplifier which develops a high peak voltage output pulse once per line when the 'flyback' part of

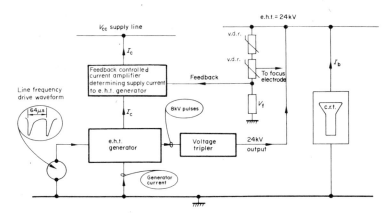

Fig. 17.2 *Showing the basic principles of an e.h.t. generator stabilized by a feedback controlled amplifier which determines the collector supply current to the e.h.t. generator transistor*

the input waveform cuts the transistor off. The output is rectified and multiplied by a voltage tripler to produce the e.h.t. Stabilization is achieved by placing the power supply current to the generator under the control of a feedback loop. This loop is activated by a feedback current which is proportional to the e.h.t. voltage. If the e.h.t. voltage tends to rise, the feedback current increases. This causes a decrease in the supply current to the collector of the generator and the output voltage delivered to the tripler drops correspondingly. Conversely, a tendency for the e.h.t. voltage to fall (i.e., on peak whites) causes an increase in the supply current to the generator and the e.h.t. voltage is maintained.

There is one further facility which must be considered. It is desirable to include a beam current limiter circuit to ensure that the c.r.t. is not called upon to pass an excessive current. The need for this may be seen by considering the constant current systems described under Fig. 17.1(a) and (b) above. Suppose that the constant current loading is 1·4 mA. On black parts of the picture the beam current is zero and the full 1·4 mA is passed by the shunt stabilizer. Conversely, on peak white, the c.r.t. beam current is 1·4 mA and the shunt stabilizer current is then zero. Clearly, these are the limits of the control range. If, because of a transient condition, or perhaps a fault, the c.r.t. should now be driven harder, the shunt stabilizer can do nothing to prevent the c.r.t. current rising above 1·4 mA. For this reason a protective beam-current limiting circuit is usually included, to take over control of the e.h.t. current at the limit of the shunt stabilizer's control range. It will be appreciated that such circuits

280

only come into operation under abnormal conditions to prevent damage to the expensive c.r.t., whilst the e.h.t. voltage stabilizer forms a dynamic part of the circuitry which functions *all* the time the receiver is working normally. Some examples of the e.h.t. circuitry are now studied.

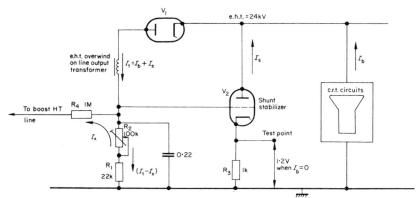

Fig. 17.3   *E.h.t. shunt stabilizer circuit*

The negative bias on the grid of the shunt stabilizer is controlled by the total e.h.t. current

Figure 17.3

Triode V_2 is the shunt stabilizer. The current I_s passed by it depends upon the negative bias voltage developed across resistors R_1 and R_2.

The total e.h.t. current I_t is the sum of the current I_b passed by the c.r.t. and the anode current I_s of the shunt stabilizer. This current, $I_t = I_s + I_b$, passes downwards through R_2 and R_1, driving the top of R_2 negative to chassis. Also passed through R_1 and R_2, but in the opposite direction, is a reference current from the boost h.t. line via resistor R_4. The line output stage is stabilized and the boost voltage is therefore sensibly constant.

Setting up the e.h.t. circuit usually involves two operations. The line output stage stabilizing circuit provides a bias to the line output valve grid. A potentiometer allows this to be adjusted. With a normal locked picture, this bias is adjusted until the e.h.t. voltage measured at the c.r.t. anode terminal is 24 kV. (Alternatively the boost voltage itself—as measured at a stipulated point—is set to a given level.) Following this, the shunt stabilizer grid circuit potentiometer is adjusted, with the c.r.t. blacked-out (so that $I_t = I_s$), until a reading of 1·2 V at the cathode indicates that the required e.h.t. current is 1·2 mA. It should be noted that the 1000 Ω cathode resistor is included to provide a convenient means of monitoring the shunt stabilizer current in order to set up the circuit for correct operating conditions which in this circuit is for a maximum shunt stabilizer e.h.t. current of 1·2 mA. The significant bias on the valve is developed in the grid circuit; not at the cathode.

Under typical conditions, the net current downwards through R_1 and R_2 when $I_t = 1·2$ mA is 0·3 mA. This indicates that the reference current upwards through R_1

281

and R_2 to the boost h.t. line is $(1\cdot2 - 0\cdot3) = 0\cdot9$ mA. This current may be regarded as constant under normal circumstances.

When the brightness control is turned up to bring the receiver into normal operation, the total e.h.t. current I_t tends to increase above $1\cdot2$ mA. This causes the negative bias on the grid of V_2 to increase and I_s is reduced. The control loop is efficient enough to hold the total e.h.t. current-loading virtually constant at $1\cdot2$ mA.

The stabilized line output stage is capable of maintaining a reasonably constant boost voltage for normal variations in mains voltage. Should the variation be severe and the boost voltage fall slightly, the $0\cdot9$ mA reference current up through R_1 and R_2 falls and the net negative bias on V_2 increases. This lessens the loading on the e.h.t. system giving some compensation for the drop in e.h.t. voltage which accompanies the fall in boost voltage. This represents a secondary stabilizing action, which tends to reduce the degree of degradation of picture quality under very abnormal conditions such as a marked fall in the mains supply voltage.

The resistors R_1 and R_2 are decoupled by a $0\cdot22$ μF capacitor which prevents the bias voltage from being modulated by short term transients and random variations.

Figure 17.4

This circuit is similar to Fig. 17.3 but the arrangements in the grid of the shunt stabilizer valve V_2 are somewhat different.

Instead of the total e.h.t. current passing to earth via the grid resistors, in this circuit it is taken through the 470 kΩ resistor R_f to the boost H.T. line. The voltage drop across R_f due to the e.h.t. current, exceeds the boost H.T. voltage so that the junction of R_f and the low potential end of the e.h.t. winding, is negative to the main H.T. line. Since the grid resistor R_1 is connected between this junction and the H.T. line, the negative bias on V_2 is essentially $(V_{R_f} - V_{boost})$ plus the small potential across the cathode resistor R_7. As in the previous circuit, the latter provides a convenient method of monitoring the stabilizer current and R_7 is fitted for this purpose; not to provide bias.

The net bias on V_2 is arranged to be of the right order to make V_2 pass about $1\cdot2$ mA when the c.r.t. is blacked out. When the brightness control is turned to normal, the increased e.h.t. current down through R_f drives the grid of V_2 more negative. This in turn reduces the current passed by V_2 and the total e.h.t. current remains sensibly constant at about $1\cdot2$ mA.

Also shown on this diagram is an overload protection circuit which operates to limit the total c.r.t. beam current to a safe level. As stated earlier, once the shunt stabilizer current is reduced to zero, the c.r.t. beam current could increase above $1\cdot2$ mA and under fault conditions it may reach a damaging level.

Under normal operating conditions the anode of the diode D_1 is negative with respect to its cathode which is returned to the grid of V_2. The diode is therefore cut-off and does not affect the circuit. When the total e.h.t. current exceeds a certain maximum permitted level (e.g., $1\cdot2$ mA) the negative voltage across R_f increases to the point where the diode's cathode is driven negative to its anode. D_1 now conducts and current passes up through the 100 kΩ resistor R_3. This causes an increased volts drop across R_3 and in turn the voltage at the slider of the brightness control becomes more negative. The anode current of the luminance amplifier is reduced and the cathodes of the c.r.t. are driven more positive which reduces the c.r.t. beam current to a safe level. This sequence of events may take place during a momentary overload due to a transient condition. Alternatively it may protect the c.r.t. if a fault should develop which would otherwise cause a destructive increase in the c.r.t. current.

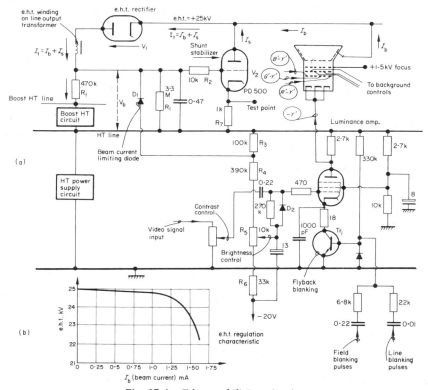

Fig. 17.4 *E.h.t. stabilizing circuitry*

The control voltage for the shunt stabilizer valve is here derived by sensing the total current passed by the e.h.t. rectifier.

The sketch at Fig. 17.4(b) illustrates the efficiency of this e.h.t. shunt stabilizer in maintaining the e.h.t. voltage constant for total e.h.t. current loadings between 0 and 1·25 mA.

The transistor Tr_1 in series with the luminance amplifier cathode resistor is normally conductive and of low resistance, but is cut-off by blanking pulses applied to its base during line and field flyback. This cuts off the amplifier anode current and raises the c.r.t. cathodes to H.T.+ potential which cuts-off the beam current so blanking out the flyback strokes.

283

X-ray radiation

Electrons accelerated by a p.d. as high as the 24 kV e.h.t. used for shadow-mask tubes, gain sufficient kinetic energy to cause the emission of X-rays from metal surfaces bombarded by them. In the design of colour television receivers care is taken to ensure that this unavoidable X-ray radiation does not become a hazard. As an example, the stabilizer valve anode is at the full e.h.t. and emits a dangerous level of radiation. This valve is enclosed in a metal box which prevents the X-rays from 'escaping'. Service manuals draw the attention of engineers to the danger of operating the receiver with such screening boxes removed. Warnings of this kind must be treated very seriously. Radiation is an insidious danger; it produces no sensation to warn of its presence.

The c.r.t. itself is made of lead glass which, in conjunction with the external earthed aquadag coating, limits X-ray radiation.

In addition to the X-ray hazard, an e.h.t. system capable of delivering 1·2 mA at 24 kV is lethal and manufacturers' instructions for testing and adjustment must be strictly observed. When the e.h.t. connection is removed the c.r.t.'s capacitance must be discharged by a shorting lead connected to chassis. The chassis connection must be made before that to the final anode.

E.H.T. voltage triplers

It is common practice to reduce the e.h.t. overwind voltage to the order of 8 kV and then to multiply the rectified voltage by a tripler circuit. This method avoids the necessity of using a valve rectifier capable of working on the full e.h.t. voltage, decreases the X-ray hazard, limits the insulation problem in the line output transformer and makes for simplicity and increased safety.

E.H.T. tripler circuits are not to be confused with the conventional multipliers which work on sine-wave inputs. The e.h.t. voltage is derived from brief duration high amplitude line flyback pulses. Figure 17.5 shows a typical circuit using a tripler. The circuit is in all other respects similar to that of Fig. 17.3 already described. The e.h.t. tripler from Fig. 17.5 is redrawn in Fig. 17.6 and four fictitious switches are included to allow a step-by-step explanation of the action to be made. Without this simplified break-down approach it is difficult to describe how the circuit works.

The input to the tripler from the line output transformer overwind is represented by the waveform shown. On the flyback stroke the applied voltage is +8 kV falling to 0 V during the scanning stroke. S_1 is imagined to switch the tripler input between these two voltage levels at line frequency. In the explanation which follows S_1 is imagined to work continuously, resting at (a) for the duration of the flyback pulse and at (b) for the scanning stroke. The circuit is first studied with S_2, S_3, and S_4 open and then, by closing S_2, S_3, and S_4 one at a time, the effect of adding in successive sections of the tripler may be studied. This is easier than trying to picture the entire circuit operation by one logical argument which at once embraces all the diodes and capacitors from the moment the circuit is switched on.

284

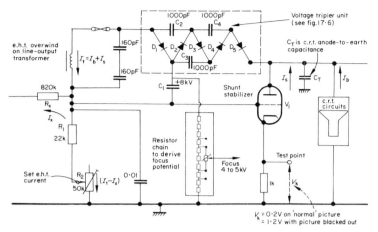

Fig. 17.5 *E.h.t. circuit using a voltage tripler*

(Associated diagrams: Figs. 11.8, 12.5, 13.2, 14.3, 15.2.)

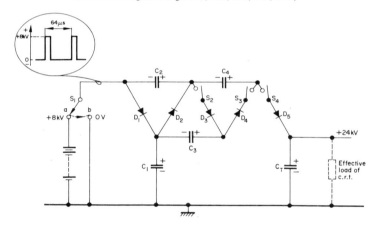

Fig. 17.6 *E.h.t. voltage tripler*

Step 1. Let S_2, S_3, and S_4 be open

Then, with:

S_1 at 8 kV C_1 charges to 8 kV via diode D_1. D_2 is cut-off.

S_1 at 0 V D_1 is cut-off and C_2 charges to 4 kV from C_1 via D_2 (i.e., the 8 kV p.d. across C_1 divides equally between C_1 and C_2).

S_1 at 8 kV C_1 charges from 4 kV back to 8 kV via D_1. Meanwhile D_2 is cut-off.

S_1 at 0 D_1 is cut-off and C_2 charges from 4 kV to 6 kV via D_2. This is because, with S_1 at 0 V, the net voltage facing D_2 is $(V_{C_1} - V_{C_2}) = (8 - 4)\,\text{kV} = +4\,\text{kV}$ and D_2 conducts until the charges on C_1 and C_2 equalize leaving $V_{C_1} = V_{C_2} = 6\,\text{kV}$.

285

S_1 at 8 kV	C_1 charges from 6 kV to 8 kV via D_1. Meanwhile D_2 is cut-off.

S_1 at 8 kV C_1 charges from 6 kV to 8 kV via D_1. Meanwhile D_2 is cut-off.

S_1 at 0 D_1 is cut-off and C_2 charges via D_2 from 6 kV to 7 kV. (*N.B.* the net voltage facing D_2 is $(V_{C_1} - V_{C_2}) = (8 - 6)$ kV $= +2$ kV and this divides equally between C_1 and C_2 so that V_{C_1} falls from 8 kV to 7 kV while V_{C_2} rises from 6 kV to 7 kV.)

S_1 at 8 kV C_1 charges from 7 kV to 8 kV via D_1 whilst D_2 is cut-off.

S_1 at 0 D_1 is cut-off and C_2 charges via D_2 from 7 kV to 7·5 kV. (*N.B.* The net voltage facing D_2 is $(V_{C_1} - V_{C_2}) = (8 - 7) = +1$ kV which divides equally between C_1 and C_2.)

In a short time the voltage across C_2 rises to 8 kV and thereafter no further current flows since no shunt load has yet been considered to be connected. The process is rather like a pumping action as a result of which, after several successive strokes of the line timebase, both C_1 and C_2 charge to a p.d. of 8 kV.

Now suppose that S_2 is closed

S_1 at 8 kV   The anode of D_3 now faces $(V_{C_2} + 8$ kV$) = 16$ kV but D_3 cathode faces $(V_{C_3} + V_{C_1}) = (0 + 8$ kV$) = 8$ kV. D_3 conducts and C_3 charges from 0 V towards 8 kV.

S_1 at 0 D_3 is now cut-off because its cathode voltage $(V_{C_3} + V_{C_1})$ is more positive than its anode which equals V_{C_2}. D_1 is also cut-off. D_2 conducts and the charges on C_1 and C_2 equalize as described earlier.

But it has already been established that the switching action of S_1 must result in C_1 and C_2 both being charged to 8 kV. It follows that each time S_1 rests at 8 kV the net voltage across D_3, which is $(V_{C_2} + 8$ kV$) - (V_{C_3} + V_{C_1})$, must make D_3 conduct and the charge on C_3 increases with each stroke until at length the p.d. across C_3 is 8 kV.

After several successive movements of S_1 (i.e., after several line timebase strokes), C_1, C_2, and C_3 are all charged to 8 kV and no further current flows.

Now suppose S_3 is closed

S_1 at 0   The anode of D_4 faces a p.d. of $(V_{C_3} + V_{C_1}) = (8 + 8)$ kV $= 16$ kV whilst the cathode faces $(V_{C_4} + V_{C_2}) = (0 + 8)$ kV $= 8$ kV. D_4 conducts and C_4 charges from 0 towards 8 kV. It will be observed that at the start the total voltage in the loop C_1, C_2, C_3, C_4 is $(8 + 8 + 8 + 0) = 24$ kV and the charges on the four capacitors will equalize leaving the p.d. on each at 6 kV.

S_1 at 8 kV D_4 is now cut-off, as is D_2. But D_1 and D_3 are conductive and V_{C_1}, V_{C_2}, and V_{C_3} all increase above 6 kV.

Again, by the actions previously described, it has been established that C_1, C_2, and C_3 must all at length charge to 8 kV and it follows logically that each time S_1 rests at 0 V, C_4 charges further until it also has a p.d. of 8 kV across it. At this point no further current flows.

286

Now suppose S₄ is closed

S$_1$ at 8 kV   The voltage facing D$_5$ anode is $(V_{C_4} + V_{C_2} + 8)$ kV $= (8 + 8 + 8)$ kV $=$ 24 kV. But the cathode of D$_5$ is connected to C$_T$ the lower plate of which is earthed. Hence the top plate of C$_T$ charges from 0 V towards $+24$ kV.

S$_1$ at 0   D$_5$ is now cut-off and the charges on capacitors C$_1$, C$_2$, C$_3$, and C$_4$ tend to equalize.

S$_1$ at 8 kV   D$_5$ conducts and C$_T$ charges nearer to 24 kV.

Again, since the action of the circuit as previously described must restore the charges on C$_1$, C$_2$, C$_3$, and C$_4$ until they each bear a p.d. of 8 kV it follows that C$_T$ must eventually charge until it bears a p.d. of 24 kV, after which no further current will flow.

It has now been established that with S$_2$, S$_3$, and S$_4$ closed an output voltage of 24 kV is obtained across C$_T$ from a pulse input of 8 kV. Clearly, in the practical circuit without the switches, the same result is achieved and several successive line timebase strokes after the moment of switching on, the voltage across each of the four capacitors C$_1$, C$_2$, C$_3$, and C$_4$ must increase from 0 V to 8 kV and that across C$_T$ from 0 V to 24 kV.

In a practical circuit C$_T$ is the c.r.t. capacitance between the inner conductive coating connected to the final anode and the outer aquadag coating which is earthed. The c.r.t., with the parallel shunt stabilizer, present C$_T$ with a constant load and a steady voltage is maintained across C$_T$ by the tripler action. It will be observed that five diodes and five capacitors (including C$_T$) are used in the tripler to produce 24 kV from an input of 8 kV. In general, if it is required to multiply the input voltage by a factor of n times, then $(2n - 1)$ rectifiers and $(2n - 1)$ capacitors are needed. Since, in an e.h.t. circuit for a c.r.t., the capacitance of the c.r.t. itself forms the final capacitor in the multiplier circuit, the actual number of capacitors needed in the multiplier unit is $(2n - 2)$. The diodes and capacitors should have a voltage rating of at least E_m/n, where E_m is the maximum possible e.h.t. voltage which the circuit can develop. A suitable rating for the components in a colour television receiver e.h.t. tripler is 10 kV.

Various factors can cause the e.h.t. voltage to rise above its normal level. It has been found that a 10% rise in the mains voltage can cause a 3% rise in the e.h.t. In addition if the line timebase is unsynchronized, a further 5% rise is possible. To protect the c.r.t., the maximum value which the normal e.h.t. should be designed to have, must be such that when it is increased by 8%, the e.h.t. voltage still does not exceed the maximum permitted level quoted by the c.r.t. manufacturer. A typical maximum c.r.t. final anode voltage rating is 27·5 kV. Working backwards from this figure, the maximum normal e.h.t. developed by the tripler must not exceed E' where $(E' + 8\% E') = 27·5$ kV, i.e., $1·08E' = 27·5$ kV from which $E' = 25·5$ kV.

The e.h.t. circuit in Fig. 17.5 shows a normal shunt stabilizer circuit in use with a tripler. Simpler arrangements have been employed which give a rather poorer, though still adequate, e.h.t. voltage regulation. An example of such a circuit is shown in Fig. 5.11 of chapter 5. Here a v.d.r. across the e.h.t. line is employed to derive the focus potential and also to give a measure of regulation. The e.h.t. regulation is enhanced by making the pulse input from the 8 kV overwind on the line output transformer, flat-topped rather than peaky. This is achieved by tuning the transformer to the fifth harmonic of the flyback frequency. The amplitude of the flyback pulse is held sensibly constant by the normal action of the stabilizing circuit employed in line output stages. A typical e.h.t. regulation characteristic for a tripler circuit of the type discussed (i.e., with no shunt stabilizer except the focus potential dividing v.d.r. and resistor network) is shown in Fig. 17.7. As would be expected the circuit shows a

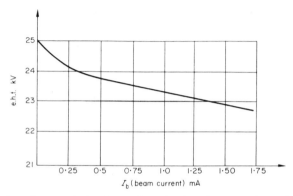

Fig. 17.7 *Regulation characteristic of an e.h.t. circuit using a tripler and no shunt stabilizer valve*

marked drop in e.h.t. voltage as the beam current increases from zero to a 100 μA or so but thereafter the slope is less steep, although not as gentle as the characteristic shown in Fig. 17.4 for a normal shunt stabilized system.

The use of a tripler simplifies the design of the line output transformer since problems of insulation are much reduced. In addition the impedance of the system is less. The semiconductor diodes in the tripler are of very low impedance and the overwind is much smaller. This leads to a more compact transformer unit. The problem of X-ray radiation is alleviated since there is no valve rectifier working on 25 kV. If there is also no shunt stabilizing valve circuit, there is no need for specially screened compartments to prevent X-ray radiation and the only precautions are then those which the manufacturer employs in the design of the c.r.t.

E.H.T. generator controlled by current feedback amplifier

Figure 17.8 shows an e.h.t. system of the type briefly described in the block diagram of Fig. 17.2.

The driver transistor Tr_{42} feeds the two line output transistors (not shown on the diagram) and the e.h.t. generator stage Tr_{43}. The input to the base of n-p-n transistor Tr_{43} is essentially a square wave which switches Tr_{43} on during the scanning stroke

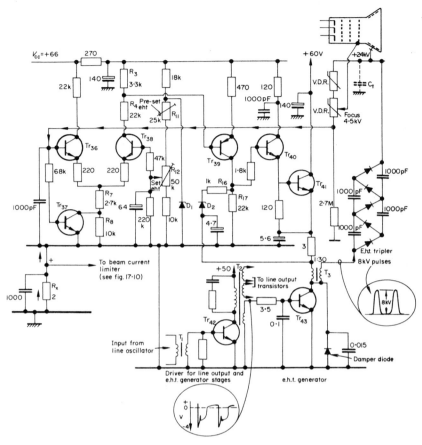

Fig. 17.8 *E.h.t. generator controlled by a current feedback amplifier*

(Associated diagrams: Figs. 12.6, 13.5, 13.7, 14.1, 15.5, 16.5, 17.10)

(when a sawtooth type current builds up in the primary of the collector output transformer T_3), and switches it off abruptly on flyback. The sudden cessation of current through Tr_{43} produces a high back-e.m.f. across T_3 primary and this is stepped up to yield about 8 kV across the secondary. (T_3 has a step-up ratio of the order of 30:1.)

The 8 kV secondary pulse is applied to the e.h.t. tripler circuit, which delivers 24 kV to the c.r.t. As in the tripler circuit previously described, the 24 kV is developed across the c.r.t. anode-to-earth capacitance. (C_t). The whole e.h.t. tripler unit is included as part of an assembly which plugs into the c.r.t. final anode socket. It follows that with the c.r.t. disconnected there is no final capacitor across the tripler and the 24 kV e.h.t. is therefore only developed with the c.r.t. anode cap plugged in.

289

Stabilization is achieved by bringing the current supply to the e.h.t. generator transistor Tr_{43} under the control of a feedback amplifier whose output current forms Tr_{43}'s collector supply current.

Tr_{43} is fed via Tr_{41}. But Tr_{41}, with Tr_{40}, forms a Darlington pair. The principle of such a circuit is shown in Fig. 17.9. In effect the pair form a high gain current

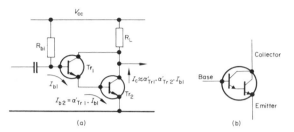

Fig. 17.9 *(a) Showing the basic principle of a Darlington Pair. (b) A composite transistor, internally connected to function as a Darlington Pair*

amplifier giving an output current which is approximately equal to the base input current of the first transistor multiplied by the product of the individual current gains of the two transistors. Hence a change δI_b in the input to Tr_1 gives rise to a collector current change of $\alpha'_{TR_1} \times \delta I_b$. But the emitter current of Tr_1 forms the base input current of Tr_2 and the change of Tr_1 collector current represents a change in the input current of Tr_2. In turn Tr_2 collector current is α'_{TR_2} times the base input current change. Hence the change $\delta I_{b(TR_1)}$ in the input to the base of the first transistor of the Darlington pair gives rise to an output current change of $\{\alpha'_{TR_2} \times \alpha'_{TR_1} \times \delta I_{b(TR_1)}\}$ in Tr_2 collector current.

With identical transistors having $\alpha' = 50$ the current gain of a Darlington pair would be $50 \times 50 = 2500$ and a change of $2\,\mu A$ in Tr_1 base current could give rise to a change of $5000\,\mu A = 5\,mA$ in the output current. Composite transistors, which are in effect two transistors connected internally as a Darlington pair, are manufactured for some applications.

Referring back to Fig. 17.8 it is clear that by making the base current to Tr_{40} increase when the e.h.t. drops, or decrease when the e.h.t. rises, the current output of the Darlington pair (i.e., the current supply to the collector of the e.h.t. generator Tr_{43}) increases or decreases respectively. In this way, a tendency for the e.h.t. voltage to drop, is countered by an increased supply current to the e.h.t. generator. On the flyback stroke, switching off a larger current through the primary of T_3 causes the back e.m.f. to rise and this in turn results in the e.h.t. voltage being restored to normal.

The Darlington pair forms the last two transistors in a five-transistor current feedback amplifier comprising Tr_{36}, Tr_{38}, Tr_{39}, Tr_{40}, and Tr_{41}. The purpose of Tr_{37} will be described later.

Connected across the e.h.t. line is a series circuit consisting of v.d.r.'s and a $2\cdot7\,M\Omega$ resistor. The focus voltage is obtained from a slider tap on the lower of the two v.d.r.'s. The voltage across the 2·7 MΩ resistor is used to drive a standing forward bias input current through the base-emitter junction of Tr_{36}, which, with Tr_{38}, forms a differential amplifier.

To understand the action of the entire circuit it is helpful to trace the sequence of events which would follow a tendency for the e.h.t. voltage to fall.

A fall in e.h.t. results in a drop in the positive voltage to which the base of the n-p-n transistor Tr_{36} is connected. This brings about a fall in base current and a correspondingly greater fall in collector current. As a result the common emitter voltage of Tr_{36} and Tr_{38} grows less positive. Since the base potential of Tr_{38} is fixed by a potential divider across the supply line, the negative-going movement at the emitter causes an increase in Tr_{38} collector current. This gives rise to a fall in the positive voltage passed on from the junction of R_3 and R_4. But this voltage is the base voltage of a p-n-p transistor Tr_{39} and a negative-going movement in Tr_{39}'s base potential causes its collector current to increase. In turn Tr_{39} collector potential becomes more positive and the base input current to the first transistor Tr_{40} of the Darlington pair, increases. Finally this causes an amplified increase in the collector current of Tr_{41}, i.e., the supply current to the e.h.t. generator Tr_{43} increases and this tends to increase the generated e.h.t. voltage to its previous normal level.

Tr_{37} forms one of a number of protective circuits which guard against damage which would otherwise result from fault conditions. An open circuit in the feedback loop to Tr_{36} would cause the base input current to Tr_{36} to drop to zero and it has already been demonstrated that reductions of Tr_{36} base current yield increases in the supply current to the e.h.t. generator and hence in the e.h.t. voltage. Zero base current to Tr_{36} would result in an excessively high e.h.t.

With the feedback loop properly connected, Tr_{37} is switched hard on by the forward bias current derived from the positive voltage at its base. Tr_{37} then effectively short-circuits the 10 kΩ resistor R_8 leaving the 2·7 kΩ resistor R_7 as the common emitter resistor for Tr_{36} and Tr_{38}. If the feedback loop is open-circuited, the forward bias on Tr_{37} is removed and the transistor switches off. This brings R_8 into the circuit and the 10 kΩ increase in the resistance of the emitter return circuit of Tr_{38} results in this transistor being biased off. The reduction in Tr_{38} collector current causes the base voltage of Tr_{39} to become more positive. This in turn limits the currents passed by Tr_{39}, Tr_{40}, Tr_{41}, and finally Tr_{43} so holding the e.h.t. voltage within safe limits.

Zener diode D_2 protects the circuit against overload currents. Under normal operation the level of back-bias across D_2 makes its resistance so high that the diode has no effect upon the circuit. The greater the forward bias on Tr_{39}, however, the higher the positive voltage on Tr_{39} collector and the greater the current passed by Tr_{40}, Tr_{41}, and Tr_{43}. As Tr_{39} collector moves more positive the junction of T_3 primary and the 3 Ω resistor simultaneously moves less positive. In total this represents an increase in the back-bias across D_2. There comes a point where D_2 reaches the Zener turn-on potential and D_2 becomes conductive. This by-passes much of Tr_{39}'s collector current since the 1 kΩ resistor R_{16} with D_2, T_3 primary and the low resistance highly-conductive Tr_{43}, are now in parallel with the 22 kΩ collector resistor R_{17}.

291

Momentary transient overloads (or sustained overloads due to fault conditions) are in this way prevented from driving the Darlington pair and Tr_{43} too hard.

The correct e.h.t. of 24 kV, as indicated on an e.h.t. voltmeter connected to the c.r.t. anode cap, is adjusted by means of R_{12}, the *set e.h.t.* pre-set potentiometer. Should this adjustment not give the correct e.h.t. a further pre-set is available. With R_{12} set to maximum value R_{11} is adjusted to give an e.h.t. of 26 kV. Then R_{12} is turned down to reduce the voltage to 24 kV.

Because the bias voltage to Tr_{38} base controls the e.h.t., further stabilization of the d.c. supply from which this bias is derived is necessary. This is given by Zener diode D_1.

Protection for the c.r.t. against excessive e.h.t. current is given by the circuit shown in Fig. 17.10.

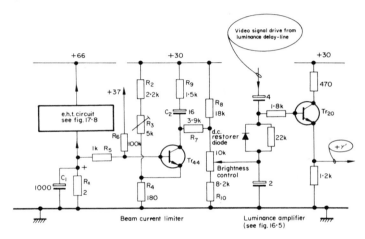

Fig. 17.10 *Beam current limiter circuit associated with the e.h.t. circuit of Fig. 17.8 and the video circuit of Fig. 16.5*

(Associated diagrams: Figs. 12.6, 13.5, 13.7, 14.1, 15.5, 16.5, 17.8)

The total supply current taken by the complete e.h.t. circuit of Fig. 17.8 passes to the supply negative terminal via the 2 Ω resistor R_x which is decoupled by a 1000 μF capacitor. Under normal conditions the beam-current-limiting n-p-n transistor Tr_{44} is cut-off because the emitter is positive to base. When the e.h.t. current exceeds a certain pre-determined level, the total current passed by the e.h.t. circuitry is sufficient to establish a voltage across the 2 Ω resistor high enough to make the base of Tr_{44} move positive to emitter. But Tr_{44} collector is taken to the positive supply line via resistor R_8, which is at the positive end of the brightness control potential divider. The current passed by Tr_{44} causes the potential at the junction of R_8 and the brightness control to become less positive. In turn the forward bias on the luminance amplifier Tr_{20} is decreased so that Tr_{20} passes less current and its emitter voltage becomes less positive. As shown in Fig. 16.5 the emitter of Tr_{20} is direct coupled to the bases of the red, green, and blue output transistors Tr_{25}, Tr_{30}, and Tr_{35}. These three n-p-n transistors conduct less when the emitter of Tr_{20} grows less positive and the collectors of the upper transistor of each output pair (i.e., Tr_{24}, Tr_{29}, and Tr_{34}) move more positive. The three cathodes of the c.r.t. are therefore driven more positive and the beam currents are cut down.

To adjust the pre-set control R_3 which determines the bias on the emitter of Tr_{44} in Fig. 17.10 (and hence fixes the threshold point of the beam current limiter), the following procedure is adopted:

(a) The picture is adjusted for normal contrast.
(b) The lead to the green cathode of the c.r.t. is unplugged and a milliammeter is inserted in series with it.
(c) The red and blue beams are switched off.
(d) The brightness control is now set to maximum and the pre-set beam limiter control R_3 is adjusted to give a reading of 800 µA on the milliammeter.

Low impedance circuits without special stabilizing circuitry

Transistorized line output stages are inherently of low impedance. When an e.h.t. tripler is fed from an overwind on the output transformer of such a circuit, the internal impedance of the whole e.h.t. system is low. The e.h.t. voltage variations which follow changes in the total beam current loading, are then much less pronounced than in a circuit of higher impedance. Satisfactory performance is possible with circuits of less complexity.

Changes in e.h.t. current present the line output stage with a varying load. If the internal impedance were negligible and the power supply feeding the line output stage completely stabilized, the e.h.t. voltage would be constant and no special e.h.t. stabilization measures would be needed. In practice the impedance is not negligible and some variation in e.h.t. voltage occurs. It is, however, possible to compensate for the effects of this in a simple way.

As stated earlier, it is the changes in picture size (i.e., 'breathing') which constitutes the main ill-effect of poor e.h.t. regulation. Since focus, purity, convergence, and light output all remain acceptable provided the e.h.t. voltage variations do not exceed a few kilovolts, it follows that if the picture size can be held constant despite changes of e.h.t. voltages of this order, then such changes may be tolerated.

The block diagram of Fig. 17.11 illustrates how this may be achieved.

Picture width may be altered by changing the supply voltage to the line output stage, which in turn changes the magnitude of the deflector coil current. The resistor R_s, which may be of the order 50 Ω to 100 Ω, is inserted between the stabilized transistor power supply and the line output stage. If the e.h.t. current rises, the increased load on the line output stage causes an increase in the volts drop across R_s. This in turn reduces the supply voltage to the line output stage and the picture width is reduced, because the deflector coil current is less. But the fall in e.h.t. voltage which follows the rise in e.h.t. current, tends to make the picture larger and the two effects therefore work in opposite directions. By careful choice of the value of R_s it is possible to make the net change of width very small for normal changes in the total beam current.

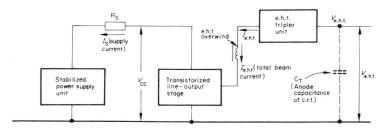

Fig. 17.11 *Showing the basic arrangement of e.h.t. systems working from low impedance transistor line output stages*

Note: A decrease in $V_{e.h.t.}$ causes the picture to grow larger, but a decrease in V_{cc} causes it to grow smaller. R_s is chosen to equalize these effects so giving automatic compensation for e.h.t. voltage changes.

The field timebase height control circuit may be fed from the same point so that the picture height is also affected by the volts drop across R_s. In this way the supply voltage to both timebases, is made to 'track' with the e.h.t. voltage and the picture size is maintained almost constant.

This system may be described as e.h.t. compensation. Its object is not to stabilize the e.h.t. but to maintain a constant picture size despite variations in the e.h.t. The inclusion of the circuit does in fact make the e.h.t. stability slightly worse. This is so because the reduction in supply voltage to the line output stage, not only reduces the line deflection current, but also reduces the amplitude of the overwind flyback pulses from which the e.h.t. is derived. It may at first appear that the result is a vicious circle with the decrease in picture size due to the drop in supply line voltage being offset by an increase in size due to the fall in e.h.t. arising from the smaller flyback pulses. This, however, does not occur because the two influences are not equal. Deflection sensitivity and hence raster size, is inversely proportional to the square root of the e.h.t. voltage, but the scanning amplitude is directly proportional to the deflector coil current which varies linearly with the supply voltage. The change in scanning current is therefore the more significant quantity and overrides the effect of the small accompanying drop in e.h.t.

Figure 17.12 shows a line output and e.h.t. arrangement of this type. A single transistor in such a circuit, would have to be capable of withstanding (during flyback), voltages in excess of 2 kV. To accommodate these high voltages, two transistors in series are used in the circuit shown. (Single transistor circuits are also now used.)

Since the flyback stroke is initiated by switching off the transistors, it is important that they both go off together. Either one of them switching off, stops the collector current of them both. If one should still be forward biased (and hence of very low

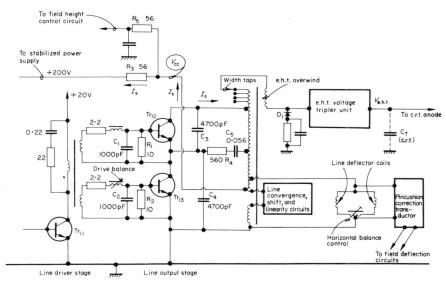

Fig. 17.12 *Transistorized line output stage and associated e.h.t. circuit*

(Associated diagrams: Figs. 15.8, 16.8)

internal resistance) when the other switches off, the one which is off (and of very high resistance) will receive the full flyback voltage between its collector and emitter. If both switch off simultaneously, the flyback voltage is evenly divided between the two. Inductors are included in the base input drive circuits and one of these is made adjustable so that balance may be achieved, causing both transistors to switch-off together.

Following normal techniques, the transformer is tuned so that the resonant frequency of the main transformer winding with shunt capacitance, is approximately one-third (or on occasions, one-fifth) of the frequency at which the overwind leakage inductance resonates with the associated stray capacitance. This 'third-harmonic tuning' (or sometimes 'fifth-harmonic tuning') of the transformer, has two beneficial effects; it increases the peak e.h.t. voltage output from the overwind and it decreases (by peak flattening) the flyback voltage developed at the collector. In Fig. 17.12 the tuning capacitance is provided by two series capacitors C_3 and C_4. By connecting one of these across Tr_{12} and the other across Tr_{13}, the flyback voltage is evenly distributed between the two transistors. When the circuit is in balance, minimum current passes through the network C_5R_4.

The supply current to the transistors passes through the resistor R_3, which provides the compensating action described for R_s in Fig. 17.11.

The diode and its RC network connected in shunt with the input to the tripler unit, becomes conductive on the second half-cycle of the flyback waveform developed at the overwind terminal. When the beam current is very low, without D_1 present,

295

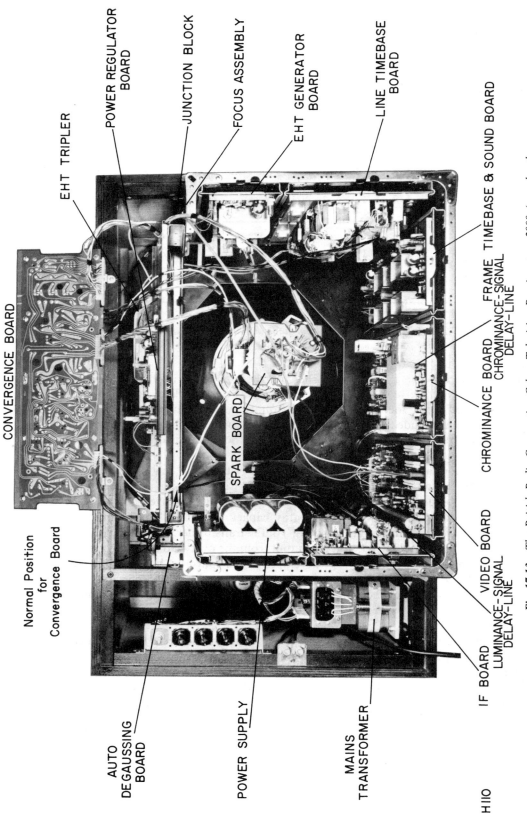

CONVERGENCE BOARD

Normal Position
for
Convergence Board

EHT TRIPLER

POWER REGULATOR
BOARD

JUNCTION BLOCK

FOCUS ASSEMBLY

EHT GENERATOR
BOARD

LINE TIMEBASE
BOARD

FRAME TIMEBASE & SOUND BOARD

CHROMINANCE BOARD

CHROMINANCE-SIGNAL
DELAY-LINE

SPARK BOARD

VIDEO BOARD

LUMINANCE-SIGNAL
DELAY-LINE

AUTO
DEGAUSSING
BOARD

POWER SUPPLY

MAINS
TRANSFORMER

IF BOARD

H110

Fig. 17.13 *The British Radio Corporation Colour Television Receiver type 2000 (see also the*
block diagram, Fig. 17.14)

(Photograph reproduced by kind permission of British Radio Corporation Limited)

the circuit is insufficiently damped and the oscillation does not cease at the end of the positive-going pulse from which the e.h.t. is developed. This added 'ringing' can affect the e.h.t. voltage and this is prevented by the damping action of D_1.

Receiver design and development

Colour television was introduced into Europe at a time when thermionic valves were fast being supplanted by transistors in monochrome receivers. The first colour

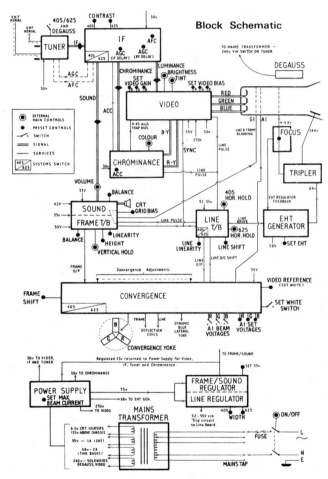

Fig. 17.14 *Block diagram of the B.R.C. Type 2000 Colour Television Receiver (see also Fig. 17.13)*

(Reproduced by kind permission of British Radio Corporation Limited)

297

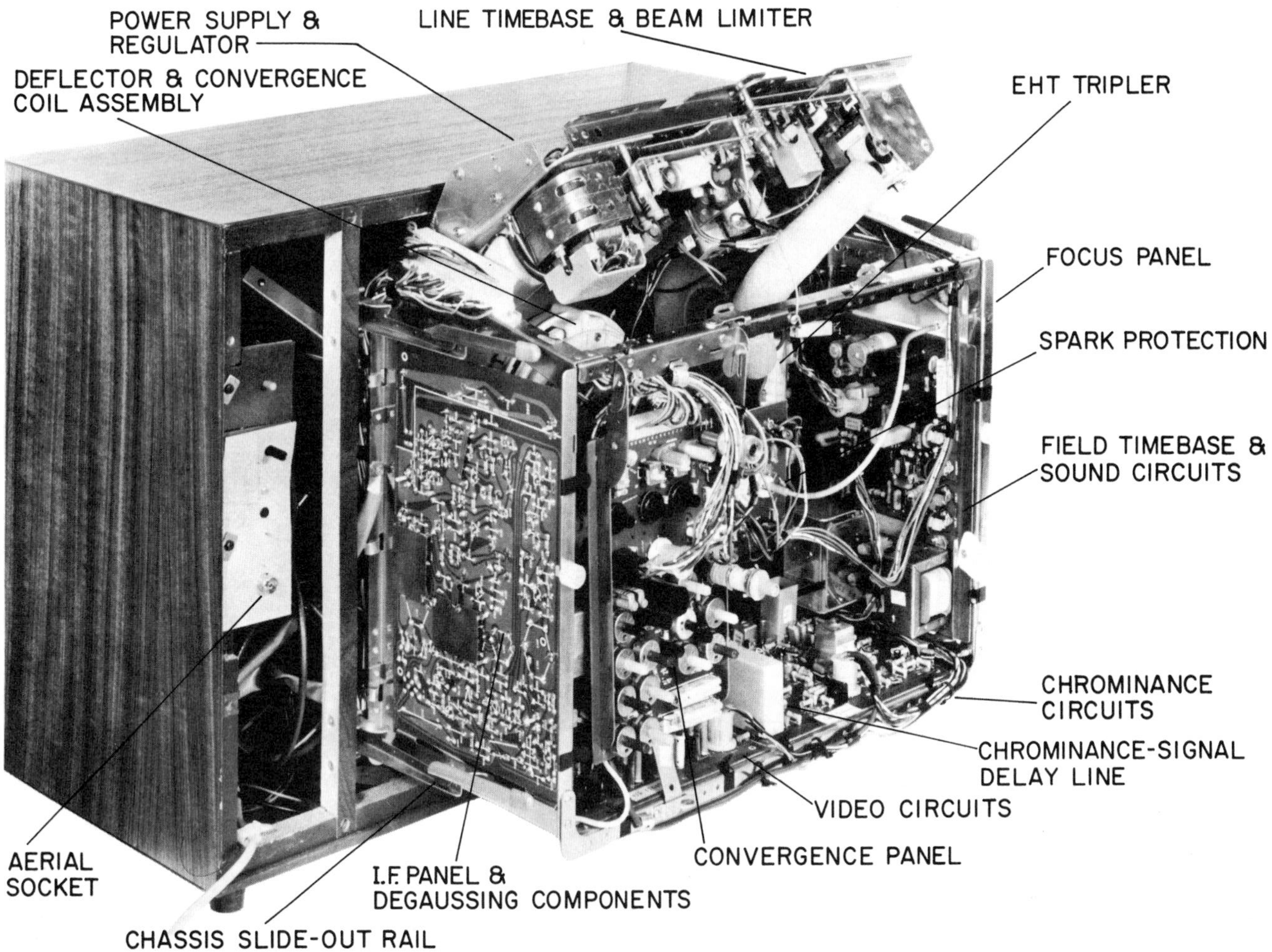

POWER SUPPLY &
REGULATOR

LINE TIMEBASE & BEAM LIMITER

DEFLECTOR & CONVERGENCE
COIL ASSEMBLY

EHT TRIPLER

FOCUS PANEL

SPARK PROTECTION

FIELD TIMEBASE &
SOUND CIRCUITS

CHROMINANCE
CIRCUITS

CHROMINANCE-SIGNAL
DELAY LINE

VIDEO CIRCUITS

CONVERGENCE PANEL

I.F. PANEL &
DEGAUSSING COMPONENTS

CHASSIS SLIDE-OUT RAIL

AERIAL
SOCKET

Fig. 17.15 *The British Radio Corporation Colour Television Receiver type 3000 (see also the block diagram Fig. 17.16)*

(Photograph reproduced by kind permission of British Radio Corporation Limited)

receivers were largely of hybrid form, containing valves for some purposes and transistors for others.

An exception was the British Radio Corporation Receiver type 2000, which was the first fully transistorized colour television receiver to be produced for the domestic market in the United Kingdom. Since then others have followed and at the same time integrated circuits have appeared, which represent the next logical step forward in receiver evolution. The first notable application of integrated circuit techniques in domestic colour television receivers was introduced by the Rank-Bush Murphy organization, who, working in conjunction with the Plessey Company, developed the decoding circuit described in chapter 16.

Figure 17.13 shows the first B.R.C. transistorized 2000-series receiver. This provides an excellent example of the tendency towards modular construction in complex electronic apparatus. The receiver is divided into a number of major sections; each built on a sub-chassis. The latter are often, perhaps more appropriately, described as 'panels'. These are interconnected in such a way that each may easily be removed. The block diagram Fig. 17.14 shows the sections into which the receiver is divided. For servicing purposes, this method of construction makes it possible to get a faulty receiver working again very quickly, by the replacement of a sub-chassis. The faulty sub-chassis, or panel, may then be returned to a central workshop where sophisticated test-procedures may be applied to localize, then identify, the fault.

The inconvenience of removing faulty colour television receivers from homes, to be returned to workshops for repair and then transported back again, is largely avoided except in a limited number of cases. By allowing receivers to be kept in working order in the home and at the same time by reducing the time necessary for a

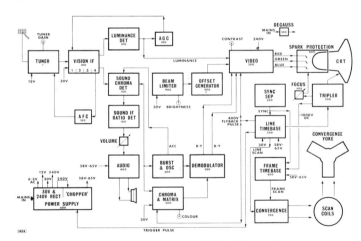

Fig. 17.16 *Block diagram of the B.R.C. Type 3000 Colour Television Receiver (see also Fig. 17.15)*

(Reproduced by kind permission of British Radio Corporation Limited)

299

service engineer to get a receiver in action again after it has broken down, the whole process of maintenance becomes more efficient and much more convenient both to the user and to the firms concerned.

Figure 17.15 shows the second generation B.R.C. chassis, referred to as the 3000 series. The associated block diagram is Fig. 17.16. This receiver includes many simplifications and innovations. A comparison of the two is a clear indication of the vigorous development work which will continue to modify the design of colour television receivers in the years ahead.

With the use of fully solid-state circuitry and the increasing application of integrated circuit techniques, it is already true that the physical size of a colour television receiver is largely dictated by the size of the cathode ray tube. As stated in chapter 5, there is continuing intensive research into other radically different display devices. Perhaps the ultimate receiver will more nearly resemble a 'picture-on-the-wall' than the present day box-like structure. Even the latter have already become acceptably slim when compared with the rather ungainly and bulky receivers of earlier years.

It is quite evident that exciting developments lie ahead and it is hoped that this book will play a part in equipping engineers and students to comprehend and interpret these developments as and when they appear.

The NTSC System

On a Q.A.M. chrominance signal phasor diagram of the type discussed in chapter 3 it was seen that any particular hue may be identified in terms of the phase angle which the phasor bears when the balanced modulators are fed with the weighted colour-difference signals V and U which correspond to the given hue.

The eye is able to resolve finer detail in some hues than in others. Subjective testing of observers shows that the eye has a maximum colour resolution for orange hues corresponding to phase angles centred upon 123° and for the complementary blue-green hues centred upon the diametrically opposite phase angle of 303°. These maxima are not sharply defined but the eye's ability to see fine detail in colour shows broad peaks in these regions. The chrominance signal axis passing through the line 123°–0–303° is referred to as the I axis; often loosely described as the orange–cyan axis. (The figure 0 is the origin of the phasor diagram; see Fig. A.2.)

In a PAL signal one of the two chrominance signal components lies along the V axis where it is directly proportional to the amplitude of the $(R' - Y')$ colour-difference signal, whilst the other lies along the quadrature U axis and has an amplitude proportional to the $(B' - Y')$ colour-difference signal.

In the NTSC system, instead of using these modulation axes, one of the two chrominance signal components is shifted so that it lies along the I axis, i.e., along the axis of 'maximum colour acuity'. Similarly, the other component, which must be placed in quadrature with the I axis, is shifted 33° anti-clockwise relative to the U axis. This is referred to as the Q axis and it lies along the line 33°–0–213°. It happens that the Q axis corresponds to hues which the eye is least able to resolve. This axis may be described as the axis of minimum colour acuity and it is often broadly referred to as the purple–yellow-green axis. Once again (as with the maxima), the minima are not sharply defined, but the eye's ability to resolve colour detail is poorest for hues, corresponding to phase angles on the Q axis.

The NTSC chrominance signal I and Q components therefore, directly represent the picture's orange–cyan and purple–yellow-green contents respectively.

With the aim of transmitting as much colour information as the eye can use, but no more, the I signal is given a broader bandwidth than the Q.

In the U.S.A. 525-line system, the video signal linear bandwidth is 4 MHz, or 4·2 MHz measured to the point where the response falls by 2 dB. For a colour signal, using this standard and NTSC I and Q chrominance components, the picture information in the signal may be divided into three groups:

(a) Chrominance signal Q component; bandwidth 400 kHz (to -2 dB point)
(b) Chrominance signal I component; bandwidth 1·3 MHz (to -2 dB point)
(c) Luminance information with a bandwidth of 4·2 MHz (to -2 dB point)

The performance of a receiver making full use of this information may be summarized as follows:

(a) Large areas and the most prominent features of the picture are fully resolved in their true colours. The smallest detail fully resolved in colour corresponds to video frequencies up to the order of 400 kHz.
(b) Any orange and blue-green content in the picture is resolved in finer detail, up to a limit corresponding to a frequency of 1·3 MHz.
(c) Finer detail still, corresponding to frequencies above 1·3 MHz and up to the limit of 4·2 MHz, is resolved in monochrome only.

This performance means that the displayed picture contains all the information that the eye could in fact perceive if the transmitted scene were viewed directly.

The colour sub-carrier frequency is placed approximately 400 kHz below 4·0 MHz ($f_{sc} = 3 \cdot 579545$ MHz, i.e., approx. 3·58 MHz). The Q component is radiated as a double sideband (equiband) signal, while the I signal is of the vestigial sideband form having an upper sideband of 400 kHz and a lower of 1·3 MHz. Figure A.1 shows this in diagrammatic form.

When the NTSC system was being considered for possible use in the U.K., where the monochrome video bandwidth is 5·5 MHz, the I and Q bandwidths proposed were 1·6 MHz and 0·8 MHz respectively. In the event, the PAL system, finally chosen, employs equiband V and U signals having compromise bandwidths of 1 MHz.

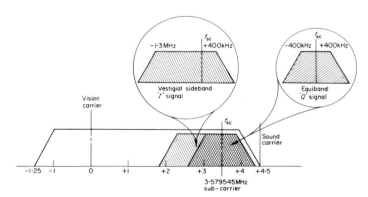

Fig. A.1 *Frequency components of the U.S.A. 525-line NTSC colour television signal*

Note:
(i) The shaded area shows the chrominance signal.
(ii) As shown by the 'balloons', the chrominance signal has two components: an equiband 'Q' signal of ± 400 kHz bandwidth, and a vestigial sideband 'I' signal having lower and upper sidebands of 1·3 MHz and 400 kHz respectively.

302

To express the I and Q signals in terms of V and U information

The best way of gaining a clear understanding of what is involved in shifting the axes of the two quadrature chrominance signal components from the V and U components which are at $90°$ and $0°$ (or $270°$ and $180°$ when V and U are negative) to the I and Q axes which lie at $123°$ and $33°$ (or $303°$ and $213°$ when I and Q are negative) is to consider a convenient hue and draw a phasor diagram corresponding to it.

For convenience magenta is chosen. This makes the V and U components both positive. Moreover, since $R' = B'$ and hence $(R' - Y') = (B' - Y')$, it follows that the magnitudes of the V and U components are in the ratio of the weighting factors, i.e., in the ratio 0·877 to 0·493.

If V and U components are drawn in this ratio, the chrominance phasor rests at $61°$. This is shown in Fig. A.2.

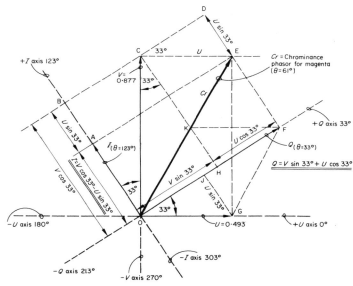

Fig. A.2 *Transformation of the co-ordinates of a Q.A.M. chrominance signal, from the quadrature components V and U to the quadrature components I and Q*

Note:

 (i) The actual chrominance phasor shown represents a magenta hue, for which the phase angle is $61°$.

 (ii) The magnitude Cr of the chrominance phasor is given by $Cr = \sqrt{V^2 + U^2}$.

(iii) Cr may equally well be resolved in terms of the two co-ordinates I and Q, where $Cr = \sqrt{I^2 + Q^2}$.

(iv) The geometry of the figure shows that: $I = V \cos 33° - U \sin 33°$ and $Q = V \sin 33° + U \cos 33°$.

 (v) These identities which are established in the text may also be proved as follows:

$$Cr^2 = I^2 + Q^2 = \{V \cos 33° - U \sin 33°\}^2 + \{V \sin 33° + U \cos 33°\}^2$$
$$Cr^2 = V^2 \cos^2 33° - 2UV \sin 33° \cos 33° + U^2 \sin^2 33° + V^2 \sin^2 33° + 2UV \sin 33° \cos 33° + U^2 \cos^2 33°$$
$$Cr^2 = V^2(\sin^2 33° + \cos^2 33°) + U^2(\sin^2 33° + \cos^2 33°)$$
$$Cr^2 = V^2 + U^2$$

(vi) Clearly any chrominance phasor, in any of the four quadrants, may be expressed either in terms of V and U or in terms of I and Q, due attention being paid to the signs of V and U when substituting these quantities in the expressions for I and Q.

303

But, having drawn this phasor, it may then be resolved into I and Q components, simply by dotting in the I and Q axes at $123°$ and $33°$ respectively and drawing perpendiculars from these axes to the tip of the chrominance phasor. The I and Q components are shown labelled as I and Q and drawn in full-line on the appropriate axes.

It is now possible to express the magnitudes of I and Q in terms of the known V and U components.

It will be seen from the geometry of the figures that:

$$I = (V \cos 33° - U \sin 33°) \quad \text{and} \quad Q = (V \sin 33° + U \cos 33°)[1]$$

Since this is so it follows that the same chrominance phasor may be generated in two ways:

(a) By using two voltages of magnitudes V and U to modulate two sub-carriers having the quadrature phases of $90°$ and $0°$ respectively.

(b) By using two voltages having the magnitudes I and Q to modulate two sub-carriers having the quadrature phases of $123°$ and $33°$.

The PAL transmitter diagram Fig. 4.6 shows an example of (a), but (b) is used in NTSC.

In practical NTSC coding circuits it is not so difficult as may perhaps be imagined, to obtain the I and Q signals. This is so because the three signals Y', I', and Q' are each simply straightforward combinations of the gamma corrected colour signals R', G', and B'.

The expressions for I and Q are:

$$I = 0.596R' - 0.275G' - 0.322B'$$
$$Q = 0.211R' - 0.523G' - 0.312B'$$

These expressions may be obtained by substituting $0.3R' + 0.59G' + 0.11B'$ for Y' in the formulae for I and Q derived earlier. For example:

$$Q = V \sin 33° + U \cos 33°$$
$$Q = 0.877(R' - Y') \sin 33° + 0.493(B' - Y') \cos 33°$$
$$Q = 0.48(R' - Y') + 0.41(B' - Y')$$

[1] An expression for I and Q may be obtained directly in terms of V and U by applying those principles of plane co-ordinate geometry which relate to the transformation of the co-ordinates of a point on a plane surface. However, Fig. A.2 has been constructed so that the result may be arrived at by inspection.

(1) *To find I.* The dimension AB = DE = JG. But $\triangle$DEC = $\triangle$JGO and from $\triangle$JGO, side JG = $U \sin 33°$

therefore $\qquad\qquad\qquad\qquad$ AB = $U \sin 33°$

In $\triangle$BCO, side BO = $V \cos 33°$

therefore $\qquad\qquad\qquad$ I = (BO − AB) = $V \cos 33° - U \sin 33°$

(2) *To find Q.* From $\triangle$OCH, $\qquad\qquad$ OH = $V \sin 33°$

Also $\qquad\qquad\qquad\qquad\qquad$ $\triangle$HKF = $\triangle$DEC = $\triangle$JGO

therefore $\qquad\qquad\qquad\qquad$ HF = DC = OJ = $U \cos 33°$

Hence $\qquad\qquad\qquad$ Q = (OH + HF) = $V \sin 33° + U \cos 33°$

304

$$Q = 0 \cdot 48(R' - 0 \cdot 3R' - 0 \cdot 59G' - 0 \cdot 11B') +$$
$$0 \cdot 41(B' - 0 \cdot 3R' - 0 \cdot 59G' - 0 \cdot 11B' - 0 \cdot 11B')$$
$$Q = 0 \cdot 211R' - 0 \cdot 523G' - 0 \cdot 312B'$$

A similar derivation leads to the expression for I quoted above.

Since Y', I, and Q are obtained directly from R', G', and B' it is usual in a block diagram of an NTSC transmitter to show one box labelled 'matrix' into which R', G', and B' are fed and out of which Y', I', and Q' emerge. Since both negative and positive amounts of G' and B' are needed it follows that the matrix must include inverters for these two colour voltages.

The I signal passes through a filter of broader bandwidth than the Q filter. The narrower bandwidth of the Q filter introduces a greater delay in the Q signal path than that existing in the I path. To bring these two components into step at the point where they are added, a delay circuit is needed in the I signal path.

Basic NTSC transmitter arrangements

The block diagram of Fig. A.3 shows the basic principles of an NTSC transmitter. When this is compared with the corresponding diagram for a PAL transmitter in Fig. 4.6 it will be seen that the main differences are:

(a) PAL uses equiband weighted $(R' - Y')$ and $(B' - Y')$ colour-difference signals to modulate the two quadrature sub-carriers of the chrominance signal, but NTSC uses the more complex I and Q signals which have different bandwidths and each of which contains both $(R' - Y')$ and $(B' - Y')$ information.

(b) The sub-carrier phases in the PAL signal for positive values of V and U are $90°$ for V and $0°$ for U (changing to $270°$ and $180°$ respectively when V and U are negative). In addition, the phase of the V sub-carrier is switched by $180°$ on alternate lines.

The NTSC sub-carrier phases for the I and Q signals are $123°$ and $33°$ respectively for positive values of I and Q (changing to $303°$ and $213°$ respectively for negative values of I and Q). There is no alternate-line switching of the I sub-carrier to correspond with the V sub-carrier switching in the PAL signal.

(c) In the PAL signal the phase of the back-porch burst signal switches from $135°$ on one line to $225°$ on alternate lines; the 'average' burst phase being $180°$. With NTSC the burst phase is constant at $180°$ on all lines.

Basic NTSC receiver arrangements

Figure A.4 shows in outline form, the main sections of an NTSC receiver. The purposes of all the sections will be apparent from the text about the very similar PAL receivers discussed in this book.

A point of interest arises in connection with the I and Q signals.

To extract the I and Q colour-difference signals from the chrominance signal it is

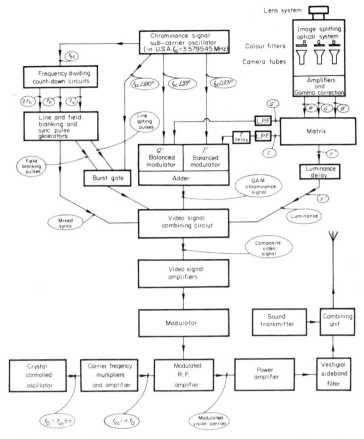

Fig. A.3 *Basic NTSC transmitter arrangement*

necessary to demodulate along the I and Q axes, i.e., the reference sub-carrier inputs to the I and Q synchronous demodulators must have phases equal to those of the suppressed carriers at the transmitter. These are 123° and 33° respectively. When this is done the full transmitted information is available. By matrixing I and Q the colour-difference signals $(R' - Y')$, $(B' - Y')$, and $(G' - Y')$ are recovered.

A study of the phasor diagram in Fig. A.2, however, shows that the chrominance signal may equally well be resolved directly into the weighted $(R' - Y')$ and $(B' - Y')$ components (i.e., into V and U).

To accomplish this the synchronous demodulators must receive sub-carriers at 90° and 0° instead of 123° and 33°. This leads to a simpler receiver but the broader bandwidth information carrier by the I signal is sacrificed. The U and V components are now treated as equiband signals having bandwidths equal to that of the Q signal. There is thus a loss of the finer detail information in orange–cyan hues. Such receivers

306

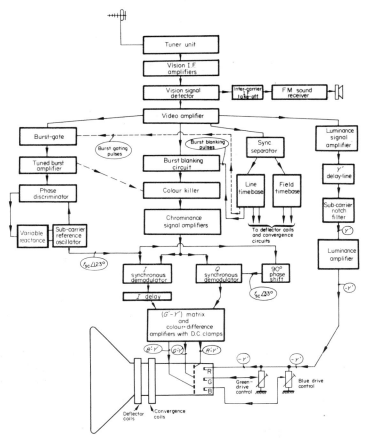

Fig. A.4 *Basic NTSC receiver arrangement*

are sometimes referred to as narrow-band chrominance receivers whereas those using *I* and *Q* demodulators are known as broad-band chrominance receivers. Because of their relative simplicity the former are in the majority.

It is useful at this point to read again the brief comments at the end of chapter 11 which refer to the other demodulation systems in use, i.e., demodulation along the *X* and *Z* axes, and also the system using three synchronous demodulators to produce the three colour-difference signals directly. A study of all these systems leads to a better comprehension of the nature of Q.A.M. signals generally.

Colour Television Test Card F

(TEST CARD F—designed jointly by the BBC, BREMA, EEA, and ITA)

Test cards are designed to provide on the screen of a television receiver, visible evidence of its performance. In addition, they provide signals which allow stringent electronic testing of the system itself.

The details of Test Card F given in this appendix, are reprinted by kind permission of the BBC, from the BBC Engineering Information Department; Information Sheet 4306(3) dated March 1970 (see Plate 9 inserted between pages 102–103).

The pattern shown in the illustrations includes the electronically-generated colour bars which replace the first twenty-four lines of the test card proper for the reasons stated in paragraph 1 below. The test card includes coloured edge castellations to check colour synchronization effects and picture size; a grid with corner diagonals and centre circle enabling picture geometry and focus to be assessed; a 'letter-box' pattern to test low-frequency effects, frequency gratings for assessment of bandwidth, and a six-step grey scale. Colour information is included in the edge castellations and within the circle.

The electronically generated colour bars transmitted with the test card enable colour decoder performance to be checked.

1. Checking decoder performance

The top of the transmitted test card starts about 12 lines after the end of the field blanking period in each field on 625 lines (or about 8 lines on 405). Thus about 24 lines (on 625) or 16 lines (on 405) of each picture are made available for the electronic colour bar signal. An electronic signal is used to avoid the problems of generating a high-accuracy signal by optical means. The decoded colour-separation signals corresponding to the coloured bars in this part of the picture should take up values of 100% or 25% (according to the colour of the bar) of their value for peak white. This form of signal (sometimes referred to as '100 per cent amplitude, 95 per cent saturation') has been adopted in agreement with the British Radio Equipment Manufacturers Association as being representative of the high-saturation and high-luminance signals obtainable from colour cameras and is regarded as a stringent but realistic test of colour television systems. On black-and-white receivers, and in any case on 405 lines, the colour bar signal will appear as a grey scale with the bright bars at the left and dark ones at the right.[1]

Faults or adjustment errors in a colour receiver are easily recognized as asymmetry or changes in shape of the waveform and/or differences in amplitude from line to line in the waveforms of the red, green and blue components of the colour bars at the output of the decoder. If the colour bars are observed on the face of the tube, an assessment of the decoder performance can be obtained by switching off individual guns of the tube.

2. Colour-receiver reference generator faults

The colour bars, being located at the top of the picture, also enable the recovery of the reference generator after the field-sync period—during which the reference bursts are absent—to be clearly seen as variations in the saturation of the bars. The bottom castellations, being green, provide a means of assessing the reference generator performance at the end of the field as compared with the start.

The red and blue castellations on the left-hand side will give rise to the greatest disturbance of the displayed colour picture if the gating circuits permit picture information to pass to the reference generator. Thus, if this fault is present in the receiver, either bands of saturation changes or 'Venetian Blinds' will be visible in coloured areas across the picture depending on the decoding circuits employed.

3. Colour-receiver convergence checking

Certain lines in the grid have been outlined in black to assist in checking display-tube convergence. Others have no outlining so as to avoid the confusion which might otherwise result from the low-frequency ringing seen when certain types of quadrature distortion are present in a receiver. The blackboard and white cross also provide a check on static convergence.

4. The colour picture

The colour picture in the centre circle contains areas of flesh tones and of bright colours to facilitate overall picture quality assessment and the correct adjustment of saturation. A child was chosen as the model rather than an adult so as to avoid the effects of changes in make-up fashion.

The circle containing the colour picture is outlined in white to avoid any 'optical illusion' effects which might occur if the coloured areas abutted directly on to the

---

[1] Author's note:

At the time of writing the ITA were in fact using a 75% amplitude 100% saturated colour-bar signal (see the reference in chapter 16 to the EBU 100/0/75/0 signal) as distinct from the 100% amplitude 95% saturated signal (reference 100/0/100/25) used by the BBC.

background grey and white grid. It must be emphasized that Test Card 'F' is intended primarily for technical purposes and is only secondarily a demonstration picture. Further, although provision is made for the critical appraisal of convergence it is not intended that the colour test card should be regarded as a substitute for a grid pattern generator when setting convergence.

5. Transmitted picture limits

The limits of the transmitted picture are indicated by the points of the opposing arrowheads in the border. For receivers having a display area with an aspect ratio of about 5:4—the transmitted picture aspect ratio is 4:3—it is usual to adjust the receiver so that the visible picture height extends from the top line of the inserted colour bars to the point of the bottom arrowhead; if the picture width is then adjusted so that the side castellations of the test card appear in the display area of the receiver, the aspect ratio of the picture will be correct.

6. Contrast

To the left of the centre circle of the test card is a column of six rectangles with an overall contrast range of about 30:1. The difference in brightness between adjacent rectangles should be approximately constant on a correctly adjusted receiver. Within the top and bottom rectangles are small lighter spots, both of which should be visible; white or black crushing results in the merging of the top or bottom spot respectively into its surrounding area.

7. Resolution and bandwidth

At the right of the centre picture are six gratings each consisting of vertical stripes corresponding to the following fundamental frequencies in megahertz (MHz):

625-line UHF services	1·5	2·5	3·5	4·0	4·5	5·25
405-line VHF services	1·0	1·6	2·25	2·6	2·9[1]	3·4[1]

The gratings, on a correctly adjusted receiver, will appear to extend in value from white to black with their surrounding area white.

8. Scanning linearity

The white lines in the background should enclose equal squares and the central white ring should appear truly circular.

[1] These bars are likely to be indistinct on most 405-line receivers due to the removal from the transmitted signal of colour information to avoid degradation of the converted 405-line picture.

310

9. Line synchronization

The left, right and bottom borders of the test card are formed by a pattern of alternate rectangles in black and colours with a high luminance value. On black-and-white receivers these rectangles appear as black and various lighter tones ranging from grey to white. The right side of this border serves as a test signal to check the line synchronization of receivers. Faulty line synchronization shows as horizontal displacement of those parts of the picture on the same level as the lighter toned rectangles in this side; it will also give the central ring the appearance of a 'cog-wheel'. The right-hand castellations, being yellow and white, provide a check on sync-separator performance in the presence and absence, in 625-line transmissions, of the colour sub-carrier. The spacing of the left- and right-hand castellations has been staggered to make it clear from which side any disturbance arises and to give the maximum possibility of phase change resulting from a gating error.

10. Low-frequency response

Low-frequency response can be checked from the appearance of the black rectangle within the white rectangle at the top centre of the test card. Poor low-frequency response shows as streaking at the right-hand edges of these rectangles and also of the border castellations.

11. Reflections

If there are reflections of the television signal, from hills or large buildings, these may result in displaced 'ghost' images of any significant feature of the picture. This effect will be most readily seen as displaced images of the white or black vertical lines, particularly where these are adjacent. The effects of short-term reflections are often most clearly shown by the noughts and crosses on the blackboard.

12. Uniformity of focus

In each corner of the test card there is a diagonally-disposed area of black and white stripes; the focus in these areas as well as in the central area of the test card should be good.

Index

Printed and bound in Great Britain by
William Clowes (Beccles) Limited, Beccles and London